UNDERSTANDING MICROWAVES

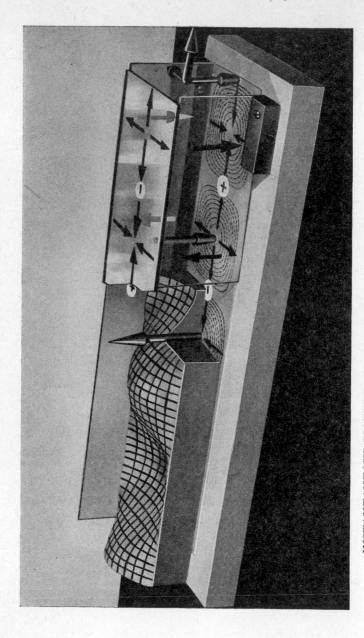

INSTANTANEOUS PICTURE OF ENERGY FLOW IN WAVEGUIDE. (See page xi)

Courtesy of Paul H. Nelson, Research Associate, The Ohio State University Research Foundation.

UNDERSTANDING MICROWAVES

BY

VICTOR J. YOUNG

Senior Project Engineer, Sperry Gyroscope Co.

JOHN F. RIDER PUBLISHER, INC.

404 Fourth Ave.   New York 16, N.Y.

Printed in the United States of America

Dedicated to

MY WIFE

PREFACE

THE TITLE of this book explains what the author has tried to do as well as any two words can describe a goal. More completely, the book is intended to present material which will form a basis for understanding microwave radio and radar. Certainly the book makes no claim to cover the field completely as it exists today; that could hardly be done in a score of books the size of this one. Instead material has been chosen which it is believed will aid those who have not yet considered radio waves shorter than 10 centimeters and allow them to go on into the various advanced ideas which are now being published or which will soon be coming forth in great volume. It is also hoped that the book will aid in correlating the isolated facts concerning microwaves which have come to the attention of many people and give them a perspective which has not been possible during the past few years because of the requirements of military security measures.

One difficult objective has only been partially realized. It is the elimination of mathematical explanations. Because of a strong desire to make the book pleasant reading and understandable to others than those directly concerned with the design of the various components, the mathematics are relegated to footnotes wherever possible and even there it is written out in detail so as to be easier to follow. Because of this, and because of the introductory nature of the first few chapters, it is hoped that the book will be helpful both to engineers and to those interested in radio from the standpoint of service or operation. It is believed that the only prerequisites that are necessary in order to read this book are a small knowledge of the conventional uses of electricity plus a willingness to think in terms of physical ideas and experiments.

As a secondary objective, the book tries to break down the psychological bar to electromagnetic theory which is often experienced because of the mathematical manner in which that subject is usually introduced. The physical ideas of electromagnetic fields are greatly emphasized, although in order to avoid completely "sugar-coating" the subject, a section on Maxwell's equations is also included. It is hoped that this section will keep the introductory nature of the rest of the book in its proper perspective.

The almost universal difficulty with units has been experienced and met by using the gaussian system everywhere, except when a different set of units is explicitly mentioned. This has been done in the face of the growing popularity of another system, namely the MKS or Giorgi system. The logic followed is that in the face of the present use of many kinds of units by many authors, there can be no entirely satisfactory solution for the reader that is short of understanding all systems. In a book like the present one, it is therefore logical to use whatever units make the explanations the most palatable.

Special acknowledgment is due to *Radio Magazine* and its editor, Mr. John Potts, for the release of copyrights on certain parts of the text which were originally published in that journal. The staff of the John F. Rider Publisher, Inc. made a large contribution to the book, not only by editing but also by suggesting technical issues which needed further explanations. Mr. Jay E. Browder and others of the Sperry Gyroscope Company Research Laboratories aided by many technical discussions of various points and especially a part of Chapter XI was the result of the combined efforts of the author and Mr. Browder. Finally, an acknowledgment to the many books and articles which have been consulted must be made. As in any book of this sort, very little completely original material is included.

VICTOR J. YOUNG

March, 1946.

TABLE OF CONTENTS

SECTION II

THE FRONTISPIECE

The frontispiece shows an instantaneous picture of the flow of energy from left to right through a rectangular waveguide operating in the $TE_{0,1}$ mode. The plus and minus signs indicate the way in which portions of the inner surface of the top and bottom of the waveguide are charged. The lines at the left end show the strength of the electric field by virtue of their rise above or depression below an imaginary centrally located horizontal plane. The vertical arrows at the center of the waveguide show the direction of the electric field; the broken lines and the centrally located horizontal arrow at the right end, describe the magnetic field. The arrows shown on the walls of the waveguide describe the current which is flowing. The arrow at the right-hand end pointing out of the waveguide shows that energy will come out at that point.

UNDERSTANDING
MICROWAVES

SECTION I

Chapter 1

THE ULTRA HIGH FREQUENCY CONCEPT

THE UNIVERSE of which the Earth is a tiny part, is almost completely made of electricity. Metal, cloth, glass, and even your own right hand consist of electricity more than anything else. These objects are composed of atoms such as hydrogen, carbon, oxygen, and dozens of others, and each of these atoms is now known to be composed mostly of three basic building blocks: *protons* (positive charge), *neutrons* (no charge), and *electrons* (negative charge). In the ordinary course of events, the electricity of these common objects does not make itself known, because in the atom and molecule the two kinds of charge are so accurately paired off and divided into such small units that almost regardless of how small a sample of material is examined, it is found to contain equal amounts of positive and negative charge which neutralize each other almost completely.

It is a very fortunate property of nature that makes possible the easy separation of negative and positive charge so as to create what are called *charged bodies*. As is diagrammatically illustrated in Fig. 1-1, such charged bodies are still very far from being all charge of one sign. Out of the some 17 million coulombs of charge [1] in the balls

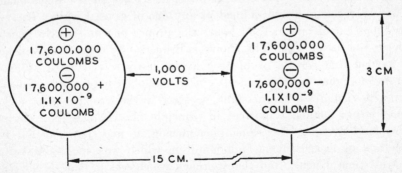

FIG. 1-1. The amount of charge in two 3-cm aluminum balls separated by 15 cm. An excess of only 1.1 x 10⁻⁹ coulomb is sufficient to raise the potential to 1,000 volts.

shown, an excess of only 1.1 thousand millionths of a coulomb is sufficient to raise the potential to 1000 volts.[2] The preponderance of the charge is still paired off and is essentially non-existent as far as its electrical properties are concerned. Only an excess or deficiency of charge of one sign causes a body to have an electric potential that is different from its uncharged counterpart. The greater this excess or deficiency of charge is, the greater will be the voltage between the two bodies.

It is also fortunate that when chemical batteries or generating machines are used to effect the separation of charge, it flows through metallic conductors as electric currents, and in doing so performs all the useful results with which everybody is in part familiar. These things are fortunate, but the full exploitation of the electrical properties of nature also rests on our diligence in formulating the rules which are followed, so that machines can be built which will cause electricity to perform ever new and more useful tasks so as to add to our well being and convenience. It is the main purpose of this volume to explain as simply as possible the rules most pertinent to electric charge which is made to oscillate back and forth so fast, that even when as a current it moves with extremely high velocity, it does not have time to travel far in any given direction. These rapid and brief motions of charge may correspond to very short radio waves which are descriptively known as *microwaves*.

Nature of Definitions

It is a common experience of physical science that a phenomenon may be recognized and defined in any one of several ways. There is no question of one method being the proper one or even in general being the better way. The choice is instead only one of convenience. The fact that certain problems may be easily solved when attacked from one point of view and all but impossibly complicated when approached from a different slant, does not in the least change the fact that either method is correct in principle. In the case of a second problem involving the same phenomenon, it may happen that the method of measurement and definition which was successful before is this time difficult, and the approach which was previously so complicated, turns out in this later case to be able to yield a design with the least difficulty.

The small back-and-forth movement of a simple pendulum, which is an example of what is called *simple harmonic motion,* may be quoted as a mechanical example of this sort of thing. Such motion may be defined in terms of the restoring force which always urges the pendulum to return to its center position when it is displaced, or it may equally well be initially described as a motion in which a plot of displacement versus time will yield a sinusoidal curve. If either of these properties is taken as a starting point the other may be derived as a property of the motion. Neither can be said to be the correct definition in contrast to the other, although either will completely describe the motion. If it is desired, however, to construct such a motion by the use of springs or magnetic forces, it is clear that the force definition is much the easier with which to work. On the other hand, if it is desired to design an instrument such as a recorder, which makes use of the motion to actuate some other mechanism, it is better to work with the sinusoidal properties of simple harmonic motion.

This sort of situation also exists in the study of electricity. The flow of electrical energy may be described in either one of two commonly used ways. When considering direct current or low-frequency alternating current, a quantity of current called the *ampere* and a quantity of potential called the *volt* may be established and it may be shown that their product at any instant is a measure of the energy per second which is then being transported by electrical means. The reasoning behind this type of definition of electrical energy flow is very simple. The number of amperes shows how many electrical charges move from the source to the load each second, and the number of volts is by definition the amount of energy that is carried by each unit of charge. Their product is, therefore, a measure of the total energy transported per second, just as the product of the number of buckets of sand moved in a second and the pounds of sand in each bucket would give the total amount of sand moved in a second.

The current—voltage picture of electricity is a very convenient one when currents and voltages are restricted to wires or relatively slim conductors, so that no ambiguity concerning the path followed by the charge is encountered. In fact, it is the ease with which ammeters and voltmeters can be built that has influenced us in learning to accept so universally these measurements as proper for circuit design. It is not, however, entirely necessary that even a simple storage-battery circuit be analyzed in terms of current and voltage. A perfectly satisfactory analysis, although a more complicated one, may be constructed by talking about measurements that can be made in the space surrounding the conductors which carry current to or from the storage battery. In Chapter 6 such a method of computing a simple circuit in terms of electromagnetic fields is discussed in some detail for the purpose of demonstrating how this can be done and in order to show the operation of quantities such as E, H, and Poynting's vector in a type of problem which is assumed to be familiar to everyone.

Electromagnetic Fields

The electromagnetic-field method of analyzing the transportation of electrical energy is less well known to many people for several reasons. For one, radio wave propagation problems are not nearly so common in the ordinary household as are troubles with the door bell or with the cord for the electric iron. For another, instruments for measuring electric and magnetic fields are somewhat more involved to use than are their counterparts of ammeters and voltmeters. Some may also say that the theory of electric fields is intrinsically more difficult than that of circuits and may attempt to prove it by showing the very involved mathematics that often enters into any discussion of electromagnetism. Perhaps they are right. The fact remains, however, that this kind of talk is necessary in order to get a proper understanding of microwave apparatus. Although some parts of electromagnetic theory are very mathematical, there are nevertheless many valuable yet very simple things that can be said about electromagnetic fields.

In order to become familiar with the functioning of modern microwave radio, it is absolutely essential that both methods of electrical analysis be understood. Consequently, the first part of this book endeavors to review the elementary facts of electricity in such a way as to lay a foundation for such an understanding. The following few chapters then revert to discussions which are mostly in terms of circuit theory, while the last part of the book uses both methods of description.

Fig. 1-2 illustrates why it is impractical to talk in terms of currents when the operation of one particular piece of microwave equipment is under discussion. The piece of hollow waveguide shown is of the sort that is commonly used as a microwave transmission line. Such a hollow-pipe waveguide may in general be of almost any shape if it has the proper dimensions; circular as well as rectangular pipe is commonly used. Much more will be said about this later, but for the moment the illustration of Fig. 1-2, which indicates that it is possible to pass electrical energy through a pipe just as an ordinary pipe can

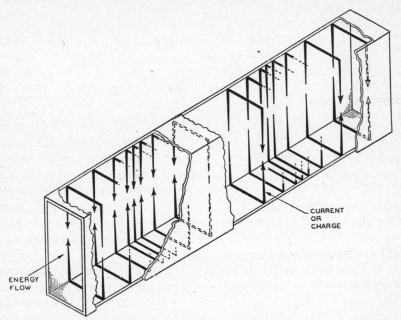

FIG. 1-2. A cut section of a rectangular waveguide showing the current flow lines in one mode of operation at a given instant. The current transports charge into a distribution like that of the arrow heads.

transport water or gas, will be sufficient. The absence of a second conductor in such a device makes it difficult for the uninitiated to see how a closed circuit, which is so necessary in circuit theory, can be possible, and thus how the device can operate.

The beginning of an answer to such confusion probably lies in showing an example of how the charge moves around on the inner surface of the walls of the pipe as electrical energy flows through the guide. Currents do exist in such a device just as much as they do in a house lighting system. Discussions concerning the flow of radiant energy through hollow pipe usually say little, if anything, of current, simply because it is far too difficult to make a direct measurement of a current which is spread non-uniformly over metallic surfaces. If it is desired to describe completely the current shown in Fig. 1-2, it must be borne in mind that that illustration is only an *instantaneous* view of the flow. An instant later the whole pattern shown there will have moved on down the guide in the direction of the energy flow. Charge in the metal itself moves constantly back and forth from the bottom of the waveguide up to the top, and back again.

As the pattern is shown in Fig. 1-2, current in accord with the direction of the arrows is at one place flowing from the bottom inside surface up to the top inside surface, while in another place it is moving the other way. As the pattern of current flow moves along the waveguide from the source to the load, the places where upward or downward current flow is required, are constantly changing. Thus, at a given point on the guide, charge is alternately urged to move upward and downward.

FOOTNOTES

1. A normal aluminum atom contains 13 electrons of negative charge and an equal amount of positive charge. Since the negative charge of an electron is 1.6×10^{-19} coulombs, each atom carries 20.8×10^{-19} coulombs of negative charge. An aluminum ball 3 centimeters in diameter weighs 382 grams, and an aluminum atom weighs 4.5×10^{-23} grams. Such a ball therefore contains

$$\frac{382}{4.5 \times 10^{-23}} \text{ atoms, or a charge of } \frac{20.8 \times 10^{-19} \times 382}{4.5 \times 10^{-23}}$$

This yields approximately 17.6×10^{6} coulombs.

2. The capacitance of two equal spheres of r centimeters radius, the centers of which are separated by d centimeters, and where d is very much greater than r, is given by the expression

$$C = 2.2 \ \pi \ \frac{r}{d} \ (r + d) \times 10^{-12} \text{ farads.}$$

Thus the capacitance of the two 3-cm spheres shown is 11.9×10^{-12} farads. The charge necessary to produce a voltage on a condenser is the product of capacitance and voltage, so the charge needed here to produce 1000 volts is 1.14×10^{-9} coulombs, or 1.14 thousand millionths of a coulomb.

Chapter 2

STATIONARY CHARGE AND ITS FIELD

IN AGREEMENT with usage, negative charge may be defined as that charge which appears on a hard rubber rod which has been rubbed with wool. Similarly, positive charge may be defined as the charge which appears on a glass rod when it is rubbed with silk. Experiments may be performed which show that the charge obtained by such frictional means is the same as that which comes from batteries or generating machines, but for the moment this is assumed to be true, and the properties of static charge shall be described without paying much attention to the way in which it is obtained. It is advantageous to discuss first the properties of static charge, because the situation is much simpler when no motion of charge is involved. As long as electric charge is held stationary in space, or as long as magnetic fields are kept at a constant strength and location, electricity and magnetism are completely unrelated subjects and may be studied separately. This makes it possible for the facts of this chapter to be presented in a straightforward discussion which is complete in itself, and which forms a foundation on which to build.

A convenient way to study the action of static charge involves the use of very light bodies, such as two pith balls. If two such balls are suspended by light silk threads, as is shown in Fig. 2-1, any charge which is collected on the surface of the balls will be held there because of the insulating qualities of the pith and silk thread. When a glass rod is rubbed with silk, electrons are removed from the surface of the

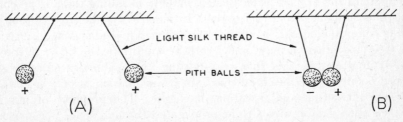

FIG. 2-1. Attraction and repulsion of electric charge as demonstrated by means of two pith balls, those in (A) being of like charge and those in (B) being of unlike charge.

glass, and small areas on that surface have a resulting excess of positive charge. Since the glass itself is a relatively good insulator, it is not possible for electrons that are normally located elsewhere in the glass to come to these shortage areas and even partially make up for the loss. It is a property of a conductor that electrons may move about freely in the material, and a property of an insulator that they cannot. If such a charged glass rod is rubbed along both of the pith balls, the pith material comes so very near to parts of the charged regions of the rod, that charge is transferred in spite of the insulating properties of the materials. If both balls are thus charged with electricity of the same sign, they will be found to repel each other, as shown in Fig. 2-1(A). On the other hand, if one ball is exposed to the glass rod and the other to the previously mentioned hard rubber rod, so that the balls carry charge of opposite sign, they will be attracted toward each other, as shown in Fig. 2-1(B).

This illustrates the well-known fact that electric charges of like sign repel each other, while those of unlike sign attract each other. This ability of charge to affect other charge at a distance is perhaps the most startling of the elementary facts of electricity. Usually no attempt is made to explain this phenomenon in more elementary terms. Instead, rules are formulated concerning the action, and in every case that involves microscopic dimensions (i.e., dimensions that are larger than those of atomic structure), it is possible to predict what will occur when electricity is used in any given way. At least we know how to make the predictions, even though they may sometimes involve calculations that are too laborious to perform. In any event, the ability of one charge to affect another which is some distance away, is an integral part of electromagnetic theory, and is no more strange than the action of gravity.

A wrench thrown from an airplane feels a gravitational force which pulls it to the ground, even though while it is falling there is no connection between it and the ground. In much the same way (although it is believed that this is an entirely different phenomenon) charge in a receiving antenna may, under certain conditions, be made to move in sympathy with that in a transmitting antenna many miles away. It is not meant to intimate that radio transmission is only a matter of the attraction and repulsion of charge. The property of nature which allows radio waves to be propagated through space is considerably more complicated than the results of charging two pith balls.

It is not surprising that the phenomenon, which allows a charge to affect another located some distance away, is so important in radio and especially in microwave radio. It is convenient to make many calculations in terms of the effect that charges have on each other. The strength of a remote interaction between charges depends upon several things, such as the magnitude of the charge, the separation between the charges, and the medium in which the charge is immersed. For the specialized case of stationary charge to which this chapter is limited, a complete specification of the interaction between two charges may be stated with one simple statement called Coulomb's Law. Before stating it, however, a suitable unit must be defined in terms of which the amount of charge present in a given region can be expressed. This, in turn, demands a qualitative notion of how stationary charge may be handled in general.

Use of an Electroscope

Fig. 2-2 shows a simple electroscope which may be used to detect the presence of a static charge. It consists of a well insulated metal

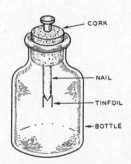

FIG. 2-2. A simple electroscope made by inserting an insulated metal rod in the neck of a bottle; at the bottom of the rod two strips of tinfoil are fastened.

rod mounted in the neck of a bottle with two small pieces of tinfoil fastened to the lower end. The purpose of the bottle is to serve as a convenient support and to protect the tinfoil. Such an electroscope can be made by driving a large nail through the rubber or cork stopper of an empty glass bottle. The tinfoil pieces, which should be about ¼ inch by ½ inch wide, can then be fastened to the point of the nail by removing the stopper. If the foil is light and thin enough, a little moisture will be sufficient to make the tinfoil pieces stick to the nail point.

Whenever the nail, and in consequence the foil, becomes charged for any reason, the mutual repulsion between the two foils causes them to separate, and this demonstrates the presence of the charge. If the electroscope is first partially charged with a particular polarity by proper manipulation of a glass or rubber rod, and then an unknown charge is added, it is possible to determine the polarity of the unknown charge. If the sign of the unknown charge is the same as that of the charge originally placed on the electroscope, additional charge will simply make the leaves spread wider; if it is of the opposite sign, the addition will neutralize some or all of the charge originally placed on the instrument. The leaves will then collapse, although they may open again because of an excess of electricity from the unknown charge, if that source is strong enough.

It is also possible to make quantitative measurements of charge strengths by the use of an electroscope. To do so, a scale must be added so that the angle of divergence of the foils may be measured. By taking a number of more or less obvious precautions, and by arranging a very delicate suspension of the leaves, it is possible to obtain a very sensitive and quite accurate instrument. Except for special vacuum-tube devices, as ionization chambers and Geiger counters, such a carefully constructed electroscope is one of the most sensitive known methods of detecting small electric currents.

If it is desired to charge an electroscope or any other isolated body, there are two possible methods of procedure. One may be called *charging by conduction* and the other *charging by induction*. The method of conduction is the simplest and has already been mentioned. It consists of simply touching a charged body to the electroscope and allowing the charge to flow over to the new body at the point of contact. If the source body is a conductor this will work very well, but if the source is a rubbed glass or rubber rod more difficulty will be experienced and it will be impossible to transfer more than a small fraction of the charge to the electroscope. This is so because charge will be transferred only when the electroscope rod comes so close to certain charged areas on the rod that charge is transferred in spite of the insulating properties of the rod.

When an isolated body is charged by the method of induction, this difficulty does not exist, because the source body does not need to touch the electroscope at all. The method is now described in detail not only because of its own intrinsic interest, but also because it gives a further insight into the way in which a charge may affect another which is located some distance away.

Fig. 2-3 shows drawings of the procedure at five different stages of the operation of charging by induction. In Fig. 2-3(A) the uncharged electroscope is represented. An absence of plus and minus signs indicates that the positive and negative charges are paired off, and shows that an uncharged body only contains charge of both signs which cancel the effect of each other. In Fig. 2-3(B) a positively charged rod has been brought near the electroscope. As a result, the position of the residual charge in the electroscope is disturbed. Some of the positive charge that was originally located at the head of the nail is repelled and sent to the bottom point of the nail while some

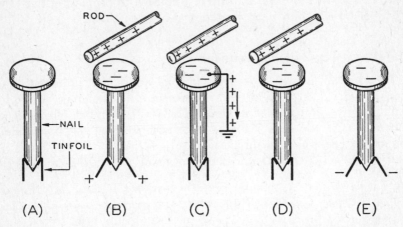

Fig. 2-3. The five stages of charging an electroscope by induction.

of the negative charge at the point is attracted to the head of the nail. As a result, even though the electroscope as a whole is still uncharged, there is an excess of positive charge at the leaves and they are forced apart as is shown in Fig. 2-3(B).

If at this moment the charged rod were removed, all the original charges in the electroscope would return to their original positions as in Fig. 2-3(A) and nothing would have been accomplished. If instead, the electroscope is now grounded, as is shown in Fig. 2-3(C), charge of one sign will flow off the electroscope to ground, so that when the ground connection is broken as in Fig. 2-3(D), and then the charged rod removed as in Fig. 2-3(E), a preponderance of charge of one sign will remain on the electroscope, and this will distribute itself over the head and point of the nail. It is of particular importance to notice that in Fig. 2-3(C) it is the positive charge and not the negative charge which flows off into the ground. The negative charge becomes an example of what is called *bound charge*. It is almost as if each charge on the rod were tied to one of the charges at the top of the electroscope so as to prevent that charge from escaping, while urging a charge of the other sign to move away as far as possible. Actually, of course, the bonds are not tangible things at all but only another example of a charge being able to establish a field which affects another charge which is remotely located. It is also interesting to note that when a body is charged by the method of induction, it ends up with a sign that is opposite to that of the source. This fact is often a cause of confusion to people working with static electricity and must be thoroughly understood.

Faraday's Ice-Pail Experiment

An experiment which is very famous and quite illuminating is known as the "Faraday ice-pail experiment." The reference to an ice pail does not imply that any thermal properties are taken into account, but only that the experiment is done with a small metal container similar to one which might be used to hold ice. With Faraday's ice pail it can be shown that the amount of induced charge is equal to the

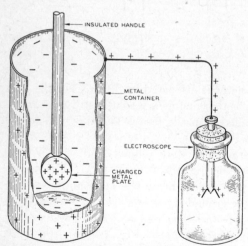

INSULATED HANDLE

METAL CONTAINER

ELECTROSCOPE

CHARGED METAL PLATE

Fig. 2-4. The equality of the amount of induced charge to the neighboring charge causing the induction is demonstrated by the Faraday ice-pail experiment, the apparatus for which is illustrated at the left, consisting of a metal container connected to an electroscope.

neighboring charge causing the induction, and that a grounded metal shield placed around a configuration of static charge is sufficient to insure that the effects of that charge cannot be detected at a point outside the container. The latter fact forms the basis of electric shielding, which is so commonly used in radio design, while the first fact is useful in explaining the action of electric condensers.

The arrangement for Faraday's ice pail experiment, as it is shown in Fig. 2-4, consists of a metal container connected to an electroscope, both of which are initially entirely uncharged, and also a charged flat metal plate mounted for convenience on an insulated handle. This little test plate, which is called a *proof plane,* may be charged by the use of the induction method previously described, or it may receive a charge from a high-voltage battery or generator arrangement as is shown in Fig. 2-5. When the positively charged proof plane is introduced into the uncharged metal container, as shown in Fig. 2-4, paired

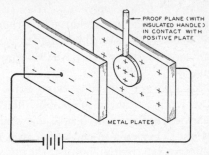

Fig. 2-5. A static charge can be obtained on a proof plane by placing it in contact with a plate connected to one side of a high-voltage battery or generator.

positive and negative charges in the container will rearrange themselves in the ice pail. Negative charge is attracted to the inner walls of the container while positive charge is made to move to the outer walls and also into the electroscope where its presence is manifested by the spreading of the electroscope leaves. Now starting with this arrangement as shown, if the charged proof plane is allowed to touch the container, then the negative charge of the inner walls will simply neutralize the positive charge on the plate without affecting the positive charge on the outside of the container or in the electroscope. This is true because of the fact that such direct contact of the metal container with the proof plane does not affect the electroscope deflection. This is proof that the magnitude of the induced charge on the inner surface of the can is exactly equal to that on the original source.

The fact that whenever charge is placed inside a hollow metal container, an induced charge appears on the inner surface in a quantity that is exactly equal to the original charge, is an indication that electrostatic shielding is possible.

The fact that a grounded metal shield will carry no charge on its outer surface can also be directly demonstrated with the apparatus of Fig. 2-4. If, after obtaining the condition shown there, the can is connected to ground, the free positive charge on the outer surface of the can and in the electroscope will, of course, flow away through the ground connection and cause the electroscope leaves to collapse. If next the ground connection is broken and then the proof plane removed, the negative charges on the inner surface of the can which were originally bound in place, are freed and spread throughout the metal of the can and into the electroscope where they cause the leaves to open. Now, if the same charged proof plane is reinserted, the negative charge of the metal can is again drawn to the inner surface of the shield can. This is observed by the action of the electroscope, the leaves of which just close. Here, in effect, a grounded shield was first placed around some charge and then by disconnecting that ground it was shown that the shield had automatically adjusted itself with ground so that its exterior was charge free with the internal charge present.

All of this may seem to have little to do with microwaves. The point which it is desired to establish is that electric charge is not something which is just poured into one end of a wire and allowed to run out of the other end, even though in a discussion of simple wired circuits it can be treated in just that way. Instead, electric charge is something which is plentiful in all materials and is especially mobile in metals. When attention is restricted to charge which is moving along in a wire, the resulting phenomena can be observed by metering the amount of charge which passes a given point (amperes) and by measuring the energy which is carried by each unit charge (volts). On the other hand, when microwaves are dealt with and devices such as waveguides and resonant cavities must be used, it is often found more convenient to work with field measurements which fortunately do not need to specify the exact location of every charge. What has just been described is an attempt to indicate that under various conditions charge will move around in a conductor and form a distribution which has varying effects on external indicators.

Electric Field

A great advantage of working with electric field (force on a unit charge) lies in the fact that it is not necessary to know the location of the charges which are causing the force. If a chalk mark is made on the top of a table and its position called P, the question can be asked as to what force would be exerted on a test charge placed at point P without first obtaining any information concerning other charge which may be in the neighborhood. More definitely, what force would appear to work on a unit positive charge which is placed on the table and held at the chalk mark?

Such a unit positive charge is looked upon as a test charge and is used (at least theoretically) as a measuring instrument. When this unit charge is placed at P and there found to experience a force of n dynes, the electric field at P is said to have a strength of n. (The size of this unit is defined later in the chapter.) It is possible, of course, that nothing at all will happen when the test charge is placed at the chalk mark P. Nothing will happen if no other charge is in the neighborhood. If a positive charge is fastened to the bottom of the table directly under the chalk mark, however, a force will appear which tries to push the test charge off the table. From the observation of such a force, one might be tempted to guess that there was charge glued to the underside. Such a deduction might very well be wrong. Instead, a much stronger charge may be located on the floor directly underneath the table, or an even stronger charge in the basement which would give the same effect. Other charges may, for example, be placed around the elge of the table, and if they are of the same sign and are symmetrically located around the test charge on the table, their effect on the test charge will cancel out and not be observed. Therefore when the electric field of a point is measured by making use of a test charge, all that can really be said is that the point in question has the property that a charge placed there is subject to a force. It cannot be stated that any single or definite array of charge is the cause of that force. Actually in most cases, interest is only in this force.

The known facts can be very briefly stated: there is a certain electric field at the point in question. It must be very clearly understood that electric field is a quantity which measures the properties of a point in space. It is not at all necessary that a charge be there or indeed that anything else be there at all. The so-called test charge is to be regarded only as a tool for detecting and measuring that field.

Other kinds of fields are similar to the electric field. For example, when the earth's gravitational field which surrounds the earth is considered, it is meant that a test mass in that field will feel a force pulling it toward the ground. It is not necessarily meant that anything in particular is in the space around the earth; the field is presumed to be there all the time even in the absence of any test object. Similarly, radio waves propagated through space may be assumed to create electric and magnetic fields in the absence of all matter, although they are detectable only when an antenna or a test charge is present.

Like any true force, electric field is a vector quantity. If a test charge is placed at a point in order to measure the field there, it is not enough to say that there will be so many dynes or so many pounds of force acting on the charge. It is also necessary to say that there will be so many pounds acting upward or downward or to the right or left. This is precisely what a vector quantity shows. In the case of the table and the chalk mark referred to before, a perspective sketch showing an arrow drawn with its tail at the chalk mark can represent a vector picture at this point of the field. The direction of the arrow shows the way in which the force urges the test charge, and the length of the arrow indicates the magnitude of the force on the unit test charge.

The meaning of an electric field can also be understood by saying that it is *the voltage per unit length that exists in a medium.* If two very large plates are separated by a distance of 1 meter and have V volts connected between them, the electric field in the medium between the plates is said to be equal to V volts per meter directed perpendicularly to the surface of the plates and pointing toward the plate of negative polarity. This is equivalent to the force picture just given, inasmuch as a unit positive test charge placed in the region between the plates would be urged to move toward the plate of negative polarity under a force of V units. Without going into detail concerning the ideas of voltage and potential, this equivalence may be made apparent from the definition of a volt. Voltage is energy divided by charge, and energy is force times distance. Thus voltage per unit length is the same as force per unit charge.

To discuss quantitatively the effect of charges upon each other, some method of measuring a quantity of charge is required. This is done by basing the definition of a unit charge upon the property of attraction and repulsion. If two identical quantities of charge of the same sign are placed one centimeter (about 2/5 of an inch) apart and the repulsive force between them measured, and then if the amount of each charge is adjusted while always keeping the two equal until the repulsive force is equal to one dyne (about 2.3 millionths of a pound) of force, then the quantity of each charge is said to be equal to one electrostatic unit. This unit of charge is very small. Three thousand million such charges are in a coulomb, which is the ordinary practical unit of charge.

Three kinds of units are occasionally referred to in many books on electrodynamics. One is the *electrostatic* system of units (*esu*) which is based upon measurements made with static charges. Another is the *electromagnetic* system of units (*emu*) which is based upon measurements made with magnets and is generally useful for magnetostatic work. The third is the so-called *practical system* of units, which is most commonly used in circuit work and which includes quantities such as the ordinary volt, ampere, and watt. To make matters worse, none of these systems are very satisfactory for computations which must include phenomena in all three realms of electromagnetic theory. One or two additional compromise systems of units are therefore commonly used when it is desired to cover the whole field. One of these is known as the *gaussian system* of units and the other is called the *Giorgi or MKS system*. The latter system seems to be increasing in popularity.

Coulomb's law describes the force which acts between two neighboring, but otherwise isolated charges. *It states that two unit charges will repel each other with a force of one dyne when they are one centimeter apart (according to the definition), that they will repel each other with a lesser force when they are further apart, and that furthermore the force will become less in a manner which is proportional to the square of the separation.* At 2 centimeters the force between two unit charges will be 1/4 dyne; at 3 centimeters it will be 1/9 dyne. From Coulomb's law it is known that the force of attraction or repulsion will depend upon the medium in which the charges are immersed. In other words, the definition of unit charge should strictly have been set up by referring to the charges being located in a vacuum. In any other medium, the force will be less. The factor which dictates how much less is given by a constant K, which is called the *dielectric constant*. In esu, K has the value of unity for a vacuum, and has a greater value for other media, depending upon how much those media reduce the force. Coulomb's law may be stated as

$$F = \frac{Q_1 Q_2}{Kr^2}$$

where Q_1 and Q_2 are the two charges, r is their separation, and F is the force between them.

Field Arising from Charge

Although it is quite possible and often desirable to consider field strength without taking into account anything about the neighboring charges which give rise to the measured value, it is also possible to predict the field strength which will be obtained as the result of known arrays of charge. From Coulomb's law alone it can immediately be seen what the electric field in a region surrounding an isolated charge is like. Consider the special case in which 15 units of positive charge are located at an isolated point in space; what electric field will be observed 10 cm to the north of that location? In accordance with the definition, this is equivalent to asking what force will appear on a unit charge placed at the point in question. The magnitude of the force can be calculated as

$$E = \frac{Q}{Kr^2} = \frac{15}{1 \times 100} = 0.15 \text{ esu}$$

Because like charges are known to repel each other, the force and hence the field are directed to the north.

In Fig. 2-6, a somewhat more complicated case is considered. The problem here is: what field will be observed at point P because of 81 units of positive charge located 3 cm to the east and 72 units of negative charge 6 cm away in a direction 60° north of east? To solve

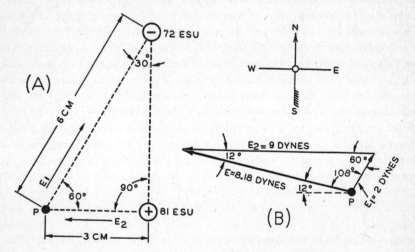

Fig. 2-6. The electric field arising from two charges.

this sort of problem the procedure outlined before is followed, inasmuch as a unit positive charge is introduced at P and then the force that will be exerted on that test charge is found. It is apparent that there will be an attractive force which will urge the test charge to move toward the negative 72-unit charge and a repelling force which will push the test charge away from the 81-unit positive charge. These forces, the magnitudes of which may easily be computed from Coulomb's law, are shown in Fig. 2-6(B) as vectors E_1 and E_2. They indicate that the test charge will be urged to move 60° north of east with a force of 2 dynes and in a westward direction with a force of 9 dynes. The problem of finding the electric field strength at P therefore reduces to one of finding a single force which is equivalent to these two.

If two forces act in different directions on a body, the body will be caused to move in a direction that is a compromise between the directions indicated by the forces. If after the direction of motion is established, the two forces are replaced by a single force of suitable magnitude which is directed so as to cause the proper motion, then that force may be said to be equivalent to the original pair of forces and hence represent their sum. This is really the definition of the sum of two vectors and is very simple. *To add two vectors so as to obtain a single vector that is the sum of the pair, one vector is drawn so that its origin is coincident with the head of the other, and their sum is a new vector which extends from the origin of the first vector to the head of the second.* This simple rule, which may be applied either through mathematical formulas or may be used graphically by drawing actual vector arrows to scale, is a valid method no matter what physical measurement the vectors represent.

It is true if the vectors represent displacement. If a man walks three miles east, the fact that he has displaced himself three miles in that direction may be represented by a vector arrow three units long pointing to the east. If the man then continues his walk by going four miles north, that displacement may also be shown by an arrow four units long and pointing northward. This second arrow would be drawn with its origin at the head of the first arrow, since the first arrow represents the man's position after the first part of his journey. After the respective three- and four-mile walks, however, the man does not find himself displaced from his initial position by seven miles, even though he has walked that far. Instead, his displacement is only five miles in a general north-easterly direction, because that is the length of the third side of the triangle formed by his two movements. It is also the length of the vector arrow necessary to complete the vector addition performed in accordance with the definition.

Returning now to Fig. 2-6, it is clear what procedure should be followed to find the actual electric field at point P which arises from the components E_1 and E_2 induced from the fixed charges. The vectors E_1 and E_2 are added, which has been done in Fig. 2-6(B). E_1 was first drawn with the same direction and magnitude as was computed, and then E_2 added on with its origin at the head of E_1. The vector sought is E, and it can be determined either graphically or by methods of trigonometry,[1] that E is an arrow 8.18 units long which is directed in the manner shown. It is therefore finally found that the electric field at P in Fig. 2-6 is 8.18 dynes per esu of charge directed **12 degrees** north of west.

Electric Displacement

Although it is often true that too brief a mention of a subject is confusing, if not dangerous, nevertheless a discussion of the electric displacement field is very necessary. This is particularly true, because some later mention of this idea occurs in Chapter 9. It is therefore advisable to introduce the idea here, even though it does not play an important role in an introductory discussion of microwave radio. Perhaps this mention in addition to the discussion in the terminology section will suffice for some and make it easier for others to understand the more elaborate treatments in other books on electrodynamics.

The electric field **E** at any point in space is a field which arises because of contributions from all charge in the neighborhood. It is a vector quantity that is the sum of field components from each and every charge. Another kind of field also proves to be useful in electromagnetic theory. It is usually called the *electric displacement field* and represented by the capital letter **D**. It is a field which arises only from "real charge" and is unaffected by polarized charge pairs. The crux of the situation is summarized by a more careful consideration of the constant K, which was introduced in the statement of Coulomb's law. If the force between two isolated charges is measured and then, without disturbing the separation of the charges, they are immersed in a gas or fluid and the force measured again, in general it will be somewhat smaller. In order that Coulomb's law shall be correct for both cases it is necessary that the law include a constant K, which is dependent among other things upon the medium in which the charges are placed. The electric displacement is defined as the product of K and E. In simple cases the displacement field is a vector directed in the same direction as E but greater in magnitude by a factor K.

The reason that the force between two charges may be expected to be reduced upon immersion in a medium is that the medium itself although neutral, inasmuch as it contains equal amounts of charge or both signs, is nevertheless a substance made up of charge and therefore not without electrical properties. Any small but microscopic portion of the medium will contain equal positive and negative charge, and when a field is present these small entities tend to deform themselves so as to obey the laws of attraction and repulsion as best they can. Such action is called *polarization* and such charge is called *polarization charge* in contradistinction to free charge, which was mentioned before. *Free charge* is that kind which is ordinarily meant in current flow problems, and this is in contrast to polarized and *bound charge* to which we have just referred as polarization charge. As polarization charges become polarized, they may reduce the electric field arising from one charge and hence the force exerted on the other. The electric displacement D, however, is larger than E by just the factor necessary to make it independent of polarization. D does not depend upon the medium and is often easier to compute. In a vacuum, D and E are numerically the same in the Gaussian system of units; in gases they are also very close in magnitude. In the esu system, K for air is only 1.00058 at normal temperature and pressure and ordinary electrical frequencies.

Electric Potential

Another way of describing the condition of a point in space with respect to charge in the neighborhood has to do with the measurement of the energy necessary to carry a unit test charge to that point. In one important way this is easier than it is to measure the field at the point in question. It is easier because energy is not a vector quantity but is only a scalar, and the point is therefore characterized by just a number rather than by a number and a direction. It is unfortunate that such calculations are not quite as useful, nor are they applicable to magnetic phenomenon in a simple form.

The magnitude of the energy necessary to carry a unit test charge from a ground reference to a given point in space is known as the *potential* of that point and is measured in volts. It may be esu volts, or in another system, it may be practical volts just like those used to measure a storage battery. It is common experience among those who work with circuits that voltage alone does not tell the whole story of a power supply. A high-impedance spark coil may generate a high voltage and yet only cause slight discomfort when touched to the hand, whereas a low-voltage source of high current supplying ability may be able to burn through a substantial piece of steel. Voltage alone, however, does indicate to what extent an existing charge wants to move. *Voltage is the energy per unit charge.* Since it is customary to speak of high voltage at a point where there is not much charge, it is only one step further to use potential to describe the condition of a point where no charge exists, except possibly a unit test charge carried there in imagination for the purpose of measurement. *The potential of any point is the work which must be done upon a unit positive charge in order to move it from some ground reference to the point in question.*

If a region of space is empty except for a single charge Q and the potential of a point r units distant from that charge is to be found, it may be computed from the relation

$$V = \frac{Q}{Kr}$$

where V is the potential, and K is the dielectric constant mentioned previously. It will be noticed that this expression is quite similar to Coulomb's law. In fact, the only difference is that here r enters only to the first power rather than as the square. This is not accidental. Energy which is essential in the unit of potential (volts equal energy per unit charge) is stored by virtue of a force working through a distance. The Coulomb law expression for force must therefore be dimensionally multiplied by a distance to become a measure of energy. It develops that this multiplication is simply one by r, so the strong similarity of form in the equations occurs.

If, in Fig. 2-6, the potential of point P arising from the two charges shown is to be found, the task will be somewhat easier than was the case with electric fields. Two potential components may be computed as

$$V_1 = \frac{-72}{6} = -12 \qquad\qquad V_2 = \frac{81}{3} = 27$$

These are added algebraically and the potential of point P is found to be $27 - 12 = 15$ esu units.

FOOTNOTE

1. By the law of cosines, $(9)^2 + (2)^2 - (2 \text{x} 2 \text{x} 9 \cos 60°) = E^2$

   Therefore $\qquad\qquad\qquad E = 8.18$

   By the law of sines $\qquad \dfrac{\sin \theta}{2} = \dfrac{\sin 60°}{8.18}$

   Therefore $\qquad\qquad\qquad \theta = 12°$

Chapter 3

MAGNETOSTATICS

O ACCOUNT FOR the properties of radio waves and particularly to understand something about energy flow through space, it is not enough to discuss charge and electric field alone. Another equally important kind of field, which is called *magnetic field*, must also be understood. It turns out, in fact, that a measure of the radio energy flow through a region of space may be made from the product of the electric and magnetic fields in that part of space. A quantity called *Poynting's vector* may be obtained from the vector product of the electric and magnetic fields. Poynting vectors play the same role in space phenomena as do watts as computed from voltage, current, and power factor, in circuit theory.

Particularly in microwave radio, where hollow metallic bodies may be used as resonant devices just as tuned circuits are at longer wavelengths, it is necessary to understand as much about magnetic fields as possible. This is essential in order to understand the way in which these hollow resonators function and in order to see how to make an external connection to them. Also, in dealing with microwave transmission systems, it is often convenient to define a special kind of impedance in terms of the electric and magnetic fields and to use this as an aid in matching lines to sources and loads. These reasons and others make it necessary to consider and review certain facts concerning magnetism.

Magnets

When a piece of iron or steel is treated in a certain way, it becomes a magnet and exhibits magnetic properties. These magnetic properties have a degree of permanence that depends upon the hardness of the material and the treatment experienced by that material after magnetization. Hard steels retain their magnetism best, although a soft iron is the easiest to magnetize in the first place. Heating and pounding will remove magnetism. In an examination a student was presumably within his rights when he answered the query of "How do

24

you demagnetize a watch?" by "Heat it red hot and pound it with a hammer," even though a somewhat gentler answer concerning a variable alternating current was expected. In any event, magnetization is a process of orientation of sub-microscopic particles, and demagnetization is a disrupting of that orientation.

Pounding disrupts the order in a purely mechanical way; heat imparts additional energy to the molecule so that they can upset any magnetic order that may have been present. Strong alternating currents in the neighborhood can set up strong magnetic forces which will shift the order of the innermost iron particles with a back-and-forth motion as the polarity of the alternating current changes back and forth. If such an alternating current is slowly reduced in strength, a demagnetizing effect is realized.

One simple way to magnetize a piece of iron is to wrap wire around it in one direction and pass a direct current through that wire. Modern theories of exactly what happens when this is done are extremely complex in detail, and are not even entirely satisfactory in some cases. The general explanation, however, is one based upon the observation that a current circulating in a circle will give rise to magnetic effects that are qualitatively the same as those of a magnet lying along the axis of that circle. The conclusion is that all magnetic fields are caused by moving charge. At least this is a good picture, if one wishes to work with a mechanical idea of the atom that is similar to the one first put forward by Bohr, namely, miniature planetary systems are imagined with electrons of negative charge circulating around a positive core or nucleus, much as the planets revolve around the sun. All materials effectively contain such rotating systems which, however, are normally oriented at random so that no gross magnetic effect is observable. Materials containing iron and, to a much lesser extent some other metals, have the peculiar property that when they are placed in a magnetic field, these submicroscopic systems become partially aligned so that the overall piece acts as a magnet.

In Fig. 3-1 is shown the relation between a circulating current and the magnetic poles which are obtained. A simple rule for relating the facts is known as the right-hand rule. If the fingers of the right hand are directed so as to point in the direction of positive current flow, the thumb will be pointing toward the *north* pole of the magnet. The important fact is that although electric fields are found whenever charge is present in a neighborhood, magnetic effects will be observed only when there is a current that is not completely random in its flow.

Magnetic Poles

The earth itself has the properties of a huge magnet, which extends roughly but not exactly along the earth's axis of rotation. Magnetic measurements indicate that a magnetic pole of the earth exists in the Arctic and another in the Antarctic. The fact that the one in the Arctic near the north geographic pole is a south magnetic pole, while

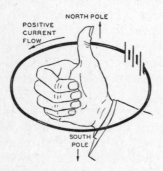

Fig. 3-1. The relation between a circulating current and the magnetic poles which are obtained is illustrated by the right-hand rule. When the fingers of the right hand are pointed in the direction of the positive current flow, the thumb points towards the north pole.

the one in the Antarctic is a north pole is a cause of some confusion, although it is simply a matter of definition. The situation is easy to remember when the logic of the basis of the definition is understood.

If a small bar magnet is suspended from a fine thread and placed at a point well removed from other magnetic materials, the magnet will turn like a compass and come to rest with one end pointing north and the other south. By definition, the end pointing north is called a north pole, while the end pointing south is called a south pole. Strictly, the poles should be named north-seeking or south-seeking, since they are the ends of the bar which point in those directions when undisturbed. The simpler forms are almost universally used, however, and mean the same thing. Since, as may be quickly determined by experiment with two or more magnets, the poles of which have been named in this manner, like poles repel each other, and unlike poles attract each other, it follows that the magnetic pole of the earth which caused the north pole of a bar magnet to point toward the Arctic, must itself be of the kind which has been named a south pole.

Magnetic Moment

To go beyond what has already been said, magnetic poles are rather unsatisfactory to discuss. This is true because no one point on a magnet nor near a coil of wire exhibiting magnetic properties, can be said to be a pole. Magnetic poles are at best not points, but rather regions at the end of a rod of iron or near the end of a helix of wire. Since they cannot be located precisely nor bounded accurately, it is inconvenient, if not impossible, to make precise calculations in terms of them.

It is equally impossible to isolate a magnetic pole of one kind from an accompanying one of the other kind: whenever a north pole is found, a south pole must exist close by. If a bar magnet is cut in two, a new north or a new south pole will be formed at the cut, so that both halves immediately become magnets complete with both poles. The same sort of thing is true no matter what is done to magnetic material. North and south poles always exist in pairs.

For this reason it is more logical to measure magnetic entities in terms of a quantity which involves a *pair* of magnetic poles. To do so is to recognize that magnetism is a different sort of thing than the attraction and repulsion of charge. This means that an analysis of magnetic fields may be started without a prejudice that is based on an analogy with the electrical system, which would require comparing positive charge to north poles and negative charge to south poles. This furthermore allows the immediate consideration of quantities that have actual measurable values. The quantity to be defined as the *magnetic moment* is one which can be used to characterize the strength of any bar magnet, and this, in conjunction with physical dimensions, will serve as a complete description of the magnetic properties of any magnet.

In Fig. 3-2 a pair of very large magnetic pole pieces is shown having a strength of some constant amount. The task of establishing absolute

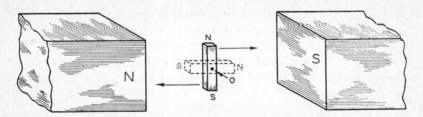

Fig. 3-2. The magnetic moment is obtained from the measure of the torque which urges the small magnet to rotate between the pole pieces of the larger magnet.

units will be left until later, because this becomes easier after the field idea is introduced. For the present merely assume this large constant magnet for the purpose of examining the behavior of other magnets in terms of how they act when they are placed between its pole pieces.

If, for example, a small magnet is placed midway between the large poles in the position shown in Fig. 3-2, the magnetic forces will be applied in the manner that is indicated. Since on the small magnet there is an equal amount of force to the left and to the right, there will be in this case no tendency for the magnet to be moved toward either of the large poles. It will only be urged to rotate about a point O, and ultimately come to rest with its north pole opposite the south pole of the large fixed magnet as shown by the dashed lines. It is from the measure of the *torque* which urges the magnet to rotate, that a simple measurement of the quantity called *magnetic moment* is obtained. If a second small magnet were to replace the one first used and were found to require twice the torque to hold its orientation in the crosswise position, then that magnet would be said to have twice as great a magnetic moment as the first.

If you lay your pencil on the flat top of a desk and twist it around as the magnet of Fig. 3-2 is twisted, you will probably be doing so with a thumb and forefinger. The thumb is pushing in one direction and the forefinger in the other, just as are the magnetic forces of Fig. 3-2. Especially if your pencil is a heavy one, you can notice that the rotation is easiest when the thumb and forefinger are separated the furthest. *Torque* is more than a force; it is two equal and opposite forces, the magnitude of which is multiplied by the perpendicular distance between the vectors representing them.

Torque may also be said to be a single force multiplied by the perpendicular distance from a hinge, although that definition has no concern here except perhaps as it allows further mechanical explanation. Try opening a door by pushing only an inch out from the hinge. It is difficult and requires a hard push. A small push at the door knob will accomplish the same thing by applying the same torque. The torque is the same for both cases because the force of the small push on the knob is multiplied by the large distance to the hinge to produce the same product that can be obtained from a large force at the small distance.

In Fig. 3-2, the torque may be measured by applying a pair of restraining forces and adjusting them so that they just resist the torque of the magnetic forces. As has been said before, that torque is a measure of the magnetic moment of the small magnet; it is also a measure of how strongly the big magnet is acting on the small one. It will result that under conditions of orientation like that shown in Fig. 3-2

$$T = M \times H$$

where **T** is the torque, **M** is the magnetic moment of the small magnet, and **H** is the magnetic field in the area where the small magnet is located.

Magnetic Field

As in the case of an electric field, a magnetic field is to be regarded as a property of a point or region of space. It is a property which depends upon the strength or arrangement of permanent magnets or currents in the neighborhood of that point or region, but does not uniquely determine what that arrangement must be. To determine the magnetic field at or near a point P, such as that shown in Fig. 3-3,

FIG. 3-3, right. Measuring the magnetic field **H** at a point P in space.

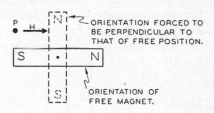

ORIENTATION FORCED TO BE PERPENDICULAR TO THAT OF FREE POSITION.

ORIENTATION OF FREE MAGNET.

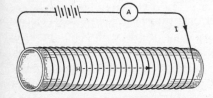

FIG. 3-4, left. A long solenoid can be used to establish the definition of a unit in which to measure magnetic moments and field strengths.

a small freely-mounted magnet of known magnetic moment is placed there. The direction in which the north pole of that compass points is the direction of a vector representing the magnetic field. If that magnet is then forced to rotate 90 degrees to take up a position like that shown by the dashed lines in Fig. 3-2 and the torque necessary to hold it there measured, the magnitude of **H** can be computed from the relation already given. Solved for **H**, this is simply $H = T/M$. Knowing the magnitude and direction of the field, only a set of units need be established in order to draw a vector to specify it.

A very satisfactory way to get at the definition of a unit in which to measure magnetic moments and field strengths is through the use of a long solenoid like the one shown in Fig. 3-4. Experiment shows

that the field inside and near the lengthwise center of such a device
is very constant. If a current of I amperes flows through the coil, it
is convenient to state simply that the internal field is a certain amount.
In one set of units the field is said to be **H** oersteds where

$$\mathbf{H} = \frac{4\pi}{10}\, nI$$

The number of turns of wire on the solenoid per centimeter of length
is given by n.

If with a solenoid like that shown in Fig. 3-4, a known magnetic
field is created in accordance with the definition of the oersted, and
then a small test magnet is inserted into the region of known field
strength and a torque measured, it is easy to compute the magnetic
moment of the test magnet in terms of oersteds and centimeter-dynes
of torque.[1] The same relation is used between **H**, **T**, and **M**, only
this time the equation is solved for **M**. After this is done, there is a
small magnet for which we posses a numerical value of the magnetic
moment. This calibrated magnet can then be used as a tool to measure
fields at other points.

Magnetic Field Arising from Current

Even though it is to be emphasized that magnetic fields, like electric
fields may be measured and used in solving problems without making
any reference to their cause, still it is also entirely legitimate to ask
what magnetic field will be found at a point in space because of current flowing in known circuits in the neighborhood of that point. The
fact that the magnetic field could also be influenced by permanent
magnets or changing electric fields which might also be present, are
added complications which are recognized or will be discussed again
later, but which do not affect the validity of the present idea. The
general rule for computing magnetic field arising from current is
known as the *Biot-Savart law*.

In Fig. 3-5, what magnetic field will be found at point P because
of a current flowing in the circuit shown to be located nearby? The
question is similar to the one which was asked about the electric field
arising from a multiplicity of charges. The field components which
arise from each small piece of the circuit first are found and then
the vector sum of all those components is made to get the net field
that is observable because of the whole circuit. The Biot-Savart law

shows what contribution to expect from each small length of current. For example, in Fig. 3-5, point P will experience a field component $d\mathbf{H}$ because of the current I flowing in the short length of circuit which is labeled dl. According to the right-hand rule, the field component

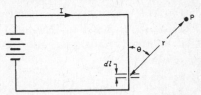

Fig. 3-5. The magnetic field component $d\mathbf{H}$ at the point P due to the current I flowing in the small length of circuit dl will be directed out of the paper, according to the right-hand rule.

$d\mathbf{H}$ will be directed out of the paper toward the reader. The Biot-Savart law shows that $d\mathbf{H}$ will have a magnitude that depends upon the distance r, the length dl, the angle θ, and the current I. The exact relationship which the Biot-Savart law states is

$$dH = \frac{I \sin \theta \, dl}{10r^2} \ oersteds.$$

The problem of calculating actual fields at points near actual circuits is a matter of making a vector addition of a very large number of components, each of which arises from a separate small current. In many complicated cases this proves to be too laborious to be worthwhile, but in a large class of geometrically symmetrical cases it is not too difficult. In most hollow pipe waveguide cases for example, it is feasible to predict the current configuration in the walls from a knowledge of the fields throughout the interior space. The reverse predictions of field configuration from current distribution could equally well be made. Since it is the field which is most easily measurable, however, the current is the factor that is more often computed.

Particularly in cases where the current flow is restricted to a single plane or a set of planes essentially parallel to each other, the contributions predicted by the Biot-Savart law are easily added by methods of calculus, because all the vector components of the field are headed in the same direction. The fact that the magnetic field is perpendicular to the planes of the current flow is important. Three examples of simple geometric circuits and the fields at places nearby, as calculated from the Biot-Savart law follow:

$H = \dfrac{2I}{10r}$ where r is the distance away from a long straight wire as shown in Fig. 3-6 (A). The field is directed circularly around the wire in a direction which would be indicated by the fingers of the right hand if the wire were grasped so as to cause the thumb to point the direction of positive current flow.

$$H = \frac{2\pi nI}{10r}$$ at the center of a ring r centimeters in radius and containing n turns carrying I amperes as shown in Fig. 3-6(B). The field is directed in accordance with the right-hand rule.

$$H = \frac{4\pi nI}{10r}$$ for the center of a long solenoid in accordance with the definition of the oersted, as shown in Fig. 3-6(C). This equation may also be derived from the Biot-Savart law. The field is directed in accordance with the right-hand rule.

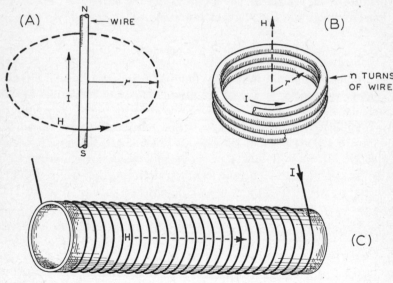

FIG. 3-6. The locations of the magnetic field component **H** in three simple circuits.

Magnetic Induction

A second kind of magnetic field known as *magnetic induction*, and usually represented by the letter **B**, is often of more fundamental importance than **H**. Since $B = \mu H$, where μ is the permeability of the medium, there is usually no difficulty in changing from one kind of field to the other. In fact, in gaussian units μ is unity, or approximately unity for all but a few materials such as those containing iron. In iron-core transformers, on the other hand, the values of **B** and **H** can be very different. Since the values can be so different and since **B** and **H** are physically different even though often measured by the same numerical values, it is well worthwhile to try to distinguish between them.

H is a field quantity that represents the magnetic results of a flowing current; **B** is the measure of a magnetic field which tells of the ability of changing magnetic field strength to induce a voltage. Without getting too far away from static magnetic fields, perhaps the situation may be summarized as follows:

H

(1) Stationary charge shows no magnetic effect.
(2) Moving charge or current produces a magnetic field called **H**.

B

(1) Stationary and constant magnetic fields produce no voltage along stationary electrical conductors.
(2) When motion or change of field strength is properly incurred, the strength of the field may be deduced from the magnitude of the voltage induced in a conductor. When the magnetic field is measured in this way, it is said to be a field of strength **B**.

In Fig. 3-7 is shown a pair of pole pieces of the dimensions indicated. The magnetic field **B** (checkered area) which we wish to measure, is presumed to be constant and, in accord with the methods mentioned before, it could be represented at any point by a vector arrow which gives magnitude by its length and direction in accordance with its orientation. Here, however, it is desired to indicate a constant intensity over a region and it is found more convenient to do so by the use of a large number of direction-indicating lines; these have no particular significance attached to their length but rather portray the magnitude of the field in accordance with the density with which they are drawn. Such lines are called *lines of magnetic induction,* and the total number of them passing between the two pole pieces is said to be the *total magnetic induction flux.* The number of lines shown per unit area on the pole pieces is the value of **B**.

Now if a piece of wire connected to a voltmeter is moved between the pole pieces at a uniform velocity so that all the lines of flux are cut in t seconds, a voltage will register on the voltmeter while the sweep is being made. It takes 10^8 lines of magnetic flux cut per second to generate one volt. Thus if V volts are observed, the total lines of induction cut in t seconds must be $Vt \times 10^8$. This must be just the

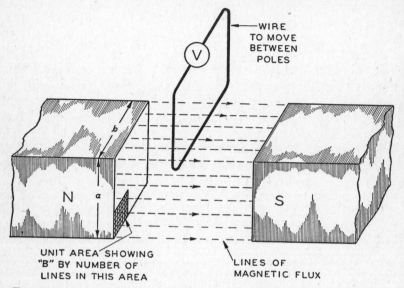

WIRE
TO MOVE
BETWEEN
POLES

UNIT AREA SHOWING
"B" BY NUMBER OF
LINES IN THIS AREA

LINES OF
MAGNETIC FLUX

FIG. 3-7. Magnetic induction and its measurements in terms of the total flux.

total flux between the two pole pieces, and this divided by the area of the pole pieces will give the density of the induction lines, or **B**. In this case

$$B = \frac{Vt \times 10^8}{a\,b}$$

FOOTNOTE

1. A centimeter dyne of torque is defined as the torque resulting from two oppositely directed forces of one dyne applied at points 1 cm apart. A dyne is the force necessary to cause 1 gram of mass to be accelerated so that its velocity increases 1 cm per second during each second that the force is applied.

Chapter 4

ALTERNATING CURRENT AND LUMPED CONSTANTS

I N ORDINARY ALTERNATING-CURRENT circuit theory, inductance, capacitance, and resistance may usually be regarded as lumped constants. A coil of wire may almost always be thought of as a pure inductance, or at most as an inductance in series with a resistance. Such an element can be shown on a circuit diagram with the usual symbol and, generally speaking, the impedances of the wires which connect it to other parts of the circuit, are entirely negligible. At UHF and microwave frequencies, this is not true. The whole circuit, including the connecting waveguide, then has properties which resemble those of resonance and are consequently dependent upon frequency. Because of this, waveguide connections are not usually discussed in terms of inductances connected to capacitances and resistances. The units henry, millihenry, or microfarad, are virtually never used. These are differences between a-c power engineering and UHF communication. What concerns us more, at the moment, are the many similarities.

The things which are common to microwave radio and to power engineering are very necessary to both subjects. The fact that in both cases oscillating charge gives rise to currents which constantly change in magnitude and periodically reverse in direction, is one similarity. The fact that in both cases electric and magnetic fields are generated must be recognized either explicitly or implicitly in order to account for observed results is another. Even the terms inductive and capacitive will be found in discussions of waveguides. When the words are used in this connection, they have a meaning closely akin to an ordinary inductance or capacitance, although they do not refer to anything which can be measured in farads or henrys. They refer instead to phase relations between voltage and current or between electric and magnetic fields. It is the purpose of this chapter to discuss some concepts pertaining to lumped constant circuits in those terms which can most easily be carried over to microwave connections.

Inductance

Whenever a current in a conductor changes, the surrounding magnetic field, which was caused by that current, also changes. If a passive circuit is located nearby, the magnetic flux linkage in that circuit will, in general, be changed in consequence, and a voltage will be generated therein, which will cause current to flow in the second circuit. This action, which is more fundamentally described by speaking of the change of magnetic fields so as to cause a varying flux linkage to induce a voltage, may also be described by attributing a *mutual inductance* to the two circuits.

Consider two coils of wire which are placed near each other, as shown in Fig. 4-1. One coil (the primary) is connected through a rheostat to a battery, so that the current can be set at any definite.

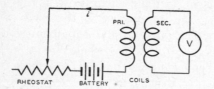

FIG. 4-1. Arrangement of two coils for studying their mutual inductance.

level, or else continuously varied by changing the rheostat. It is found that as long as the rheostat is left at any fixed setting, no voltage is induced into the second coil (the secondary) even if the resulting magnetic field is of great strength. When the rheostat is varied, however, a reading does appear on the voltmeter connected to the secondary. The faster the rheostat is turned, the greater the induced voltage becomes. It is found, in fact, that the voltmeter readings are directly proportional to the speed with which the rheostat is varied, and is consequently directly proportional to the rate at which the current in the primary changes. Such a proportionality between two quantities may be expressed by writing an equation, in which one factor is set equal to a constant term times the other factor. Such an equation shows that when one quantity changes the other quantity must also change in order for the equality to remain. The constant term takes care of the fact that one quantity may change at a different rate than the other quantity, and is essentially a number which quantitatively describes the proportionality. In this case we will call the constant of proportionality M, and write the expression as

$$e = M \frac{di}{dt}$$

where e is the voltage read on the voltmeter and $\dfrac{di}{dt}$ is a calculus notation for the rate of change of current in amperes per second. M is a quantity which is called *mutual inductance*.

If the rheostat and battery of Fig. 4-1 are replaced with an alternating-current source, the current in the primary coil will change continuously, and an alternating voltage will be generated in the secondary. If the primary current is a pure sine wave of a single frequency, its rate of change in amperes per second will be $2\pi f$ times the current, where f is the frequency in cycles per second. Thus, in this special case we have

$$e = 2\pi f i M.$$

Two coils are said to have a mutual inductance of one *henry* when a current change of one ampere per second in one coil causes a voltage of one volt to appear in the other.

It is not necessary for there to be two coils of wire in order to observe the phenomenon of inductance. When the effect is observed in a single coil, it is said to be *self inductance*, or inductance, as distinguished from mutual inductance. In Fig. 4-2 there are shown a coil, a resistance, and a variable direct-current voltage source which illustrates this. The voltage source may be a potentiometer connected

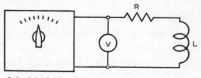

Fig. 4-2. Arrangement of apparatus for studying the self inductance of a coil.

D.C. SOURCE

across a storage battery or it may take some other form. In order to avoid confusing details and not be concerned with the exact mechanism, it shall be regarded as a box with a knob which will cause continuously variable and repeatable voltage readings to appear on a voltmeter connected across the terminals. Furthermore, assume that the coil is wound with such large wire that it has only negligible resistance. Under these conditions, the coil of wire will play no role at all for any fixed position of the knob on the voltage source. Current flowing through the coil will be steady d.c. which will maintain a constant magnetic field about the coil. Since constant magnetic fields do not induce voltages into conductors, the situation is the same as if only the resistance were connected to the source. The voltmeter across the source shows the amount of energy carried by each charge as it leaves the source so that if another voltmeter, which is not shown in Fig. 4-2, is connected across R, it will be found to read the same as the one across the source. This indicates that all the energy leaving the source is entering the resistance.

When the knob on the voltage source is being turned, the situation is different. Suppose, for the sake of definiteness, that the knob on the voltage source is being rotated in a direction which causes the voltmeter across the voltage source to increase its reading constantly. If a voltmeter is then connected across the resistance, a series of readings will be observed there also, but they will all be of smaller magnitude than they would be for corresponding stationary settings of the source voltage. If the coil contains many turns of wire and the source control knob is turned rapidly, the readings on the voltmeter connected across the resistance will be quite small. Furthermore, if during the process another voltmeter is connected across the coil, it will also be found to give an indication of voltage, instead of reading zero as it would for a fixed setting of the voltage source control. Changing the source voltage changes the current in the circuit, and this in turn changes the strength of the magnetic field. A changing magnetic field causes a voltage to be induced in nearby conductors. Unlike the mutual inductance case, the induced voltage does not this time appear in a second coil, but instead is found across the very terminals of the coil producing the magnetic field.

The magnitude of the voltage appearing across a resistanceless coil of wire is proportional to the rate at which the current through it changes. The proportionality again can be described by an equation containing a constant, which in agreement with custom shall be called L.

$$e = L\frac{di}{dt}$$

where e is the voltage observed across the terminals of the coil, and $\frac{di}{dt}$ is the rate of change of current through the coil in amperes per second. The constant L is known as the *coefficient of self inductance* or simply as *inductance*, and is effectively a number which describes the inductive character of a coil.

If the voltage source of Fig. 4-2 is replaced with an alternating-current source and the resistor is removed from the circuit, the current in the coil will change continuously and an alternating voltage will continue to appear across the source or coil. Proper fuses in the a-c supply will not be blown even though there is no resistive component to the load current. If the a-c source voltage is a pure sine wave, its rate of change is again just $2\pi f$ times the current and the equation for L may be written as

$$e = 2\pi f i L$$

where e and i are the effective a-c voltage and current respectively and f is the frequency in cycles per second.

From this, it should be apparent that in ordinary circuit theory, as well as in microwave work, the functions of magnetic fields are important. It happens that in the property called inductance there is a number which can, in many cases, save the trouble of thinking of the field theory explicitly.

Energy in a Magnetic Field

At the instant that a battery is connected to a coil or, for that matter, whenever a current through a coil is increasing, work must be done to build up a magnetic field in the neighborhood of the inductance. This increase in the magnetic field, which occurs only while the current is increasing, is really a storage of energy. The energy put into an inductance while the magnetic field is being built up, can be recovered when the field is allowed to disappear. When an unloaded transformer is connected to an a-c source of voltage, practically no net power is used. In each cycle, energy is required to build up a magnetic field, but in a later part of that same cycle the energy is returned to the source again. In the case of a d-c supply voltage that is connected to an inductance, energy is required when the connection is first made, but no more is needed after a steady condition has been reached. When, at a later time, it is necessary to break the circuit, arcing of the switch contacts will be noticed. That is what becomes of the energy which was originally fed into the inductance.

If a current level, i, in a coil is built up in t seconds, the rate of increase of i may be i/t amperes per second. By the definition of L, (Li/t) is the voltage across the coil during the build-up time. Since voltage times current is power P, and since the current has an average value of $i/2$ (half its final value) during its build-up, it is apparent that the transient power is

$$P = \frac{Li^2}{2t}$$

This means that P units of energy are fed into the inductance during each second that the current increases. Multiplying P by the total build up time, t, therefore gives the total energy W that is used in generating the magnetic field. This is

$$W = \frac{1}{2} L i^2$$

which is an expression of general applicability. Whenever a coil of inductance L is observed to be carrying a current i, W joules of energy were used in connecting the circuit and the same amount of energy will make an appearance whenever the current is interrupted.

In propagation problems and in microwave transmission lines, the storage of magnetic energy also must be considered. The forms of the circuits, and the fact that magnetic and electric storage usually occur together, make it generally impossible to use the simple formula just given, but the fundamental facts are the same.

Capacitance

A condenser consists of two conductors which are separated from each other by an insulator. In the most common form two parallel plates, or a series of interleaved parallel plates, are used, and the insulator is a material such as air, paper, or mica. Like an inductance, a condenser will accept energy from a d-c source only when the connection is first made, and will store that energy until a proper circuit change causes it to be released. A sufficiently large condenser connected in series with an a-c circuit will not absorb any appreciable power from that circuit. During a part of each cycle, energy will be stored in the condenser, but during a later part of the cycle that energy will be returned to the circuit. A condenser momentarily connected across a battery will contain stored energy, as can be seen from the spark which is generated when the condenser terminals are later short-circuited.

In Fig. 4-3 is shown a variable voltage d-c source like the one of Fig. 4-2, except that this time it is connected to a condenser through an ammeter. It will be found that the ammeter will read only when the source voltage is being changed, or for a short time after a change in voltage has been made. If the average value of the current, which flows during and after a change of source voltage, is multiplied by the time over which the average is taken, a proportionality between this product and the magnitude of the source-voltage charge will be observed. Since an ampere is by definition a current in which a coulomb of charge is moved each second, the product of current and time is charge. The proportionality of charge and voltage may be indicated with a constant C

$$Q = CV$$

where Q is the charge on the condenser, V the voltage across its terminals and C a constant which measures the size of a condenser. The unit of *capacitance* or *capacity* is the *farad*.

A condenser is said to have a capacitance of one farad when a potential difference of one volt will charge it with one coulomb of electricity.

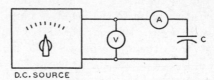

FIG. 4-3.   Arrangement of apparatus for studying the charging of a condenser.

D.C. SOURCE

If a condenser is large enough and the charging periods small enough, a rather large current can flow into it without causing enough charge to be accumulated, so that only a small voltage will appear across the condenser terminals. This is the situation when a high-frequency voltage is applied to a condenser of appreciable capacitance. Even though a rather large current flows, the reversals are so frequent that not much charge is accumulated.

When an alternating current is said to flow through a condenser, it is not meant that charge actually passes through the dielectric, but only that it is stored on the plates and then released at a later time, so as to give the effect of a current flow through the condenser.

Energy in an Electric Field

As charge flows into a condenser, the plates connected to one terminal obtain an excess of positive charge, while those connected to the other terminal receive extra negative charge. As these charges of opposite sign confront each other across the condenser dielectric, they exert a force of attraction on each other which is counteracted by the structural mechanical rigidity of the condenser. Moreover, positive charge which is already present on one plate, repels any additional positive charge which it may be desired to add to this plate. If n coulombs of charge are present on each plate and m coulombs are to be added, energy must be used to push the charge up the wires onto the plates. This energy is stored in the condenser, and may be released at a later time when the impressed voltage is removed and the condenser short-circuited. It is convenient to say that the energy is stored in the electric field which arises betwen the plates because of the presence of charge on the condenser plates. From the fundamental idea that work or energy is force times distance and from our concept of an electric field, this is a logical way to look at the matter. If, inside the condenser, a positive charge is mechanically transported with a proof plane, work will be involved during the actual motion between the electrodes. If it is a positive charge that is moved from the positive plate to the negative plate, a force aiding the transportation will occur. In fact, this force may be utilized so as to extract energy from the space between the plates.

In ordinary circuit theory as well as in microwave work, the energy of the electric field plays an important role. As with the case of inductance, this importance of the field may be overlooked, because it may be handled implicitly through the use of capacitance measured in farads. The facts are still the same, however, and can assist in understanding those microwave quantities which require the explicit use of field notation. From pure circuit reasoning, the energy stored in the electric field of a condenser is now derived.

The first charge to enter either plate of a condenser requires no urging at all since there are no like charges already there to repel it. Later charges must overcome increasingly high voltages, i.e., they must carry more and more energy per unit charge in order to enter. To place a total of Q charges on a condenser, an average of $V/2$ volts must be overcome, where V is the final voltage to which the condenser is charged. Q charges each on the average requiring $V/2$ units of energy mean that a total energy of $QV/2$ is needed to charge the condenser. From the definition of C, Q may be written as CV, and consequently the expression for the energy stored in the electric field of a condenser is finally written as

$$W = \frac{1}{2} CV^2$$

where W is expressed in joules provided C is expressed in farads and V in volts.

Alternating Current

In power engineering, direct current was first used in major installations, not only because it was simpler to understand but also because it was easier to build direct-current motors, the speed of which was controllable. Except for transient conditions, which momentarily arise when switches are first opened or closed or power levels abruptly changed by other means, direct currents are unaffected by inductance or capacitance and demand only proper resistance and insulation in order to operate satisfactorily. Likewise, by winding suitable combinations of series- and parallel-connected coils onto the field and armature of a direct-current motor, almost any torque and speed characteristic can be obtained. Specifically, by introducing relatively low-level control of the current flowing in the fixed field windings of such a motor, a very convenient method of changing the torque and speed may be obtained. On the other hand, when long transmission lines were used to carry considerable power, the possibility of using transformers with alternating current, so as to make the transmission at high-voltage level was found a great advantage. Transformers, which can only be used with a.c., allow power to be stepped up to high voltage before transmission and then reduced again at the far end of the line before being given to the ultimate consumer. Since power may be calculated from the product of voltage and current, this means that for the transmission of a given amount of power, a much smaller amount of current has to flow through the long wires. Only the magnitude of the current determines the size of the wire needed for transmission, so a.c. can be carried over long distances much more economically than d.c.

Generating Alternating Current

Because of these facts concerning transmission and because an alternating-current generator is simple to build, engineering efforts to displace d-c equipment with equally good or better a-c devices, have been consistently made and have long been successful in many places. Fig. 4-4 illustrates the construction of an a-c generator. Mechanical energy causes the rotor to turn. In so doing its windings cut the magnetic field of the electromagnet so as to generate first a voltage of one polarity and then one of the other. In the position of the rotor shown, the horizontal wires are cutting the fewest number of magnetic lines of force per unit time, thus inducing a minimum voltage in the wire. When the top half of the rotor has traveled through 90°, bringing it midway down the south pole piece, and the lower wire is similarly placed in regards to the north pole, a maximum voltage is induced in the loop as the wires are cutting the greatest number of lines of force per unit time. Because the top half of the loop is descending through the magnetic lines of force, a voltage is induced in a direction from

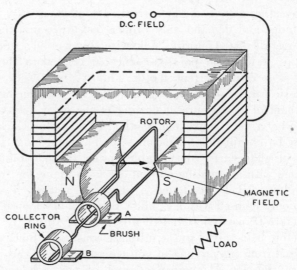

Fig. 4-4. Pictorial diagram of a single-turn coil rotating in a constant magnetic field by means of which an alternating current is generated.

back to front, i.e. towards the collector ring at A. As the bottom half of the loop is going up through the lines of force, the voltage induced will be from front to back, i.e. away from the collector ring at B. Since the horizontal portions of the loop are connected, the voltages induced in each horizontal portion are in series, and the total voltage induced is in a direction from the collector ring at B to the one at A.

As the loop continues to rotate through a second 90° to a vertical position, each side of the loop cuts fewer lines per unit time until a minimum number is cut when the loop is again vertical. In that position, the voltage induced is a minimum. During the next 180° of rotation, the voltage induced in the loop follows the same rise to a maximum value and fall to a minimum as above described, except that the direction of the induced voltage has been reversed. This is because the two horizontal portions of the loop are traveling through the magnetic lines of force opposite to the way they did in the first 180° of rotation, i.e. the side that passed down across the face of the south pole piece has now traveled up across the north pole piece. This means then that the direction of the induced voltage will be the same in the wire that is passing up the north pole, for instance, but taken from the viewpoint of the collector ring *A*, the direction of the voltage will be reversed to what it was descending across the south pole piece. One complete revolution corresponds to a complete cycle of change in the alternating voltage. If the rotor is revolving at the rate of 60 rps, 60-cycle a.c. is fed into the load.

An alternating-current generator requires only slip rings or collector rings to make connection to the rotating coil, instead of a commutator such as is needed to get d.c. Alternators have even been used to generate radio waves. Multiple-pole machines were used and high rotational speeds were then able to reach the lower r-f range. Simple methods of generating low power r-f voltages only came after the invention of the vacuum tube. These well-known methods are entirely satisfactory, and are moreover vastly superior to mechanical means, which certainly can never be used at high radio frequencies, to say nothing of using them for microwave generation. Nevertheless, the fundamental idea of an alternating current is the same no matter what its frequency. The fact that power engineering led the way into a-c theory, and the fact that a mechanical generator emphasizes that an alternating voltage is only a direct voltage which rapidly changes in magnitude and sign, is reason enough for our discussion.

Graphical Representation of A.C.

When an alternating voltage is generated by a machine like the one shown in Fig. 4-4, the change from one polarity to the other is not abrupt or discontinuous. Instead, it is sinusoidal, that is, it changes with time like the plot shown in Fig. 4-5. Voltages of one polarity, as shown by positive ordinate values above the X-axis, change smoothly into voltages of the opposite polarity, which are shown by negative ordinate values below the X-axis. The curve drawn is just sufficient to account for one complete cycle of change. It will, of course, continue to repeat itself indefinitely for as long a time as the machine is run.

In Fig. 4-5 a trigonometric device is also shown which is often used to define a sinusoidal curve, and which illustrates a very common and useful method of measuring phase. The idea is that in a circle like the one shown, a counterclockwise rotating radius may be made to generate the curve. The X-axis, which indicates time, is simply relabeled in degrees. Then each degree point is plotted in accordance with the distance from the X-axis which the outer end of the revolving radius finds itself when it has rotated through that number of degrees.

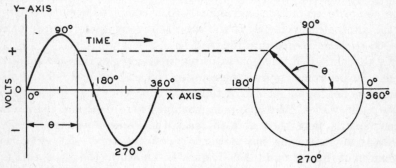

Fig. 4-5. Representation of the variations of an a-c voltage plotted in degrees against time.

For example, the radius vector is shown after it has turned through θ degrees. In that position it determines a point on the curve as can be seen from the construction lines. The point determined is one which is θ degrees along the X-axis in terms of the new time scale.

The sort of idea just discussed has caused it to become common practice to measure such things as time in degrees. This makes sense only when it is clearly realized that there is not a generally fixed relation between degrees and seconds. When one refers to a point 127 degrees along an a-c voltage wave, one only means that reference is made to a point which is 127/360 of the time for a complete cycle. To convert to seconds, milliseconds, or microseconds, it is also necessary to know the frequency, i.e., how many complete cycles occur in a second.

The device of universally calling the duration time of one cycle of a.c. equal to 360 degrees is particularly valuable when it is desired to state the phase difference between two waves, as shown in Fig. 4-6. Assuming that both waves have the same frequency, the illustration shows that they have a phase difference of 90 degrees, no matter what their frequency. If phase differences were measured in time, these curves of Fig. 4-6 would represent different values of time for each frequency. The fact that phase differences are measured in degrees makes it easy to represent an a-c quantity by a vector. In Fig. 4-6, for example, there is shown a vector representing curve B. First some reference sine wave is chosen and represented by a horizontal arrow like the one marked A. Curve A has been chosen as a reference from which to measure phase. Now curve B is 90 degrees behind A, so it is represented by an arrow which has been rotated 90 degrees clock-

FIG. 4-6. Representation of two a-c waves differing in phase by 90 degrees. Here wave A leads wave B by the amount indicated by the vectors at the right.

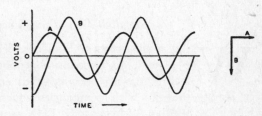

wise from the position of arrow A. *When a vector represents an alternating current or voltage, the length of the arrow represents the magnitude of the current or voltage and the amount which the arrow is rotated clockwise from some reference direction, shows how much the phase of the voltage or current leads the voltage or current to which the reference is made.*

Chapter 5

TRANSMISSION LINES

Parallel-Wire Transmission Lines

WHEN IT IS DESIRED to transmit electrical energy from a source to a load, no impedance problem exists in the connection itself if the distance is small enough. It is only necessary to bridge the gap with conductors which are of sufficient size and which are adequately insulated. Then the desired energy transfer will take place with good efficiency, provided that the source and load impedances are reasonably well matched. On the other hand, if the separation between the source and load is large, the problem is different. In that case it is necessary to pay attention to the properties of the connecting wires. The connection between the source and load is then made by a transmission line.

The question of how large the separation must be for a connection to become a transmission line is one that can be answered in terms of wavelength. With direct current, a wire of any length can be judged adequate to transmit power on the basis of its size and insulation alone. At audio, broadcast, and even conventional short-wave frequencies, the situation for wire lengths of a few inches or a few feet is not much different. Shielding may be necessary, and in certain circumstances lead capacitances may be important, but, generally speaking, the radio engineer is usually not much concerned with transmission lines, except in the design of the feed to the antenna. This is so because his connections are generally shorter than a quarter wavelength of the energy being carried. It is not true when he starts to deal with ultra-high frequencies and microwaves. When ten-centimeter waves are utilized, a connection less than an inch long (approximately one-quarter wavelength) becomes a transmission line.

When the length of a parallel-wire line is of the same order of magnitude as the wavelength of the alternating current which is to be carried, the wires are frequently referred to as *Lecher wires*. It was through a study of the now classical Lecher wires that the action of traveling electrical waves first became well understood.

A discussion of parallel-wire transmission lines naturally divides itself into three parts. The first has to do with action at low enough frequencies so that radiation may be dismissed with a statement concerning the way in which the fields cancel; the second deals with operation at high and ultra-high frequencies where radiation is important but still may be minimized if proper precautions are taken; the third is a discussion of the failure of such a simple line when an attempt is made to utilize it for microwave frequencies. The first part of the discussion is illustrated by long telephone lines and many antenna feeds; the second part is in the domain of the Lecher wire; the third part indicates the inescapable difficulties which can be overcome only by the use of coaxial lines and waveguides.

The Long Line Problem

In an electrically long line, the fact that its resistance and reactance constants are distributed along its length is of great importance. In a lumped-constant circuit it can be said that a certain inductance or capacitance is inserted at a given point. This cannot be done with transmission lines. In these lines the constants—resistance, conductance, inductance, capacitance—are distributed; that is, they are all over the line instead of being collected in a few spots. This is shown

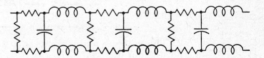

FIG. 5-1. Distributed constants in a two-wire transmission line.

conventionally in Fig. 5-1. The series resistances and inductances in this illustration represent the distributed constants present in the two wires themselves, while the shunt resistances and capacitances represent the distributed leakage resistance and capacitance between the wires.

It is not particularly helpful to know the inductance of a loop of wire formed by two long parallel wires spaced 6 inches apart and short-circuited at the far end, nor is it of direct value to know the capacitance that these two wires represent when they are used as opposite plates of a condenser. These lumped values of themselves cannot help in analyzing the operation of a transmission line, because an equivalent lumped-constant circuit into which the measured values could be inserted cannot be set up and solved. Instead a return must be made to first principles, the question asked what it is that is wanted, and then a way of obtaining a solution sought. This will be quite different from the usual way of solving problems which concern coils, condensers, transformers, etc.

The first point to remember in setting up the new method of solution is that actual physical distances are of great importance, so that the problem has a geometric aspect. Because of this, it is convenient to set up a coordinate system about the lines. In effect, the voltages and currents will be viewed on a graph.

In Fig. 5-2, a point O has been arbitrarily chosen at some place along a parallel-wire transmission line, but midway between the two wires. The idea is that if a way is formulated for determining what

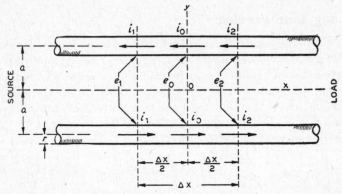

Fig. 5-2. The voltages and currents in a short length of a parallel-wire transmission line.

is happening in this region, the same data will be applicable in explaining what is happening throughout the length of the line. The only difference will be that at a point nearer the source the numerical values of voltage and current will be somewhat larger, and nearer the load they will be smaller, because of progressive losses which occur along the line. Naturally, the values considered here are to be taken over a period of time, rather than instantaneously. Since alternating currents and voltages are under consideration, the *instantaneous* value may be very large at a considerable distance from the source, while it may have zero magnitude at the same time near the source.

A coordinate system has been erected about O as the origin. The X-axis extends parallel to the length of the line, and the Y-axis therefore cuts perpendicularly across the wires. At the points where the

Y-axis intersects the wires, the peak values of the currents are always equal though opposite and are called i_o. At very short distances both before and after the points where i_o is measured, the current in general, will be somewhat different. In Fig. 5-2, the current at a distance $\Delta x/2$ before O has been called i_1 and the current at a distance $\Delta x/2$ beyond O has been called i_2.

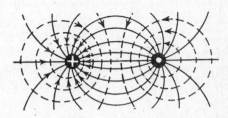

FIG. 5-3. The electric field (solid lines) and the magnetic field (dashed lines) as seen from the end of a two-wire transmission line.

The radius of each of the two wires is taken to be r and the distance between their centers is $2a$. The peak voltage between the two wires has also been correspondingly labeled at the three points as e_1, e_o, and e_2. Fig. 5-3 shows a portion of the electric and magnetic fields due to the voltage between the wires and the current through them, respectively, the electric field being represented by the solid lines and the magnetic field by the dashed lines.

General Problem

In terms of all these quantities the general problem for long lines can be established. Furthermore R can be defined as the resistance *per unit length* of the line (i.e., twice the resistance per unit length of one wire), G as the leakage conductance [1] *per unit length* between the conductors, ϕ as the number of lines of magnetic flux *per unit length* passing between the conductors, and q as the charge present in each conductor per unit length of the line. These last two quantities vary constantly both with time and position along the line. Since a definite very short length of line Δx has been chosen, however, good approximate expressions can be written for the loss of voltage and current in the line over the length Δx. These expressions are

$$e_1 - e_2 = R\Delta x\, i_o + \left[\begin{array}{c} rate\ of\ change\ of\ flux \\ per\ unit\ length \end{array} \right]\Delta x \tag{1}$$

$$i_1 - i_2 = G\Delta x\, e_o + \left[\begin{array}{c} rate\ of\ change\ of\ charge \\ per\ unit\ length \end{array} \right]\Delta x \tag{2}$$

These equations have been written by inquiring what it is that can cause the voltage or current to change with distance along the line. This is answered in the voltage case by stating first, that there will be a loss due to the resistance through which the current must flow and, second, that there will be a voltage change caused by the building up or collapse of a magnetic field between the wires. It is well known, and demonstrated in every electric transformer, that a voltage can be produced by a change in a magnetic field. The change in a magnetic field surrounding the primary winding of a transformer causes a voltage to appear across the secondary winding. It is not primarily the strength of the field that generates the secondary voltage, but rather it is the fact that it changes. This is the reason that transformers can be built only for a varying current, and not for direct current, wherein strong magnetic fields also occur but do not change with time.

Actually, the second term of the right-hand member of equation (1) is closely akin to the idea of inductance, as it is commonly known in lumped-constant circuits. Because of the changing currents in transmission lines, a continual change in the magnetic fields results. These changing magnetic fields induce along the line a voltage of opposite polarity to that which urges the current to flow. The result is that the net voltage causing the current flow is reduced. This is the nature of the second term of equation (1).

Equation (2) explains why the current i_2 is different from that of i_1 in the same manner. The first term indicates a loss due to leakage between the wires and the second term takes into account the fact that the amount of charge between the two sides of the line in the interval Δx changes. The fact that the amount of charge can change along the transmission line is a matter that is closely akin to the action of a capacitance in a lumped-constant circuit. Sections of the wires which are directly across from each other, act like opposite plates of a small condenser, and whenever a voltage appears between sections of the line, a certain amount of charge is drawn to or repelled from their inner surfaces in the same way that voltage changes applied to an ordinary condenser cause it to become charged or discharged. As far as the current is concerned, it is a matter of a change in the amount of charge. The amount of charge stored along the line does not cause the current entering a given section to be different from that which is leaving. But if during the time of observation an additional charge is stored, then during that time some of the current entering the section is diverted for this purpose and the exit current is lessened.

From equations (1) and (2) a reasonable definition of inductance and capacitance can be obtained as the terms are applied to transmission lines of this sort. This obtains since as simple equations as possible are desired which will describe the voltage and current situation at each and every point of the line at any time.

The mathematical derivation of this can be found in several places and will not be performed here. Essentially the procedure is to make an approximate calculation involving the actual magnetic and electric fields arising from the currents which flow in the section of line shown in Fig. 5-2. Approximations are made for at least two reasons. First, in order to keep the equations from becoming too involved, it is expeditious to omit the relatively small terms which appear as the equations are solved, and second, although for the same reason, components of the magnetic field arising from the so-called displacement currents of the capacitance, are ignored. It develops that both these approximations become progressively worse as higher and higher frequencies are encountered. Guillemin,[2] for example, states that for No. 10 conductors and 10-inch spacing, a frequency of 152 megacycles is the highest for which reasonable results may be expected from this type of analysis. Although this is a low frequency in terms of microwaves, it is many times higher than anything that is met in what might be called classical communication engineering.

As a result of such field calculations, equations (1) and (2) may be rewritten in a new form.[3] These new equations, which are rather formidable in appearance, are actually not at all hard to solve. An examination of these equations would show that they do not contain the concept of inductance or capacitance; instead they show the constants of the geometrical arrangement of the wires. This sort of thing must be done when waveguide is considered. There the idea of inductance and capacitance will play only a subordinate role. Calculus notation may also be employed as well as a distributed kind of inductance and capacitance to make the equations look simpler.[4]

In this form they would be recognized as equations of a type which are known as wave equations. They are so called because their solutions call for waves of current and voltage which move just as other waves do. The inductance and capacitance per unit length of line may be obtained,[5] namely

$$L = 4\mu \, log_\epsilon \left(\frac{a + \sqrt{a^2 - r^2}}{r} \right)$$

$$C = \frac{R}{4 \, log_\epsilon \left(\dfrac{a + \sqrt{a^2 - r^2}}{r} \right)}$$

These expressions are definitions of L and C. It is fortunate that they have the same sort of use as they would if the wires were used as a lumped unit of inductance or capacitance. It is because of that similarity that the expressions are named with the same symbols, L and C, which are used for lumped inductance and capacitance. It is the failure of such a simple arrangement to appear in the study of waveguides that necessitates a somewhat different approach to the problem.

The wave equations are capable of solution in many ways to give expressions which show the performance of any given parallel-wire line in terms of its dimensions, excitation, and load. Books such as the one already mentioned spend hundreds of pages on these various solutions. For the purpose of forming physical pictures which can be carried over to uhf tank circuits and waveguides, however, it is not necessary (even though advisable) to go through all this in detail. It is absolutely necessary, however, to realize that the equations are wave equations and that solutions of them will call for currents and voltages in a transmission line to move just as do other waves.

Low Frequency Lines

Before going into the wave picture, however, it is of some interest to cite certain formal results of the wave equations under the assumption of certain simple boundary conditions. These equations can be made to yield expressions for voltage e and current i which in the general case are quite unwieldy and include arbitrary constants that must be fixed in accordance with the way in which the line is excited and the way in which it is loaded, that is, in accordance with the boundary conditions.

If a very long line is imagined so that the line is effectively of infinite length, and if only a section near the source end of the line is considered, these solutions for e and i are much simplified. They include a constant α called the *propagation constant*. Its value depends upon R, G, L, C, and ω (2π times the frequency of the oscillating energy transmitted along the line). This constant is made up of two components which can be separated mathematically. The components [6] are the phase constant a and the attenuation constant b. The phase constant gives the phase of the sinusoidal variation along the line relative to the input, and the attenuation constant gives the attenuation with distance as the energy proceeds along the line.

If e is divided by i for the case of the infinite line, an impedance function is obtained which is known as the *characteristic impedance* of the line. This function is represented by Z_o, and it is independent of the individual values of e and i whose ratio it represents. Its numerical value [7] is given by

$$Z_o = \left(\frac{R^2 + \omega^2 L^2}{G^2 + \omega^2 C^2}\right)^{1/4}.$$

Since at high frequencies R is generally much smaller than ωL, and G is much smaller than ωC, the equations may be simplified to the form

$$Z_o = \sqrt{\frac{L}{C}}$$

This characteristic impedance, Z_o, is the actual impedance of an infinite line. That is, if an oscillator is connected to the input of a transmission line of infinite length, the ratio of the voltage across the input to the current entering the line is actually Z_o, as required by Ohm's Law; therefore, Z_o is a very important quantity. If, for example, we are given two finite wires of stated size and spacing, enough information is now available to use them in the most efficient possible fashion. First, the values of L and C can be calculated from the dimensions of the line and with them a numerical expression can be obtained for Z_o. Now no matter how short the line, if then the source and load are arranged so that they exhibit an impedance equal to Z_o, the line will act as if it were infinite in length.

This fact is perhaps entirely evident only after a thorough study of the properties of traveling waves, but it is certainly true and seems reasonable, since the matched impedance makes the connections smooth and lacking in any discontinuity which can be interpreted electrically as the end of the line. Thus, after matching to the characteristic impedance, any line acts like an infinite line, and a calculation of the attenuation constant for the infinite line will give a description of the way in which a signal is attenuated in its travel along the finite line.

UHF Lines

In dealing with parallel-wire lines as they are used for tank circuits in uhf oscillators, it usually becomes impractical to use all the symbolism just discussed. The general ideas of wave motion along the lines still hold, however, and discussions of the currents and voltages or, even better, of the electric and magnetic fields as waves, explain the operation.

In Fig. 5-4 is shown a typical circuit for a tuned plate—tuned grid uhf oscillator, which uses short-circuited two-wire transmission lines

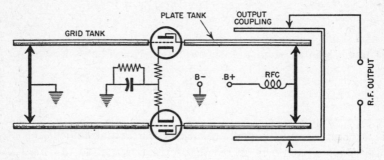

FIG. 5-4. A typical tuned plate—tuned grid oscillator which uses shorted sections of parallel-wire transmission lines as tank circuits.

as tank circuits. Here, there is no question of obtaining the most efficient possible transfer of energy through the lines. Obviously, no energy is expected to emerge from the ends of the line remote from the vacuum tubes because short-circuits appear there. One not acquainted with the action of tuned lines might believe that such a short circuit would result in the dissipation of energy into heat, which is what usually happens when a pair of electrical lines such as power lines, are shorted. That it does not happen here is because the lines are tuned; they are adjusted in length so that electrically they are just one-quarter wavelength long. This means that when a sinusoidal voltage is applied to the open end and at some instant demands a current flow in one direction, it takes a time equal to that which elapses during two quarter-wave lengths of travel for that current to go the length of the transmission line and return to the source, but headed in the opposite direction. During this time the sinusoidal driving voltage has also just had time to reverse its polarity, so there is no disagreement as to which way the current should flow.

This is just the sort of action that is desired of a tank circuit. The purpose of a tank circuit in any oscillator is, first, to time the oscillation and, second, to serve as an energy storage place. The tuned line is a timing device, because of the fixed times that are necessary for electrical energy to travel from the open end to the shorted end and back again. Such lines are energy storage places because of the electric and magnetic fields that are built up in great strength from multiple reflections of electrical energy back and forth between the essentially open and closed ends of the line.

In order to have a clear understanding of the behavior of current and voltage on a two-wire line, a pictorial representation of their distribution may be employed. Fig. 5-5 shows an instantaneous set of values of current and electric field (a measure of the voltage across

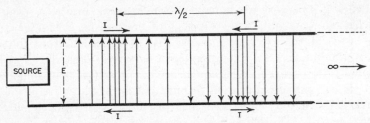

Fig. 5-5. The current and electric field distribution along an infinite parallel-wire transmission line.

the line is given by the density with which these field lines are drawn) along the initial portion of a very long transmission line. It is a matter of simplicity of representation that makes it a requirement that the line be very long (effectively infinite). If it was not infinite in length or was not loaded with its characteristic impedance, a simple description of what happens to the pattern with time would be difficult. As it is, what has been drawn to symbolize the currents and voltages of Fig. 5-5, move with time from left to right toward the load. The motion of the electric field is the sort of wave motion which has been described. A current flow of one direction in one wire and of the opposite in the other is not considered; instead, the voltage between the wires is a single measurable quantity which moves from source to load and does not return. Closed circuits do not exist for wave motion; they are not needed. To attempt to imagine the direction of the currents in Fig. 5-5 at different times is more difficult than it is to visualize the traveling waves and know that the whole pattern will move.

If the line is not infinite or matched to a load, the pattern of Fig.

5-5 will be changed by reflected waves, and the actual voltages in the line will be made up of sets of traveling waves moving in both directions. If actual measurements are made on such a line, composite values are obtained and from these it is not too difficult to deduce the strength of the waves moving in each direction. From that information then, data can be obtained on the degree of the impedance match and the efficiency of the transmission.

Radiation Limitations

From direct current up through frequencies of one or two hundred megacycles, the parallel two-wire transmission line is satisfactory, insofar as losses incident to its use are concerned. At the very high frequencies, however, which have recently come into use, even the best results achievable with this type of line are unsatisfactory. The high losses at these frequencies are due to radiation from the line; that is, the line behaves like an antenna as well as a carrier of energy. This behavior occurs at all frequencies, but is of sufficient importance as to prevent the use of these lines only at the very high frequencies.

In general, it may be stated that the amount of radiation from a parallel-wire transmission line depends upon the separation of the wires. If the wires can be kept close enough together, the radiation can be kept very small. In Fig. 5-6 are shown the magnetic fields that exist around two isolated wires; the one at the left is carrying

 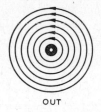

IN   OUT

FIG. 5-6. The magnetic field surrounding two wires, one carrying current into and the other out of the paper. If these fields were superimposed, they would cancel.

current away from and the other towards the reader. It is clear that if these lines were very close together, these fields would be almost completely superimposed, and so would come very close to canceling each other. To the extent that they did cancel, there would be no radiation, since both electric and magnetic fields are necessary in order that energy move out into space. It is impossible to carry this to the limit, because two separate wires must be used for a two-wire line. It may also be noted that as the wires are brought very close together, the distributed capacity of the line is increased, which is a possibly permissible condition for audio frequencies, but is not one to be tolerated for uhf.

In any event, for one reason or another it is necessary to maintain some minimum spacing between the wires for proper insulation and impedance properties. This requisite spacing cannot be made smaller at the shorter wavelengths and higher frequencies, despite the fact that the radiation field, which depends upon rate of change, becomes much more important. Because of this, it is difficult to build satisfactory parallel-wire transmission lines for operation at frequencies much in excess of 200 megacycles.

Coaxial Lines and Wave Motion

In the preceding pages it was indicated that open-wire transmission lines are of little value for transporting microwave energy; radiation losses are so great as to make them completely useless. The possibility still remains of using coaxial lines and waveguide, both of which are usable at even the highest frequencies that can be generated by vacuum tubes of any sort. As for waveguides, as well as for most of the other subjects which are treated in the rest of this book, it is necessary to think of traveling waves of electric and magnetic field, and it is hoped that the reader will find himself thinking in terms of them without too much effort. In the case of coaxial lines, however, most of the explanations can be made without use of the field concept. This is done here as much as possible, so that a good idea of traveling and standing waves may be obtained without at the same time having to think of the less familiar concepts of electromagnetic fields. Actually, what will be said about coaxial lines can in the main be applied to open-wire lines as well, but it is here specifically restricted to the coaxial line case, because it is only then applicable to microwave transmission.

Generally speaking, three distinct types of losses may be encountered in the transmission of very high frequency electrical energy. They are (1) radiation, (2) heating of the conductors due to their finite resistance through which the current must flow, and (3) loss due to an impedance mismatch of the line either at the source or at the load. As an addition to this last point, it might be added that if the line is not perfectly uniform along its length, additional mismatching may occur in the line itself. Of these three types of losses, the first is eliminated by the very fact that coaxial line is used. The complete length of transmission line is enclosed in the tube formed by the outer conductor and there is simply no way for radiation to get out. It is the purpose of this chapter to look into the mechanism by which the other two types of loss take place and to see how they may be minimized.

Mismatching

Like any other line a coaxial line becomes a true transmission line when it is used for a high enough frequency so that the line is more than a quarter wavelength long. In that case interest is focused on a property called the *characteristic impedance* of the line, and both the source and the load should be matched to that impedance. In principle, it can be seen how to do this directly by using transformers both at the load and source ends. If the transformers are perfectly adjustable and can be adjusted so that a maximum of power is drawn from the source through one transformer into the line, and then made available out of the other transformer into the load, perfect matching of the line to the source and to the load is obtained. If, with this arrangement, the line is broken at any point, the measured impedance will be the characteristic impedance and will be found to be the same in either direction. This seems reasonable since it is known that maximum electrical energy is always fed from one device to another when the impedances are equal.

Current Propagation

In Fig. 5-7 are shown plots of current in the center wire and in the shield, as well as the voltage across the coaxial line as a function of distance along the line. The curves marked with zero subscripts represent the situation at some arbitrary time at which the first plots were made. The subscripts 1, 2, and 3 then represent a perfectly matched line at successive short times later. The two current curves have been plotted out of phase, since it is apparent that the shield *A* will receive a positive charge from the source transformer when the center wire *B* receives a negative charge, and vice versa. The current will vary with time and will reverse polarity *2f* times per second, where *f* represents the frequency. Thus, if at some instant our attention is focused on a point on the wire, the direction and magnitude of the current changes with time. On the other hand if attention is focused on a given current flow, it will be found that the eyes move along the line from left to right. This is true of both the center conductor and the shield. The current wave moves down both wires from the source to the load. By looking at the curves in Fig. 5-7 in the order t_0, t_1, t_2, etc. the propagation of the current wave can be visualized.

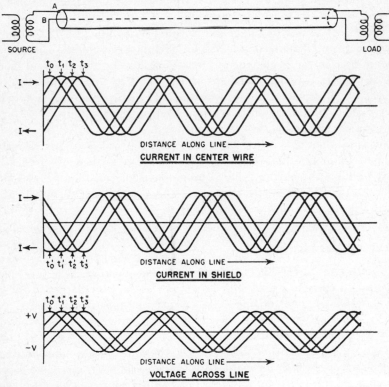

FIG. 5-7. Currents and voltages in a matched-coaxial transmission line for a sine-wave input.

Similarly, voltage waves are impressed on the line. A given voltage is at a certain instant applied to the line at the source. Successive sections of the line in turn acquire this voltage only to continue on to the next voltage dictated by the source.

Phase Relations

Next consider the phase of these three sinusoidal waves which have been visualized as traveling along the line. In doing so it must be noted that in drawing the curves of Fig. 5-7 only one possible mode of propagation is being considered. If higher modes were to be considered at this point, the curves would have to be drawn quite differently. Fortunately for the simplicity of this discussion, only this principal mode is of any importance when the diameter of the coaxial shield is sensibly smaller than a wavelength. Such a diameter is a convenient one for most applications.

The current waves of the center wire must remain just 180 degrees out of phase with those of the shield. If this were not the case, then at some time in the cycle, current would be flowing into the load from both the center conductor and the shield. This in turn would require, during that interval, a charging up of the load with respect to the source and hence assumes an external capacity coupling of the load and source. This, of course, does not exist.

The two other possibilities for change in the waves of Fig. 5-7 for specified frequency and input amplitude, are a change of phase between voltage and current, and a progressive loss of amplitude of the waves as they move along the wire. These represent mismatch and dissipative loss in the line respectively.

Effect of Mismatch

To demonstrate the effect of mismatch consider Fig. 5-8. Here the voltage and current curves are drawn as they appear across the load as a function of time for one matched and two mismatched cases. In each case a third curve is drawn representing their product. Since it is known that the instantaneous product of voltage and current is the instantaneous power, this third curve represents power. The positive lobes represent energy brought to the load, while the negative lobes represent energy fed from the load back to the source. Thus, the useful power for the load is the average over a cycle of the difference between these two. This type of power loss is said to be non-dissipative, since the energy loss is not used up in heat but rather is fed back into the source. Inspection shows that this loss becomes less and less as the phase angle between voltage and current approaches zero. Hence, a perfectly matched system is one in which there is no phase difference. The greater the mismatch, the greater the phase angle.

This physical picture of what happens with a mismatched line makes it evident that measurement of this condition is not simple.

The amount of power traveling in each direction in general cannot be easily measured. As it happens, it is much easier to make measurements on the voltage wave, as will be explained later on. To understand how this should be interpreted, it is necessary to look further at the method of representing the voltage across the line.

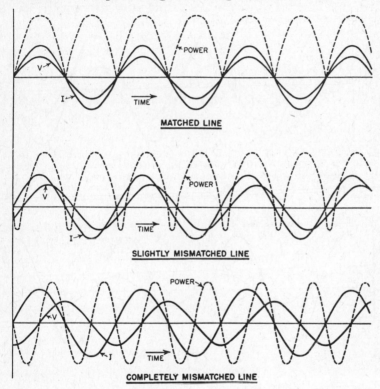

Fig. 5-8. The voltage and current waves as they appear across the load for one matched and two mismatched lines. The product of these waves represents power.

In Fig. 5-7 the voltage was shown as a sinusoidal wave traveling from the source to the load. In the mismatched case, since energy is flowing in both directions there must be two of these traveling waves, one moving toward the load and the other toward the source. It will then be found that the wave moving toward the load is in phase with a current, while the wave traveling back to the source is out of phase with its accompanying current wave. This allows one wave to carry power in one direction and the other in the opposite direction.

This concept of voltage and current waves moving in opposite directions is not inconsistent with the mismatched cases shown in Fig. 5-8, since there has been plotted what would be the sum of the two traveling waves as a function of time when measured at the load. Each wave represents a sinusoidal variation with time and it is well known that the sum of any two sine waves of the same frequency is another

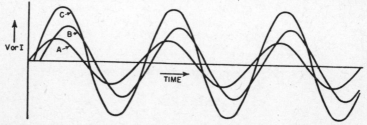

FIG. 5-9. The sum of any two out-of-phase waves of the same frequency is in general another wave of intermediate phase. Any current or voltage which can be represented by C, can be equally well considered as being two currents or voltages represented by A and B. Sine wave A plus sine wave B equals sine wave C.

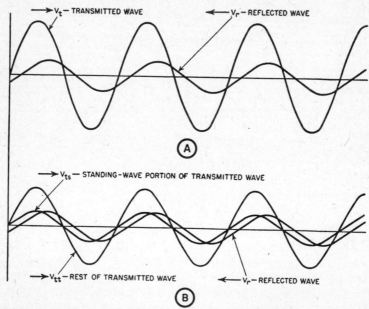

FIG. 5-10. In (A), V_t is the voltage in a mismatched line to the load and V_r is the voltage reflected from the load back to the source. The same line condition is shown in (B), but V_t has been replaced by V_{ts} and V_{tt}, their sum equalling V_t. V_{tt} represents net flow of energy to the load.

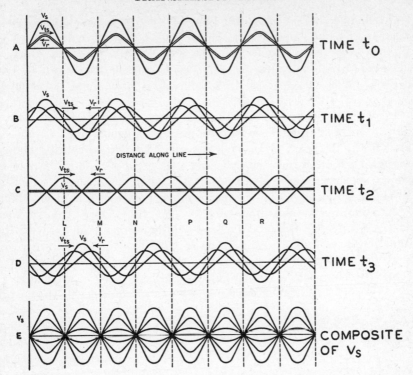

FIG. 5-11. The series of waves in (A), (B), (C), and (D) represent various conditions of V_{ts} and V_r as they travel past each other. V_s in each case is the sum of the two waves and represents the voltage actually on the line by reason of these two waves. The sums of the four conditions have been redrawn in (E) on a single baseline to show how voltage varies with time.

sine wave regardless of phase angle relation.[8] Fig. 5-9 shows how the voltage curve of Fig. 5-8 may actually be made up of two sinusoidal voltage curves.

Voltage Distribution

Two voltage waves traveling in opposite directions are shown in Fig. 5-10(A), these being designated V_t and V_r. The wave V_t is of greater amplitude than V_r because it represents all the energy moving from the source to the load, while V_r represents only that part which is reflected at the junction between the line and the load and hence is caused to travel back along the line in the opposite direction. The first step is to break up the V_t wave into two components which are designated as V_{ts} and V_{tt}, because later they will be seen to be the parts of V_t which contribute to a standing wave and to a traveling wave in the line respectively. The wave V_{ts} represents a fraction of V_t that is equal to V_r, as has been done in Fig. 5-10(B), which is interpreted as illustrating the same conditions as are shown in Fig. 5-10(A). The curves V_{tt} and V_{ts} replace V_t, while V_r is the same as before.

In Fig. 5-11 V_{ts} and V_r of the now three traveling voltage waves, have been paired and their sum for successive times t_o, t_1, t_2, and t_3, are shown. The sum of V_{ts} and V_r, called V_s, is a so-called standing wave and is one which generates no voltage at all along the line at points such as L, M, N, etc. At intermediate points an alternating voltage is obtained, which is a maximum at points such as P, Q, R, etc.

In actual mismatched line if the voltage is measured at points such as L, M, N, etc., of Fig. 5-11, some voltage other than zero will be found because of the traveling voltage wave V_{tt} (the rest of wave V_t). This will be zero, only if the reflected wave is equal to the transmitted wave. Perhaps such a case would be called a perfect mismatch. It would occur if the load end of the line were open or shorted. In general, however, as voltage along a line is measured, maximum r.m.s voltages at points like P, Q, R, and minimum voltage at points like L, M, N are found. The ratio of these voltages is known as the voltage *standing-wave ratio*. When it is unity, there is no standing wave, hence no reflected wave, and therefore a perfect match with a maximum of power available at the load. The larger the ratio, the worse the mismatch, and the less power is available at the load.

The voltage standing-wave ratio is conveniently measured by making a slot lengthwise in the shield of the coaxial cable. A very small probe, which is connected through a rectifier to a voltmeter, is then inserted into the slot and moved along. Unless the standing wave ratio is unity, two points of respectively maximum and minimum reading will be found a quarter wavelength apart. The ratio of these two readings is the standing-wave ratio, and its departure from unity is a measure of the mismatch in the system on the load side of the point where the measurement is made.

Stub Support

Strangely enough, the mismatched cases are in some places of great practical importance. For example, when air is used around the center conductor as a dielectric, some method of support must be found. The so-called stub support method represented in Fig. 5-12(A), is one possibility of practical importance. To understand its operation, examine what happens in lines one-half wavelength and one-quarter

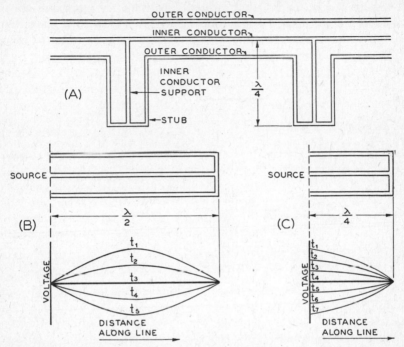

FIG. 5-12. A stub-supported concentric line is shown in (A). The stub supports are examples of a perfectly mismatched line and when properly adjusted they can be made to have practically no effect on a given frequency in the main line. In (B) and (C) are shown plots of the voltage waves in half-wave and quarter-wave stubs.

wavelength long which are shorted at the far end. The incident and reflected waves are equal in magnitude since there is perfect mismatching. No voltage can ever appear at the shorted end, so one node (a point of zero voltage of the standing wave) must be there. In the half-wavelength line, shown in Fig. 5-12(B), there must be another node at the source end. Such a line can thus have no voltage impressed across its open end. With a quarter-wavelength line, shown in Fig. 5-12(C), the situation is quite different. The unshorted end is then a point which will accept any voltage impressed on it, but will absorb no power. Thus, the stubs built out from the side of a coaxial cable can, if they are the right length, give a support for the center conductor without affecting the action of the line at all. A given quarter-wave stub will, of course, be appropriate only for certain frequencies.

At times the deliberate introduction of mismatch in a stub line can be used to correct an inherent mismatch between the main line and the load; in a sense it acts like a transformer. In Fig. 5-13 is shown how a stub of adjustable length might in certain cases be used to match

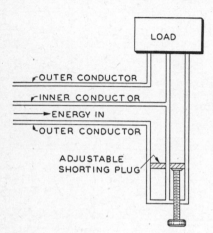

FIG. 5-13. A load can be matched in some cases to a coaxial line by the use of a matching stub, which is terminated as a perfect mismatch and adjusted in length so that its reflected wave cancels the reflection from the load.

a load to a given line. Assume, for example, that with the stub eliminated a standing-wave ratio of 5 is obtained in the main line. This means that the incident voltage wave to the load is only 1/5 larger than the reflected wave. Now suppose the shorted stub line is adjusted somewhere over a half wavelength range, but in general not precisely at a quarter or half wavelength. It will then accept a voltage wave and return it after reflection in some changed phase. With proper adjustment this returned wave may be just out of phase with the reflected wave from the load. The resulting cancellation of the load reflection will lower the standing-wave ratio in the main line and thus improve the match.

Skin Effect and Attenuation in Coaxial Lines

Over relatively short distances of twenty feet or less, ultra-high frequencies can easily be transmitted through coaxial lines with small losses. Not only can the loss due to mismatching in the line be reduced to a small amount in accord with the idea previously discussed, but with proper design the dissipative losses generating heat in the line may be kept within bounds.

If at any instant it were possible to take a snapshot which would show the position of all the charge on a high-frequency coaxial line, it would be found that the charge was mostly on the inner surface of the shield and on the outer surface of the center wire. If this is considered in terms of a line operating in its fundamental mode, which is essentially the only one that can be present when the shield diameter is sensibly smaller than a wavelength, it is quite easy to see in part why this is true. The source adds positive charge to the center conductor as it adds negative charge to the shield, and vice versa. Thus, as these disturbances, which are usually called waves of current and voltage, travel down the line, a symmetry of charge between the center and outer conductor always remains.

Fig. 5-14 shows diagrammatically what is meant. Any charge on the outer conductor is, at any instant, just balanced by an equal amount of charge of opposite sign on the inner conductor. The at-

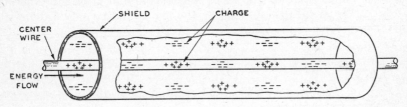

Fig. 5-14. At some particular instant the charge active in the transfer of energy in a section of coaxial transmission line is primarily on the inner surface of the shield and on the outer surface of the center wire.

tractive force between these unlike charges tries to hold the charge to the inner surface of the outer conductor and to the outer surface of the inner wire. As a result the current flows only in a very thin layer of metal. It is said that a *skin effect* is observed and current flows only in the skin of the metallic conductors. Actually, this static picture of charge is incomplete. Microwave energy causes the charge to move as a current, and to reverse its direction twice as many times a second as the frequency of the energy transmitted. Magnetic as well as electric forces are present but the result is the same.

To discuss skin effect as a function of frequency and material, it is necessary to consider the facts more carefully. It is necessary to deduce whatever is possible about the depth of penetration of energy outward through the outer conductor for two reasons: First, to arrange the dimensions so that no energy penetrates the shield and escapes as radiation; second, to determine the effective volume of metal through which the currents flow so that it will be possible to calculate the effective resistance and the I^2R loss generating heat in the line.

Line Losses

Before going into this, however, consider some actual lines to illustrate the magnitude of the effect.[9] For example, with a line made of copper and using an optimum ratio of size for the inner and outer conductor, the dissipative losses will be 5 db per mile for a line having a sheath with an inner radius of 0.6 inch and operated at 20 megacycles. A loss of 5 db per mile means that only one-half of one percent of a given input energy is lost in a 20-foot length.

It is important to understand that line losses are best expressed in db per unit length because the loss is always a given fraction of the input power. This means that with the 20-foot line just mentioned, 0.5 watt would be lost if 100 watts were put in and proper termination arranged. If 99.5 watts were put in, the loss would be only 0.497 watt; with a 50-watt input, it would be only 0.25 watt. If the line is lengthened, the absolute value of energy lost per 20-foot unit of length will gradually decrease as it goes along the line, always being one-half of one percent of that delivered from the preceding section. A convenient way of denoting this type of attenuation is by stating a coefficient in terms of db per unit length. The energy lost per unit length varies, but the db loss per unit length remains the same throughout.

To find the fraction of power passed through a mile of 5 db per mile-line, only the reciprocal of the number whose logarithm is this coefficient expressed in bels, need be considered. Thus, since the log of 3.17 is .5, a little less than a third of the input energy will be transmitted a mile. If the coefficients were 3 db per mile, then, since log 2 equals .301, about one-half the energy could be carried a mile. If from the 5-db per mile value it is desired to find the loss in 20 feet, it is first necessary to adjust the coefficient. Multiplying 5 by 20 and dividing by 5280, results in an equivalent coefficient of about 0.02 db per 20 feet. Since the log of 1.005 is .002, the transmission fraction is the reciprocal of 1.005 or 99.5%. The db losses are proportional to the length of the line; power or percentage power losses are not.

Electronics as Basis

To improve one's physical picture of electrical phenomenon it is very helpful to realize that all electrons are precisely alike. To visualize a current it is unnecessary to think of a certain electron or group of electrons moving along, but only of the motion of a region in which there is an excess of electrons. Since the days of Franklin it has been found useful to talk of two kinds of charge, positive and negative. This is always true in fact, and with ionic solutions the mobility of the two kinds of charge may well be of the same order of magnitude, so that each kind does its share of the job in the transfer of energy. In metallic conductors, however, the charge is carried by electrons. The electrons are so much lighter than the positive ions that they have a much greater mobility and account for practically all the motion of charge. An uncharged metal ball is one which has an equal number of positive and negative charges. A negatively charged body is one which has an excess of electrons; a positively charged body is one which has a deficiency of electrons. A current, which for convenience might be called one of positive charge flowing from left to right, is in reality one of negative charge flowing from right to left.

Thinking then in terms of electrons, the problem of deciding how deeply energy will penetrate the shield is simply one of finding how deeply an electron need be buried to be unaffected by the current and voltage waves traveling down the line.

In a perfectly uniform line terminated with a perfect match to the source and load, the way in which the current and voltage change with time is very simple. In Fig. 5-15, the current in the wire and shield and the voltage between the wire and shield are indicated for

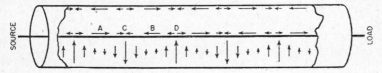

Fig. 5-15. The horizontal arrows show the direction and magnitude of currents flowing in the coaxial line at some instant. The vertical arrows indicate voltage between adjacent points on the center wire and shield at the same instant.

a certain instant of time. This assumes that the source is supplying a single-frequency voltage. As time progresses, the whole pattern simply shifts toward the load with a velocity equal to the propagation velocity of the wave which, in practical cases, will be nearly equal to the velocity of light.

In terms of an electron picture this means that in regions such as B in Fig. 5-15, the electrons in the shield are moving to the right, while those in the wire are being displaced to the left. At a point such as A, the electrons are moving in the opposite direction. At a certain time later when the pattern has shifted so that point B on the line has a pattern like that shown at A, the electrons at B will have reversed their direction of displacement. Similar remarks may be made about the voltage. At D the wire is positive with respect to an adjacent point on the shield. At C the reverse is true. After the pattern has shifted a correct amount the voltages at D will be as they are now at C.

The question now is how this will affect an electron at a depth δ in either the shield or the center wire. This electron may experience two types of forces urging it to move: one electric and one magnetic. In Fig. 5-16(A), the electric force is shown at a time when a positive loop of the current wave is approaching. It is necessary to remember

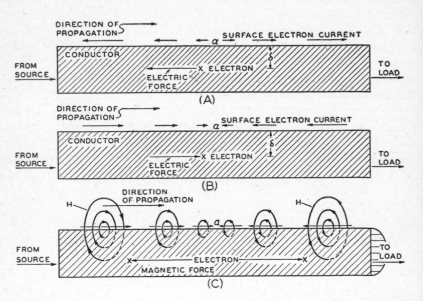

FIG. 5-16. The electric and magnetic forces on an electron in a conductor carrying high-frequency energy at some instant. The horizontal arrows indicate electron currents along the conductor; arrows pointing to the left are therefore equivalent to positive currents to the right. Note that in (C) it is the rate of change of magnetic field that exerts a force on the charge.

that electrons are responsible for all current flow. A positive voltage peak of a sine wave of current (point a in Fig. 5-16(A)) is really a point from which maximum negative charge is leaving. A positive charge density approaching the electron at depth δ is therefore the motion from left to right of the surface current vectors shown in Fig. 5-16(A) (not the motion of charge indicated by the arrows and called current, but the energy motion indicated by moving the arrows themselves.) Specifically, reference is being made to the approach of point a in that train of vectors.

Now as a positive voltage wave (a moving region of the conductor from which negative charge has departed as to leave a positive excess) approaches, the electron at a depth δ, on which attention has been focused, will, because of its opposite polarity, be attracted back toward the source, being thus equivalent to a further advance of the positive current wave. In Fig. 5-16(B), a negative wave is approaching and the electron is urged to move in the opposite direction, becoming a more advanced part of that negative wave. In Fig. 5-16(C), it is shown that the magnetic forces have the same kind of effect.

As is well known, electric currents produce circular magnetic fields. As a result, varying magnetic fields also travel along the conductor as waves. Maximum strength magnetic fields (represented in Fig. 5-16(C) by several circles) correspond to points of greatest current flow. Magnetic fields that are shown going in one direction correspond to positive current flow, while those going in the opposite direction are similar to the motion of negative charge accumulations. As this magnetic array of force lines move along the wire, particular charges embedded in the conductor at a depth δ, will start to move because of a voltage arising from the changes of magnetic field strength at their particular location. In part, the resulting motion will oppose the motion dictated by the electric field. Other electrons at different depths in the shield cause changing magnetic fields as they accelerate. The lines of force from these magnetic fields run transversely through the conductor and as they change, exert a force which tends to move the charge one way or the other along the line. This magnetic force on the electrons is in part such as to oppose the motion dictated by the electric field.

It is clear from Fig. 5-17 how the competition between these electric and magnetic forces give rise to a skin effect. Here a single conductor is carrying a rapidly changing current, as it will if operated at a very high frequency. Because of this current there will be a changing magnetic field, which will be circular in form and surround the wire. The exact distribution of the field, expressed by how close together the lines of force are drawn at various radial distances from the axis of the wire, will depend upon how the currents are allocated throughout the cross-section of the wire; but whatever it is, the center of the wire will be surrounded by more magnetic lines than the surface. This means that the electric field will have greater difficulty in moving the charge in the center of the wire and smaller currents will

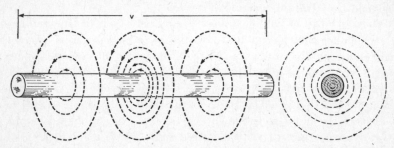

Fig. 5-17. When a cylindrical conductor carries current, the magnetic field is somewhat like that shown by the dotted circles. The instantaneous voltage, V, gives rise to a current distributed in some way over the cross-section which results in the circular magnetic field.

be found there than at the surface. It also means that the current will be shifted in phase as the conductor is penetrated more deeply. The shift will occur because the electron motion which does exist, will be a different compromise between the two fields.

Penetration Factors

It develops that it may be assumed for many calculations (especially when the frequency is very high) that all the current flows in a skin of thickness δ where

$$\delta = \sqrt{\rho/f} \ cm$$

in which ρ is the specific resistance of the material expressed in electromagnetic units, and f is the frequency of the energy being transmitted. Actually, of course, this is not true. Currents do not flow uniformly for just this depth and then suddenly cease. Instead they fall off exponentially with penetration. It is just that δ has been calculated as the depth at which the current falls off to the proper value (off to $\frac{1}{\epsilon}$ times its maximum, where ϵ is the base of Naperian logarithms or to about 0.4 times the maximum value), so that all currents flowing at greater depths added to those at lesser depths, gives the equivalent of the average current flowing in the skin alone.

It is interesting to notice how δ depends on ρ and f. At higher frequencies the current is more and more concentrated at the surface. This appears reasonable, since higher frequencies mean more rapid changes in the magnetic field and hence stronger magnetic forces. δ also becomes small if the conductivity of the material is very high. This seems reasonable, since a high conductivity material allows a skin of a certain physical thickness to be electrically equivalent to a thicker tube of higher resistance.

It must be pointed out here that the expression for the skin thickness, δ, has actually been calculated for a plane surface instead of a wire. For good conductors and high frequencies, however, δ is such a small number that this is a good approximation. Even a fairly small wire may have a large radius of curvature as compared to δ. At 3,000 mc, copper, which has a specific resistance of ρ = 1720 ohm-cm emu (1.72 x 10⁻⁶ ohm-cm), may be calculated by the equation just given to have a skin depth of 0.12 thousandths of a centimeter. This is much smaller than any wire normally used.

Calculations

Returning now to the general problem of obtaining the best possible transmission in a line, it is found that the skin effect will influence the dimensions chosen. The problem is to make the loss of energy in the line as small a fraction of the power transmitted as possible. Since the Z_o is the actual impedance of a properly matched system when the line is cut at any point and the impedance measured in either direction, it is apparent that $i^2 Z_o$ is a measure of the power being transmitted at any instant. Likewise $i^2 r$ is the same sort of measure of power dissipated at the same instant if r is the resistance of the line. The problem then is clearly that of minimizing $i^2 r / i^2 Z_o$ or more simply r/Z_o. The resistance r may be calculated in the usual way, taking into account, however, that only the skin depth, δ, is to be considered.

$$\text{Resistance} = \text{specific resistance} \times \frac{\text{length}}{\text{area}}$$

$$r = \rho \times \frac{l}{2\pi a \delta} + \rho \times \frac{l}{2\pi b \delta}$$

where ρ is the specific resistance as before, l is the length of the line, and the denominator represents areas as explained in Fig. 5-18. The first term gives the resistance of the center conductor and the second term accounts for the resistance of the shield. Since the two are effectively connected in series, the total resistance is their sum. The value of r will come out in practical units if ρ is expressed in ohm-cms and in emu, if ρ is in ohm-cm emu.

The evaluation of Z_o is a somewhat longer task not directly concerned with energy dissipation, and will not be gone into here. For a coaxial line operating in its fundamental mode, which is the only mode of much practical value, the form of the expression is the same

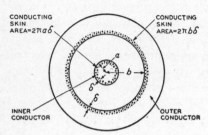

FIG. 5-18, left. For some purposes the current can be considered to flow in a skin of definite thickness, indicated in this end view of a coaxial line.

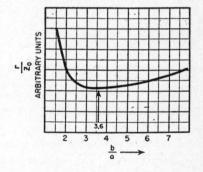

FIG. 5-19, right. This plot shows how the power loss depends on the relative size of the inner and outer conductor.

as for any continuous line. It turns out that with air dielectric it depends only on the ratio of the sizes of the inner and outer conductors.

$$Z_o = 138 \ log \ \frac{b}{a} \ ohms.$$

Now examine the expression for the fraction of energy dissipated. It reduces to [10]

$$\frac{r}{Z_o} = \frac{10^{-9} \ (a+b) \ l \sqrt{\rho f}}{2\pi \cdot 138 \ ab \ log \ b/a}$$

In Fig. 5-19 this expression is plotted against the ratio of the radius of the outer conductor to that of the inner wire. It is seen that b/a has a minimum at 3.6. This means that best lines will in general be obtained if the outside conductor has 3.6 times a radius as the inner wire. Since the minimum is rather flat, slight variations from this value will be unimportant, but a larger variation from the optimum value will result in an important increase in the dissipative loss.

The final problem of energy dissipation because of resistance is to try to see how losses in terms of db per unit length may be calculated. The db loss per mile, for example, is equal to 10 times the logarithm of the ratio of the energy passing through a line at a certain point

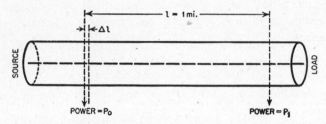

FIG. 5-20. When calculating the db loss per mile, it is convenient to find it first for a very short distance Δl, over which short length it is justifiable to assume that the current is constant.

to that passing through the same line at a point one mile closer to the source. In Fig. 5-20 such a line is indicated. It is desired to calculate a constant L where

$$L = 10 \ log \ \frac{P_1}{P_o} \ db \ loss \ per \ mile$$

The power at P_1 is just that at P_o minus the loss. If a loss, L_1, is first calculated for a very short distance Δl, so that the approximation that it is constant over that length can be made, it can be stated that

$$L_1 = 10 \ log \ \frac{P_o - i^2 r}{P_o}$$

Since $P_o = i^2 Z_o$, this expression may be rewritten as

$$L_1 = 10 \ log \ \frac{1 - i^2 r / i^2 Z_o}{1} = 10 \ log \ (1 - r/Z_o) \ db \ loss \ per \ length \ \Delta l.$$

In this last expression both P and i, which depend upon the size of Δl, have been eliminated. The quantities r and Z_o which remain are independent of the magnitude of Δl, so Δl can be any length desired. Specifically, if Δl is 1 mile, L_1 becomes L and

$$L = 10 \ log \ (1 - \frac{r}{Z_o}) \ db \ per \ mile$$

where Z_o is the characteristic impedance and r is the resistance per mile with due consideration of the skin effect. It has been already stated that r/Z_o is the fraction of power lost and an expression has been stated for that quantity which involves only frequency, dimensions, and specific resistance. If r/Z_o is the fraction of the power lost in a mile, then $(1 - r/Z_o)$ is the fraction transmitted. The ratio of this to unity is the ratio of power transmitted to that inserted so the expression for db loss per mile, as derived, is checked.

FOOTNOTES

1. The use of conductance here instead of resistance simplifies the form of the equations somewhat, but makes no other difference.

2. "Communication Networks" by Ernst A. Guillemin. John Wiley, 1935.

3. $\dfrac{e_1 - e_2}{\triangle x} = Ri_o + 4\mu \ log_\epsilon \left(\dfrac{a + \sqrt{a^2 + r^2}}{r} \right)$ (rate of change of current with time) (a)

$\dfrac{i_1 - i_2}{\triangle x} = Gl_o + \dfrac{R}{4 \ log_\epsilon \left(\dfrac{a + \sqrt{a^2 - r^2}}{r} \right)}$ (rate of change of voltage with time) (b)

where μ and K are the permeability and dielectric constant of the space surrounding the wires.

4. $\dfrac{de}{dx} + Ri + L \ \dfrac{di}{dt} = o$ (c)

$\dfrac{di}{dt} + Gl + C \ \dfrac{de}{dt} = o$ (d)

where L is the inductance per unit length and C the capacitance per unit length of the line.

5. The manner of changing from equations (a) and (b) of Footnote 3 to those of (c) and (d) of Footnote 4 deserves some special comment, because from it comes the definition of distributed inductance and capacitance. Term for term, the two pairs of equations are identical and have essentially the same meaning. In other words, equations (c) and (d) should be regarded as only a shorthand method of writing the earlier pair. That is the meaning of the new symbols.

6. $\quad \propto = aj + b$

7. Its complex value is $Z_o = \sqrt{\dfrac{R + j\omega L}{G + j\omega C}}$

8. $A \ sin \ \omega t + B \ sin \ (\omega t + \propto) = C \ sin \ (\omega t + \beta)$; where $C = \sqrt{A^2 + 2AB \ cos \ \propto + B^2}$ and $\beta = sin^{-1} \ (B/C \ sin \ \propto)$.

9. Calculated values of attenuation coefficients for various size coaxial lines are shown in a paper by Sturba and Feldman in Proc. IRE 20, 1163 (1932).

10. $r = \rho x \dfrac{l}{2\pi a\delta} + \rho \dfrac{l}{2\pi b\delta}$ emu ohms

where ρ is in ohm-cm emu. Rewriting this expression and substituting for δ we have

$$r = \frac{\rho l}{2\pi\delta}\left(\frac{1}{a} + \frac{1}{b}\right) = \frac{\rho l}{2\pi}\frac{1}{\delta}\frac{a+b}{ab}$$

$$= \frac{\rho l}{2\pi}\frac{a+b}{ab}\sqrt{\frac{f}{\rho}} = \frac{(a+b)}{ab}\frac{l}{2\pi}\sqrt{\rho f} \quad emu \ ohms.$$

To express this in ohms, we multiply by 10^{-9} obtaining $r = \dfrac{10^{-9}}{2\pi}\dfrac{l(a+b)\sqrt{\rho f}}{ab}$

Chapter 6

POYNTING'S VECTOR AND MAXWELL'S EQUATIONS

THE MOST COMMONPLACE conception of the mechanism for the transfer of electrical energy is based on the concept of charge and voltage alone. It demands that there must always be a closed electrical path. There must exist one side of the circuit to carry charge from the generator to the load and another by which the charge is returned. Each charge is then considered as a conveyor of energy, as shown in Fig. 6-1. Voltage is defined as energy per coulomb and hence the voltage across the load represents the energy carried to the load by each coulomb. The energy received by the load depends

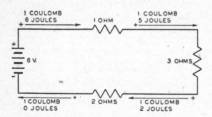

Fig. 6-1. As a positive charge of one coulomb travels around the circuit, it carries the energy to the various loads in accordance with Kirchhoff's second law.

upon the amount of charge multiplied by the voltage; that is, it depends upon the energy carried by each charge times the number of charges. The power at the load is the time rate at which energy is received, or the current times the voltage.

Kirchhoff's Laws

When the headlights of an automobile are turned on, energy must be supplied to the filaments of the lamps. Charge is carried to them by a wire from the storage battery. As it leaves the battery each charge has 6 joules of energy. It loses practically none of this on the way up to the headlight because of the low resistance of the wire. In the relatively high resistance of the headlight, however, it gives up most of its energy (i.e., a voltage drop occurs) retaining only enough to allow for the return trip to the battery, either on a second wire or through the metal framework of the car. This fact is expressed by the second law of Kirchhoff, namely, "The sum total of the voltages around any closed electrical path, when taken with due regard for polarity, must be zero." This, in connection with the first law of Kirchhoff, which effectively specifies that charge cannot be made or destroyed, is all that is needed to solve any circuit problem.

With alternating currents of even moderately low frequency, the picture becomes a little more difficult. It is necessary to think of the wires as continuously changing their functions of supplying charge to the load and returning it to the source. When capacitors are part of the circuit, allowance must be made for the fact that no charge can actually pass through the dielectric. This is considered satisfactory because all charge is exactly alike and it is known from Faraday's famous ice-pail experiment that every time a charge comes onto one plate of a condenser, another just like it is forced off the other plate; in effect, the charge flows in closed paths. Kirchhoff's laws are still valid and except for the mathematical difficulty of handling the equations, they still allow a solution to be obtained for any circuit.

In fact all that has been said is still true even when extremely high frequencies and electrically long lines are considered. In this case, electrical energy has insufficient time to make the complete trip before a reversal of direction occurs; yet correct results may often be obtained in terms of voltage and current. Repeating that all charge is alike and that although currents may be flowing in both directions at various points along a conductor, on the average, equal amounts of charge leave the generator and return at the other pole. Kirchhoff's laws still hold.

Vector Multiplication

The nature of vectors has already been discussed. They differ from ordinary scalar numbers inasmuch as vectors represent a direction as well as a magnitude. It has been shown that a 10-foot displacement to the east is quite different from a 10-foot displacement to the north, to the west, or upward or downward. It has been implied that vectors are equal only if their directions as well as their magnitudes are identical. Furthermore, it has been explained how vectors may be added by placing the origin of each arrow coincident with the head of the one before it. The sum is represented by a new vector drawn from the origin of the first arrow to the head of the last one drawn. This is merely the start of the study of vectors.

Actually an algebra of vectors is often used. Not only can vectors be added, but they can be multiplied by one another and also by scalars. A scalar has magnitude only, for example: $7, \pi, a$.

When a vector is multiplied by a scalar, the direction of the vector is unchanged but its magnitude is increased by the factor represented by the scalar. For example, a vector of 10 units magnitude that is directed east when multiplied by the scalar 7, yields a vector of 70 units magnitude with the same direction. If the 10-unit vector is represented by **A**, this type of multiplication may be indicated by

$$10 \, \mathbf{A} = \mathbf{B}$$

where **B** represents the 70-unit vector described above.

When two vectors are multiplied together by a method commonly known as obtaining the *dot product,* as indicated by a dot between the two vectors, *the result is not a vector but is instead a scalar quantity,* i.e. it is a number with no direction involved. This type of multiplication is indicated by

$$\mathbf{A} \cdot \mathbf{B} = |\mathbf{A}| \;\; |\mathbf{B}| \; cos \; \theta$$

where the vertical lines enclosing **A** and **B** indicate that only the magnitudes of these vectors are to be used, i.e. multiplied together as

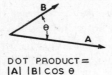

DOT PRODUCT = |A| |B| COS θ

Fɪɢ. 6-2. The dot product is the multiplication of two vectors, **A** and **B**, and the cosine of the angle θ between them; the result is a scalar quantity.

scalar quantities, and θ is the angle between the two vector **directions**, as shown in Fig. 6-2.

From this it may be seen that when the vectors are parallel, the angle θ becomes zero, making cos θ equal to unity. Furthermore, when the vectors are perpendicular to each other so that θ is 90°, the cosine factor is zero, making the dot product also zero. It is clear that the dot product of any two vectors at 90° to each other is always zero, regardless of their magnitudes.

When vector multiplication is indicated by the multiplication sign ($\times$), the product is a new vector the direction of which is perpendicular to the plane determined by the vector pair. Remembering that arrows representing vectors have only properties of magnitude and direction and that they can be moved about in any manner as long as their length is unchanged and their directions remain parallel to their original directions, it can be seen that any two vectors may be placed with their origins coinciding and that they then determine a plane. The only exception to this is incurred when the vectors are parallel to each other; in that case, the cross product is zero regardless of the vector magnitude. The cross product is given by the expression

$$C = A \times B = |A| \, |B| \sin \theta$$

where **C** is a vector perpendicular to **A** and **B** and so directed that it points in the direction which a right-hand screw would advance if an index line on its head was originally pointing in the direction of **A** and then turned through the smaller angle θ necessary to align it

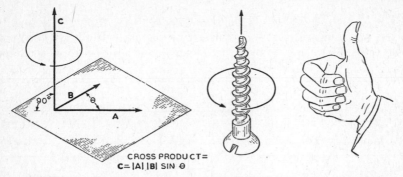

CROSS PRODUCT=
C = |A| |B| SIN Θ

FIG. 6-3. The magnitude of the vector **C** is the product of vectors **A** and **B** and the sine of the angle θ between them, the direction of **C** being that in which a right-hand screw would advance if turned in the direction from **A** to **B**.

with **B**. See Fig. 6-3. The magnitude of **C** is the product of the absolute magnitudes of $|A|$ and $|B|$ times the sine of the angle between **A** and **B**.

When **A** and **B** are perpendicular, the sine of the angle θ is unity, so the magnitude of **C** equals the product of the absolute magnitudes of **A** and **B**. In the case of **A** and **B** being parallel, the angle between them is zero; therefore the sine of the angle is zero, making the cross product also zero.

E and H Quantities

Now consider the power transmission involved in the transmission of radio waves through space, particularly the transmission of microwaves through a waveguide. The closed path travel of charge still exists, but it is difficult to trace. The difficulty arises because voltage may instantaneously appear across small lengths of a good conductor due to the time necessary for the travel of electric energy and because a conductor may at different points be simultaneously carrying current in more than one direction. When this is true, some other method of formulating the problem must be considered, as well as some quantities other than voltage and current which will supply information concerning the flow of electrical energy. Two such quantities are found in the electric field, denoted by **E,** and the magnetic field, which is denoted by **H.**

Space Energy Flow

The values of **E** and **H**-field vectors as they might be found in space, are shown in Fig. 6-4. These two vectors will always be found perpendicular to each other in free space or in any isotropic medium.

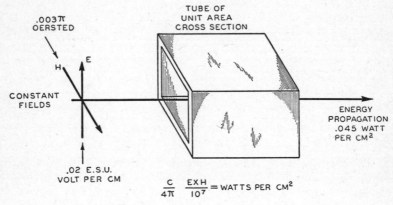

$$\frac{C}{4\pi} \frac{E \times H}{10^7} = \text{WATTS PER CM}^2$$

FIG. 6-4. The **E** and **H** vectors at right angles to each other indicate an energy flow which is at right angles to both of them. Their product measures the energy flow per square centimeter, which, in a constant field, is the power through the imaginary unit-area tube shown.

Except for a numerical factor necessary to keep the units in their proper relationship, the cross product of **E** and **H** gives the energy flow per unit area in the vicinity where **E** and **H** were measured. The result of this cross-product multiplication is a third vector, which is commonly called *Poynting's vector,* and which shows the magnitude and direction of the energy propagation. Specifically,

Poynting's Vector $= \mathbf{P} = \dfrac{c}{4\pi} \mathbf{E} \times \mathbf{H}$ *ergs per sq. cm per sec.*

where $\mathbf{E}$ is in esu volts per cm, $\mathbf{H}$ is in oersted, and c is the velocity of light in cm per second. As shown in Fig. 6-4, possible values of $\mathbf{E}$ and $\mathbf{H}$ are multiplied together to yield a numerical value of the power flow in watts per square centimeter.

There is essentially no more difficulty in visualizing these quantities and the way they transfer energy from the source to the load than there is with charge and voltage. Usually it is only a lack of familiarity that makes $\mathbf{E}$ and $\mathbf{H}$ seem more difficult. As for the mathematical details for obtaining a quantitative solution, either system of analysis may in certain cases be the better one.

At least two advantages are incurred by thinking of energy propagation in terms of electric and magnetic fields. One is that no concept of a return path is needed. It is only necessary to trace the electric and magnetic field from the load to the source. The second is that unlike currents, field quantities can travel through a vacuum or dielectric.

In general, at low frequencies where a two-wire system can be easily traced and all mutual inductances and coupling coefficients be specified, it is better to design electrical transmission systems in terms of voltage and current. At very high frequencies where the round-trip path of all currents is difficult or impossible to follow, it may be better to work with the electric and magnetic fields. In principle at least, either method will always work. Thus, to see how a problem may be solved in terms of $\mathbf{E}$ and $\mathbf{H}$ as well as V and i, first consider a simple direct-current electrical source connected to a load through particular conductors so shaped as to make the solution of the problem feasible by either method of attack.

Working Example

In Fig. 6-5(A) are shown two strips of metal each 1 meter wide and 10 meters long. One of these strips is laid flat on a table and the other is suspended 2 cm above it with air or vacuum in between. A 6-volt storage battery is connected between the strips at one end and a load resistor is placed at the other end. The resistor has such a value that 2 amperes of current flow.

To find the power by ordinary methods, the voltage and the current would be measured with a voltmeter and ammeter respectively, and upon multiplying the two together, an answer of 12 watts would be obtained. Similarly, neglecting edge effects, if the magnetic field, **H**, between the plates were to be measured, it would be found to have a value of 0.008π oersteds.[1] A measurement on the electric field, **E** would yield a value of 0.01 electrostatic volts per centimeter.[2] Here,

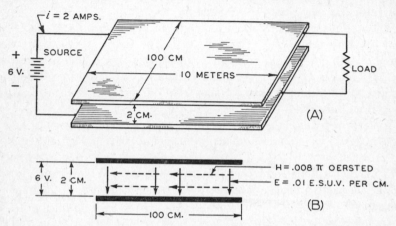

Fig. 6-5. The energy flow in this circuit (A) may be calculated in terms of **E** and **H**; in (B) is an end view of the plates as seen from the source end.

since **E** and **H** are at right angles to each other, an ordinary product of these quantities multiplied by a constant, $3 \cdot 10^{10}/4\pi$, which is necessary to keep the dimensions correct, gives the energy flow per square centimeter. Poynting's vector in this case is therefore given by

$$P = \frac{3 \cdot 10^{10}}{4\pi} \cdot E \times H$$
$$= \frac{3 \cdot 10^{10}}{4\pi} \cdot 0.01 \cdot 0.008\pi$$
$$= 6 \cdot 10^5 \ ergs \ per \ square \ cm \ per \ sec.$$

The energy is here visualized as traveling in the space between the plates. This viewpoint may seem less natural than one in which the energy is more closely associated with the charge, but it represents an equally valid way and is more helpful in explaining radiation. Poynting's vector represents the energy flow through each square cm of the space. Dividing by 10^7 so as to change the units to watts per square cm instead of ergs per square cm per second, the value of Poynting's vector is

$$P = 0.06 \ watts \ per \ square \ cm.$$

The cross-sectional area is 200 square cm, so multiplying, the total power is 12 watts as before.

In Fig. 6-5(B) this is shown more clearly. Here is shown an end view of the plates illustrated in Fig. 6-5(A). The electric field which always points toward negative charge, is represented by the vertical vectors. For the vacuum or air case the units of E are expressed in volts per cm. Since E is a vector quantity, it may be represented by an arrow, the head of which points to negative charge and the length of which shows how rapidly voltage changes through space. In previous chapters E has been defined in terms of a force, and it has been stated that E is the force on a unit charge. A positive charge might be placed between the two plates and it would be attracted to the negative plate, indicating that the electric field points in that direction. The magnitude of the force will give the magnitude of the electric field. Here the magnitude of the force will be the voltage divided by the distance between the plates, as the voltage is the work involved in transporting a unit charge between the plates and because work is defined as the force multiplied by the distance. Fundamentally, E is a property of space due to currents or charge on nearby conductors.

Also in Fig. 6-5(B) vectors have been drawn representing the magnetic field. These arrows drawn parallel to the plates and perpendicular to the electric field are also to be thought of as indicating a property of a point in space. This time it is a property which depends on whatever currents are flowing in the neighborhood. The direction in which the H vectors are to be drawn can be determined by putting a small magnet at the point in question. It will turn like a compass and indicate the direction of H with its north pole. If this same magnet is then turned through an angle of 90 degrees, the torque necessary to hold it there can show the magnitude of the H vector. It is also possible to calculate H from the known currents just as E can be found from known voltages. To do so use is made of Ampere's law. A calculation with it confirming the value of H has been given.

With the storage battery and the two strips of metal, the calculation of E, H, and Poynting's vector has been rather the long way around to find a simple answer of 12 watts. It would have been even worse if an ordinary pair of wires had been used. A justification of the difficulties is made by looking at problems solvable in terms of E and H but not in terms of V and i.

Antenna Radiation

The radiation from a transmitting antenna is in a sense just the opposite to the way a piece of resistance wire absorbs energy, this being illustrated in Fig. 6-6. Fig. 6-6(A) represents a short length of resistance wire through which a positive current is flowing from left to right. Since an electric field can be measured by the force on a

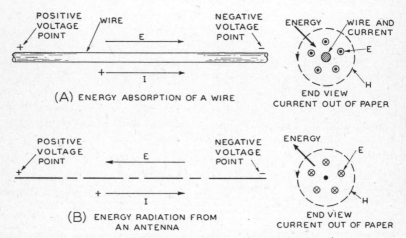

FIG. 6-6. In (A) it is shown that energy being guided along a resistance wire will flow into the wire. In (B) electromagnetic fields some distance from an antenna are so oriented that energy may move out into space.

positive charge, the electric field at the surface of the wire must also be from left to right. By the right-hand rule, the magnetic field must be as shown. Now with crossed **E** and **H** vectors, if **E** is rotated into **H** like a right-hand screw, the motion of the screw shows the direction of the energy propagation, thus with resistance wire the energy apparently flows into the wire.[3] Detailed calculations will show that with the **E** and **H** conception, this flow will be just enough to account for the heating of the wire as is usually given by the i^2r loss.[4]

With radio frequencies and low-resistance wire such as would be used in an antenna, the opposite is true on the average. It is necessary to say specifically that it is true on the average because *at the surface* of any wire whether it be serving as an antenna or a resistor, an electric field can actually only exist like the one shown in Fig. 6-6(A) and never like the one shown in Fig. 6-6(B). If as is shown in both Fig. 6-6(A) and Fig. 6-6(B), a positive voltage due to an excess of positive charge is on the left, and a negative voltage due to an excess of negative charge is on the right, the electric field (i.e. the force on a unit positive charge) must be directed from left to right as in Fig. 6-6(A) and not from right to left as in Fig. 6-6(B). Even if the resistance of the wire is made negligibly small, the value of E at the surface of the wire is only made small and its direction is not changed. In the limiting case of a perfect conductor, the condition of no tangential electric field is valid and E is actually zero at the surface of the wire. At some distance away from the surface of an antenna wire, however, the condition of Fig. 6-6(B) is valid. Such a contribution to the Poynting vector flow actually arises at a discontinuity in the antenna wire, as will be discussed in conjunction with Fig. 6-7. Here this is shown by not indicating a wire in Fig. 6-6(B), as in Fig. 6-6(A), but by only showing a center line along which a current flow could produce the desired H-field. In the sample case considered in Fig. 6-7, it will be seen that the current flow is actually to the right or to the left of this line.

If, in the case of Fig. 6-6(B), the rule of the right-hand screw is applied, it is found that energy will flow out away from the antenna. Rotating E into H yields a direction for Poynting's vector that is away from the antenna. In addition to the discussion of Fig. 6-7 which follows presently, the way in which such an outward-bound Poynting's vector arises is discussed further in the section on microwave generation. A more fundamental analysis of the way in which outward-bound Poynting vectors arise, is given there in terms of charge acceleration.

Fortunately it is quite easy with an antenna to calculate both E and H if the current is known. A rather simple expression for the radiation from a short length of wire may be formulated in terms of the current, frequency, distance, and angle from the radiating section.[5]

In Fig. 6-7, the case of a center-fed half-wave antenna is considered in some detail to show an example of how an outwardly directed component of Poynting's vector may arise from consideration of voltage and current. Fig. 6-7(A) is a schematic representation of such an antenna, while Figs. 6-7(B) and 6-7(C) show instantaneous values of the standing waves of current and voltage along the antenna at 12 times, indicated as t_1, t_2, t_3, etc. up to t_{12}. Broken vertical lines are drawn to indicate corresponding points on the two sets of curves and on the schematic representation of the antenna.

As is characteristic of standing waves, nothing changes with time in either set of curves except the amplitude and that varies smoothly from a maximum in one direction, down to zero, and then to a maximum in the other direction, and then back again. For example, at the left end of the antenna it may be seen by following the subscripts of t in order that a maximum positive voltage decreases to zero, goes on to a maximum negative voltage, and then returns through zero

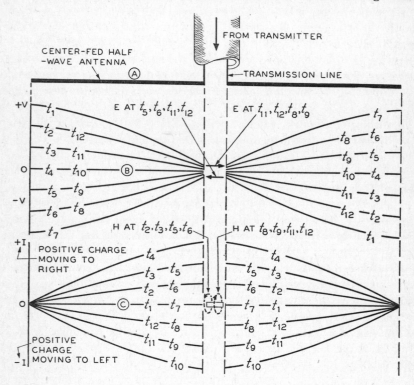

FIG. 6-7. A half-wave center-fed antenna with instantaneous plots of voltage and current at twelve different times, t_1 to t_{12}.

to a maximum positive value again. At the right end of the antenna, the voltages perform in the same way but always with opposite polarity. Similarly, the current waves also move back and forth across the zero-value line, but as can be seen from the time indexes, they move in a different phase than the voltage waves. More will be said about this phase arrangement in the chapter on waveguides when the properties of waveguide impedance are discussed.

Now in a standing-wave picture, voltage nodes and current maxima are generally drawn, but in Fig. 6-7 these are not shown, because energy is fed to the antenna at that point. The overall antenna is a half-wave in length, including the gap where the transmission line is connected. At the points where the radiators connect to the transmission line, conductors there cannot be true voltage nodes, because if there were, no voltage would ever appear at those points and no new energy could be fed into the radiators. Energy simply cannot be transferred in the complete absence of voltage or electric field. Hence, the picture of Fig. 6-7 is correct, and the standing wave acts as if a piece were cut out where the transmission line is connected. Particular interest is in this gap in the fields, because it is here that conditions are such as to generate an outward Poynting's vector at all times.

Looking first at Fig. 6-7(C), it is easy to see that the magnetic fields which are indicated in the gap, are correct. At times t_2, t_3, t_5, and t_6, a positive current is flowing to the right and the magnetic field everywhere in the neighborhood of the antenna is circular in form and directed as it is shown. This may be checked by the right-hand rule. On the other hand, at times t_8, t_9, t_{11}, and t_{12}, the current is flowing to the left and the magnetic field is reversed.

To determine the direction of the electric field in the gap it is necessary to realize that the voltage across the end of the transmission line is one that is determined by the transmitter and that its presence is the cause of all that happens. In other words, the action of the antenna is dependent upon the transmitter supplying power. Thus, during successive times such as t_{11} and t_{12} when it is desired that the positive current flow to the left shall decrease as the current curves indicate it will, the electric field in the gap must be directed to the right and exert a force to slow down the charge motion. Again, during times t_8 and t_9, the transmitter also must provide a voltage in the gap which will direct the electric field to the left as is shown, because at that time the currents flowing to the right are increasing and their doing so depends upon that urge. Similarly, it may be argued that the electric field in the gap points to the left at times t_5, t_6, t_{11}, and t_{12}.

The result of this discussion is that in the gap between the two halves of the center-fed antenna of Fig. 6-7, the electric field changes direction in unison with the magnetic field. It also may be seen by applying the rule for determining the direction of Poynting's vector that this continually gives rise to an outward direction for that vector.

Alternating Currents

In both the cases of Poynting's vector, as it is associated with a wire carrying current, the effect of the alternation of current and voltage in the wire itself has not been considered. When the case of energy absorption by a resistance was discussed, d.c. was tacitly assumed, and this is certainly justified since, at any instant, a-c energy has many of the properties of d.c., and certainly it has the same ability to lose voltage level in passing through a resistor. Also, in the antenna radiation case, the gap in the antenna was considered and it was stated that radiation came from that gap, but here again it was not shown that radiation might not arise from the actual a-c waves on the wires. Actually, standing or traveling waves of current or voltage on a wire do not cause either radiation or absorption of energy from the electromagnetic field. This is demonstrated by the discussion of Fig. 6-8 and Fig. 6-9 which follows.

In Fig. 6-8, a one-half wavelength piece of a wire is considered, and four possible arrangements of electric and magnetic field as dictated by four possible arrangements of current and voltage are shown. Fig. 6-8(B) and 6-8(D) turn out to be the same phase arrangement shown at different times. This will be discussed more fully in connection with Fig. 6-9.

The simplest part of the discussion of Fig. 6-8 concerns the magnetic field. It is always circular around the wire, and directed by the right-hand rule in accordance with the current in the wire. In the four parts of Fig. 6-8, it has been chosen to draw the current the same each time and to adjust the phase by means of different voltage curves.

The electric field near a wire carrying alternating current is less simply determined. It depends upon two things (in addition to resistance) and is, in general, neither parallel to the wire nor perpendicular to it. The parallel component accounts for the wave distribution of charge and voltage, while the perpendicular component generates a Poynting's vector which accounts for the flow of power along the wire. Only when there is infinite resistance does the perpendicular component approach zero and the electric field truly lie parallel to the wire. Only in the d-c case (and when resistance can be considered as negligibly small) is the electric field really perpendicular to the wire. It is very convenient to divide the electric field into two components, as has been done for each case considered in Fig. 6-8, be-

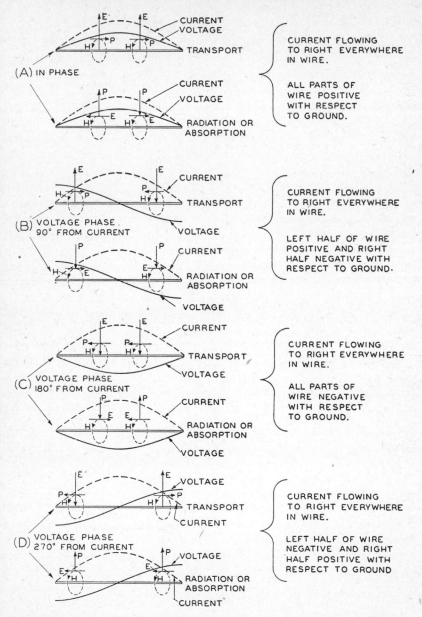

FIG. 6-8. Four possible arrangements of electric and magnetic field are shown on a half wavelength piece of wire.

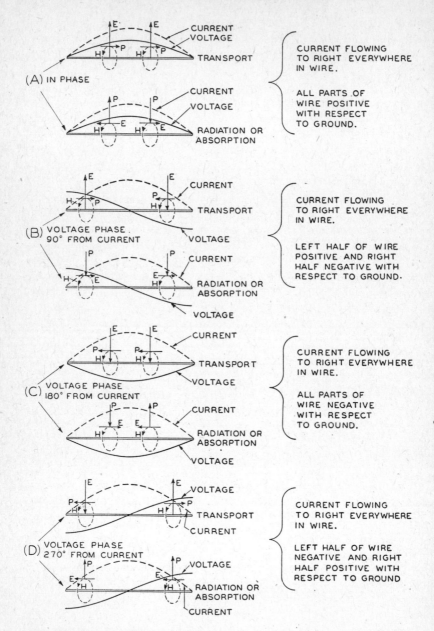

FIG. 6-8. Four possible arrangements of electric and magnetic field are shown on a half wavelength piece of wire.

cause it turns out that one component has to do with energy flow along the conductor, while the other is only concerned with energy flow in or out of the conductor. Incidentally, the in-and-out components cancel each other, as will presently be seen.

In Fig. 6-8(A) the situation for in-phase voltage and current is shown. At the time shown in the sketch, the whole wire is at a positive voltage with respect to ground, and the current is moving to the right in all parts of the wire. The current gives rise to a magnetic field like the one shown. If a positive test charge is held near the wire, it will be repelled outward from the wire because the wire is positively charged. Thus the E-field has an outward component, such as is shown in Fig. 6-8(A) in the case marked *Transport*. The Poynting vectors transporting energy along the line all point in one direction. Thus only a single traveling wave is being considered.

The same picture drawn at a later time will consist of a view showing the pattern shifted to the right. The test charge used for finding E will also feel a force urging it toward the ends of the wire and away from the center, because the greatest concentration of positive charge is at the center. This effect gives rise to components of electric field parallel to the wire, as shown in Fig. 6-8(A) in the case marked *Radiation or Absorption*. Applying the rule for the direction of Poynting's vector, we find that in Fig. 6-8(A) energy is traveling from left to right and the radiation and absorption components are both present at different points on the wire. At a later time the pattern will be shifted and in due course all parts of the wire will have a chance to radiate or absorb. Equal amount of each are present, so no net radiation or absorption takes place. The fields merely pulsate in the neighborhood of the conductor.

In Fig. 6-8(B), the left half of the wire is positive and the right half is negative. A positive test charge therefore will be attracted toward the left half and repelled from the right half; so the transport components of Poynting's vector average to zero. In other words, a pure standing wave is formed and equal flow is going on in both directions. The positive test charge will also be urged to move toward the right end of the wire because of the large amount of negative charge located there. This gives rise to an electric field directed into the wire. This would be at first seem to be a situation demanding absorption of energy by the wire but, as will presently be explained, it is only another view of Fig. 6-8(D) and together these two cases again call for complete cancellation of radiation and absorption.

The analysis of Fig. 6-8(C) is similar to Fig. 6-8(A) and will not be stated in detail. It turns out to be the case in which energy is moving from right to left as a single traveling wave.

The case of Fig. 6-8(D) is the one of apparent radiation. As in Fig. 6-8(B), the transport components of Poynting's vector average to zero. Unlike Fig. 6-8(B), however, the left end of the wire is now negative and a positive test charge feels a force in that direction. This means that all along the wire a component of electric field is directed from right to left, and in consequence, a Poynting's vector directed outward.

The pure traveling wave case of Fig. 6-8(A) and Fig. 6-8(C) can easily be seen to favor neither absorption nor radiation. Figs. 6-8(B) and 6-8(D), however, seem at first sight to yield exclusively energy absorption or radiation. The clue to the falsity of what seems to be an arrangement in which phase alone can dictate radiation is intrinsic in the components of the Poynting vectors shown in the Transport cases. Waves are shown as traveling in both directions along the wire, so time variation of the pattern must follow the changes which occur with a standing wave; this is shown in Fig. 6-9. There the current

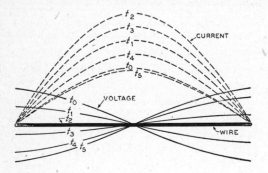

FIG. 6-9. The possible equivalence of Figs. 6-8 (B) and (D).

and voltage curves of Fig. 6-8(B) have been duplicated and labeled with t_o to indicate that they represent the situation at one certain time. At successively later times, the curves t_1, t_2, t_3, t_4, and t_5 show how the patterns look. The curves marked t_5 are the same as those of Fig. 6-8(D).

From the discussion of the past few sections it may be concluded that no matter what the phase arrangement, radiation and absorption of energy can both take place in any piece of wire. Radiation and absorption components due to the alternating current itself, always accurately cancel out. Absorption due to voltage drops caused by resistance just accounts for the heat generated in the resistance. Radiation and radiation resistance arises at discontinuities in the antenna line and depends upon the voltage drive of the transmitter.

Field Motion

It has been specifically stated that the product of **E** and **H** gives information about energy flow. What is implied, moreover, is that a given value of **E** and **H** travels along with the energy. The idea of **E** and **H** vectors actually moving through space is a very helpful one, which may be justified as follows. If at some place in space a pulse of electromagnetic energy is traveling eastward and no other energy is in the neighborhood, then, likewise only at that point must **E** and **H** have values other than zero. At a moment later the energy pulse has moved and is still traveling eastward; hence **E** and **H** may also be considered as moving through space. In fact, it may be shown that an expression can be given for the energy per unit volume in space.[6] It is

$$Energy \; per \; unit \; volume = \frac{K\mathbf{E}^2 + \mu\mathbf{H}^2}{8\pi} \; ergs \; per \; cm^3.$$

When this unit volume of energy moves through space **E** and **H** must move with it.

Waveguide Phenomenon

This idea of closely identifying the flow of electromagnetic energy with the motion of a wave of **E** and **H** is very valuable in understanding waveguide phenomenon. From this viewpoint it is only necessary to see that certain values of **E** and **H** occur at certain times at the source end and then to follow these values as they move along the pipe.

In Fig. 6-10 the **E** and **H** waves are illustrated for the simple case of a cylindrical pipe fed with an appropriate frequency. A possible way of introducing the energy into the pipe is indicated by the annular insulation placed in the otherwise closed source end. If at some instant a voltage appears across the generator, then at that time contour lines of constant **E** may be drawn between the input electrodes, as are shown at the generator end of Figs. 6-10(A) and 6-10(B). In accordance with Maxwell's equations, as these lines change, as they surely will since high-frequency alternating current is being considered, contour lines of **H** will also appear. These are also shown at the generator end of Figs. 6-10(A) and 6-10(B).

Fig. 6-10(A) illustrates what happens in the extreme case of perfect mismatch between the waveguide and its load. The maximum of the magnetic field coincides with the minimum radial electric field. (It is also the point of maximum electric field along the length of the waveguide, but that part of the electric field can have nothing to do with

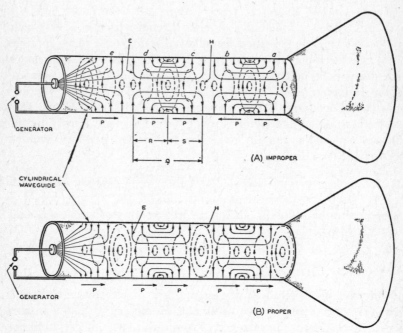

FIG. 6-10. In (A) is shown the improper and in (B) the proper phase arrangements for transferring energy along a waveguide into space.

a Poynting vector along the waveguide.) This means that a given half-wave of maximum magnetic field (that is a section along the waveguide that has magnetic field as circles directed in one direction, as along length Q) is coincident with half inward (length R) and half outward (length S) radial electric field. The result is that the Poynting vector is directed first one way and then the other, as shown beside the waveguide. The case of Fig. 6-10(A) is one of unity standing-wave ratio with equal traveling waves moving in both directions. It is certainly not the desired situation for a line to an antenna.

The case of infinite swr is shown in Fig. 6-10(B). Here the maxima of the magnetic field coincide with the points of maximum radial electric field. If at any point a radial **E** vector is mentally rotated into the **H** vector, it will be turned as if to drive a right-hand screw toward the load and away from the generator. It may be said that the waveguide has been matched to the load.

If the load end of the waveguide is perfectly matched, it is quite easy to visualize the motion of the **E** and **H** contours (lines of force). **H** moves down the pipe of Fig. 6-10 like a series of smoke rings, while the electric lines radiate out from the center of the pipe, being distributed in time (and hence in distance along the pipe) in accordance with the sine-wave form of the input voltage.

General Design

It should be remembered that this is only a single example of waveguide propagation. It is not necessary that the pipe be cylindrical, and even if it is, the waves may travel in some different manner. These various types of transmission are called *modes of propagation*. The particular mode in which a wave will travel along a pipe depends upon the method of excitation and the shape and dimensions of the guide. This will be discussed in a later chapter.

It can be stated in general, however, that in any waveguide problem a crossed electric and magnetic field must be introduced into the source end. This will then automatically attempt to transfer energy into the guide. Whether or not transmission will occur along the guide and in what mode will depend on boundary conditions. A differential equation can be written that contains the solutions of any wave problem. That equation is known as *Poisson's equation*. To design a waveguide to do a particular job it is necessary to choose such a shape and dimension as to allow such a solution of the wave equation to be obtained which will have proper boundary values at the metallic surfaces.

Fortunately, for making measurements on actual waveguide installations, the ratio of **E** and **H** is usually a constant. **E** and **H** are intimately bound up with each other. **E** for example depends upon the rate of change of **H** (really **B**) and **H** is also influenced by changes in **E**. Because of this it is not surprising that in a given geometry, one cannot be changed without changing the other. In free space the ratio is 300 to one where units of **E** and of **H** are so chosen that the ratio has units of ohms; in other words, the impedance of free space is 300 ohms. In a specific type of guide it may well have a different value but still a constant one, depending on the inductance and capacitance and hence the geometry of the waveguide. This ratio may usually be calculated so it is only necessary to measure **E** in order to compute Poynting's vector. Even if the **E** to **H** ratio is not found, measurements on **E** alone are sufficient for relative calculations of power flow. All that is necessary is to assume that the **E/H** ratio is the same at the various times when the relative measurements are made.

The Basis of Microwave Generation

If, in any radio transmitter, the electrical energy is followed from the power lines until it has been radiated from the antenna, there is some place in the path beyond which it is no longer fruitful to discuss the situation in terms of currents and voltages. Instead, it becomes necessary to describe the electromagnetic field. In ordinary broadcast and shortwave installations, this point does not usually come until the antenna is reached. Antenna currents are measured and voltage curves are drawn. Much has been written about the necessary resonance of such transmitting antennas and about the distribution of electromagnetic radiation that may be expected from various geometric arrays, but quite a bit less has been said about the actual mechanism of radiation.

Microwave Transmitters

With microwave transmitters, the emphasis must usually be changed. Antennas are not just wires but, instead, are parabolic reflectors. Energy is not brought up to these radiating surfaces on wires, but rather in a waveguide or in a coaxial line. The result is that the point in the energy path where it becomes more advantageous to consider electromagnetic waves is pushed right back to the microwave oscillator. To understand the operation of microwave transmitting tubes, such as the klystron or the magnetron, it is necessary to cultivate a physical picture of electromagnetic waves and the way in which they originate.

At power-line frequencies radiation is unimportant because, with finite currents and reasonable separation of the conductors, the radiated energy is very small. In fact, if the special case of dipole radiation in which a charge oscillates back and forth over a very small distance is considered, it becomes rather easy to calculate an expression for the total energy radiated as a function of the charge strength and the frequency. This expression is

$$Radiation = \frac{Q^2 f^2}{6\pi c^3} \; ergs \; per \; second$$

where Q is the strength of the charge, f is its frequency of oscillation, and c is a constant equal to the velocity of light. Because of the squared term in f, radiation at low frequencies is very small. At microwave frequencies it has, until recently, been impossible to build efficient radiators because of the smallness of Q.

In this same dipole case, the electric and magnetic fields arising from the oscillating charge can be calculated. It is found that in the region close to the charge, as measured in terms of wavelength, the fields become smaller with increasing distance at a more rapid rate than at greater distances. It is the strength of the field at these greater distances that gives rise to radiation, while the energy in the nearby induction field is reabsorbed by the charge as the direction of its acceleration reverses.

Here, however, there is not so much interest in the field of an oscillating charge as in the more general question of how a moving charge interacts with an electromagnetic field. Some simple and rather general ideas can be easily developed concerning the way in which a moving charge causes fields. The reverse action, by which fields affect the motion of a charge, comes rather naturally into the picture from the definitions of the fields which are given.

Wave-Trains

According to the electromagnetic theory, any accelerated charge must radiate energy in the form of an electromagnetic pulse or wave-train. If a charge that is initially at rest is set in motion, or if once it is in motion it is brought to rest, an electromagnetic pulse is sent out. If the acceleration is such that the charge vibrates back and forth, or if continual acceleration is maintained, as by the motion of the charge in a circular path, a train of waves is given out. When the charge moves back and forth along an antenna with acceleration and velocity such that it makes f complete trips per second, then a radio wave of frequency f is transmitted. This is true at all radio frequencies but is not strictly true at much shorter wavelengths, such as are encountered in light and X-rays, although even there the creation of radiant energy is brought about by electrons in the atom which rotate in orbits and are thus accelerated. An added condition expressed by a more comprehensive theory, known as quantum mechanics, is necessary to explain atomic radiation. With wavelengths which are large compared to atomic dimensions, this more complete theory reduces in such a way as to verify the simpler proposition.[7]

Before going further, ideas concerning the electric and magnetic fields themselves and how they exist around a charge under various conditions of motion must be clarified. The electric field is a quantity that can be measured at any point in space by placing a known test charge at the point in question and noting the force exerted on it due to the attraction or repulsion of other charges in the neighborhood.[8] These neighborhood charges, which determine the properties of the place where the test charge is placed, may be of two kinds. One kind is called *free charge* and, as the name indicates, this kind is completely detached from charge of the opposite sign. The other sort is *bound charge*, which is always closely associated with equal and opposite charge. The portion of the force on the test charge due only to the free charge, is a measure of the E-field at the point. The whole force depending upon the arrangement of both the free and bound charge in the neighborhood measures the **D** field. In general, it is necessary to distinguish between these two electric fields; however, since free space only will be considered where bound charge does not exist, **E** and **D** will be equal and identical.

Field of a Moving Charge

When a charge moves in a straight line with a uniform velocity the electric field usually differs very little from that when it is stationary. It takes a finite amount of time for the test charge to feel the effect of attraction from the moving charge, so that at high velocity (greater than 0.5 times the velocity of light) the field is somewhat modified. In Fig. 6-11, the electric field in terms of force lines is shown for a stationary field and for velocities of 0.5, 0.9 and 0.99 times the velocity of light. These modifications are not those which would be naively expected from simple reasoning which is based on the idea that, because of the transit time of the force line, a test charge at A feels a force dependent on the location of the moving charge at a slightly previous time. The reason for this is tied up with the theory of special relativity. According to that theory, an observer riding with the charge will see a stationary electric field and find the velocity of electromagnetic propagation to be the same in his frame of reference as that for a stationary observer. The satisfaction of these requirements calls for the fields as shown.

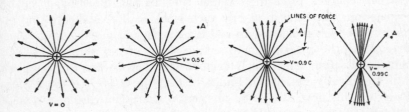

Fig. 6-11. Plots of the electromagnetic field about a charge when it is stationary and when it is moving with a velocity that is 0.5, 0.9, and 0.99 times the velocity of light.

Actually, in all microwave generators now known, no such extreme velocities are encountered. Electric field patterns like the one shown for a stationary charge are always a very good approximation of the actual distribution, although because of the symmetrical nature of the relativistic change, it is clear that the conclusions that will be drawn are valid in any event.

Magnetic lines of force around a charge which is moving with constant velocity along a straight line, are shown in Fig. 6-12. These show the magnetic field in the neighborhood of the moving charge in the same way as the electric lines of force show the electric field. The magnetic field, usually called the B or H-field,[9] is a given quantity which has a measurable value at every point in space and is hence really a property of space. To measure the magnetic field at a point such as A (Fig. 6-12), a very small test magnet may be placed at

Fig. 6-12. The magnetic field of a moving charge showing that, in connection with the electric field, a Poynting's vector is generated which is parallel to the velocity of the charge and which has no component outward from the wire.

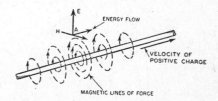

that point and oriented until a maximum torque is required to hold it. The strength of the field can then be measured by that torque and the field direction obtained by releasing the test magnet and observing the direction in which the north pole points.

In the case shown in Fig. 6-12, the direction of the magnetic field can be determined by the right-hand rule usually used to show the magnetic flux around a current carrying wire, in which resistance may be neglected. Here, the magnetic and electric fields move along with the charge. Poynting's vector showing the direction of energy propagation can be seen at any such point as A to indicate that the energy flow is in the space around the charge and moving in the same direction as the charge. The direction of the energy flow is that of a right-hand screw when the E vector is rotated toward the H vector. It is specifically noticed in Fig. 6-12 that there is no outward component of this flow. This confirms that a charge moving in a straight line with constant velocity does not radiate.

Effect of Acceleration

As has been seen, the electric field of a charge is ordinarily not much modified by constant velocities. When accelerations are present, however, the situation is changed. Referring to Fig. 6-13(A) assume that a charge Q is first observed at A and that it moves through the very short distance δx with an ever-increasing velocity. Let it be further assumed that after being accelerated to B, the voltage causing

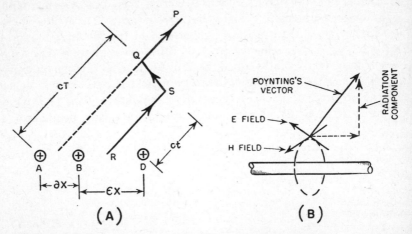

FIG. 6-13. The electric field arising from an accelerated charge is shown in (A) and the resulting Poynting's vector is shown in (B); note that a component of this vector points away from the path of the charge.

the acceleration is removed so that the charge continues with constant velocity through the small distance ϵx to the point labeled D. Now if the nature of the field around the charge is considered at the moment D is reached, the effect of the acceleration can be visualized. Representing by T the time it took the charge to travel the whole distance AD, then distant points such as P, which are farther from the charge than cT are unaffected by any of the motion until after the time of the final observation. In fact, this is true anywhere along the line QP because, although the field is propagated with the velocity of light which is represented by c, and will travel a distance cT to Q during the observations, there has not been time for it to travel farther.

Similarly in Fig. 6-13(A), during the time the charge moves with constant velocity, represented by T, the field extends out from the charge in the normal manner but, at the time of final observation, it has only had time to travel a distance ct to point S. Thus in Fig. 6-13(A), where only one line of force has been drawn it is known that the line of force must start out along RS and end up along QP. Since it is surely continuous, S and Q can be connected and the portion SQ shows the effect of acceleration.

In Fig. 6-13(B), the part of the field arising from the acceleration of the charge (section SQ in Fig. 6-13(A)) is redrawn on a larger scale, along with the magnetic lines of force and the resulting Poynting's vector. It is clear there, that the energy flow shown by that vector has a component which points outward from the path of the charge. This represents energy radiated out into space.

So far only the electromagnetic field arising from a single charge has been considered, and it has been specifically pointed out that when the velocity of that charge increases, energy is radiated. This is true whether the charge is accelerated to the right or to the left and, if the charge oscillates back and forth as in an ordinary antenna, radiation occurs at regular intervals corresponding to each acceleration. The emission of such a train of pulses is referred to as a wave-train and the oscillating charge is said to be radiating an electromagnetic wave.

Microwave Reflections

When electromagnetic waves which are traveling in a given medium, come to the interface between that medium and a new medium, some of the energy is reflected and some may be transmitted. The problem of reflection is of particular interest because of the recent successes of radar. This is, however, by no means the only circumstance where electromagnetic reflections are important. In ordinary radio communication they are also extremely important, because radio energy ordinarily travels from the transmitting antenna to the receiving antenna not only by a direct route but it also is reflected from the surface of the earth and from the ionosphere. Also, in analyzing the operation of waveguide, it is very helpful to think in terms of the reflections of waves. Just as the reflection of traveling voltage and current waves in coaxial lines has been considered, so in the discussion of waveguides must the effect of the reflection of electromagnetic energy be examined.

There is another purpose in what follows. It is desired to introduce Maxwell's equations and, without getting too deeply into the mathematical formulism which is necessary to make greatest use of that powerful set of equations, the reader should be familiar with their nature. They are the only complete theory of electricity and magnetism which, at least outside the domain of the atom, can lead to the solution of any problem of electricity and magnetism. The fact that they are often too clumsy to use in practical problems and the fact that many problems arise in which the sheer mathematical labor involved in obtaining a solution is too great to undertake, does not rob them of their generality. In electromagnetic theory they are to be regarded as the final authority. They are also a convenient starting point for a careful discussion of some topics. Electromagnetic wave reflections fall in this category, so that the combined ideas of this section work well together.

The Radar Problem

The practical solution to the problem of deciding how well a target, such as a certain type of aircraft, will reflect electromagnetic waves is almost entirely a matter of experiment and measurement. To obtain a solution by calculation of known data concerning the geometry of the aircraft construction, and the type of material from which the airplane is made, is an example of a problem which is too laborious to undertake. The surface exposed to the radar beam changes according to the orientation of the airplane; the materials of the aircraft are numerous and of odd shapes; the geometry is far from simple. Furthermore, at certain wavelengths resonant conditions may occur, because certain dimensions are equal to half wavelengths. These cause certain parts of the airplane to be much more efficient as reflectors than they would otherwise be.

In Fig. 6-14 is illustrated the nature of the reflection from an average aircraft in an average radar beam. The energy that is incident upon various exposed parts of the aircraft is essentially constant, for even at a range of only a few miles, the aircraft subtends an exceedingly

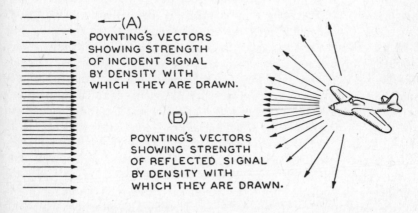

(A)
POYNTING'S VECTORS
SHOWING STRENGTH
OF INCIDENT SIGNAL
BY DENSITY WITH
WHICH THEY ARE DRAWN.

(B)
POYNTING'S VECTORS
SHOWING STRENGTH
OF REFLECTED SIGNAL
BY DENSITY WITH
WHICH THEY ARE DRAWN.

Fig. 6-14. Nature of radar energy reflected from an airplane target.

small angle at the transmitter. That is, suppose the transmitter puts out a radar beam that is 2 degrees wide. Then, if the beam is pointed at an airplane, all of the airplane will be well within that 2-degree angle, and surfaces of the airplane on the side toward the transmitter will be illuminated by the radar energy. At distances away from the airplane but no further from the transmitter, the energy density will be less because of the finite width of the incident beam. This is shown in Fig. 6-14 by drawing the Poynting vectors less densely at points away from the aircraft. In most radar problems, however, this does not enter and specifically, for formulating a criterion for reflecting ability, it is satisfactory to assume that the incident beam is of equal strength at all points where it encounters the target.

Similarly, in Fig. 6-14, it is recognized that the effect of reflection is not only to send energy directly back toward the radar set but also to send some out at different angles. In the radar example, interest is centered only in the strength of the reflection which is directed back to the radar set; that is in measuring or computing something which will compare the energy flow at A to that of B.

The conventional way to set up a quantity which will show what is wanted about the reflecting ability of radar targets, is to define what is commonly known as *reflection cross-section*. The reflection cross-section of a radar target is an area that is measured in square meters and which, when placed perpendicular to the incident beam, is just big enough so that all the energy it intercepts is the correct amount to radiate in all directions so as to produce a radiated field strength in all directions that is precisely equivalent to that which the radar target sends back toward the radar set. In terms of Fig. 6-14, this means that the reflection cross-section of the airplane shown would be an area capable of intercepting enough vectors in a region like *A*, so that those vectors could be redrawn as radiating out in every direction from the airplane with a density equal to that shown at *B*. The definition, of course, does not mean that radar reflections are really isotropic. Some other method of comparing the energy at *A* and at *B* in Fig. 6-14 could equally well be devised. The reflection cross-section, usually designated by the Greek letter sigma, σ, is only a convention, although a very useful one.

When σ is known, the predicting of how well a given radar target will be detected by a given radar set is generally possible. How this may be done shall be considered in Chapter 11. For very large airplanes σ will have values up to about 3 square meters for microwave radar signals; in smaller airplanes values down to about 1 square meter are a better estimate. For a smooth, perfectly conducting sphere, σ is equal to r^2, where r is the radius of the sphere. The properties of the target upon which σ depends may be listed as follows:

1. Dimensions of the target
2. Material of construction
3. Surface condition
4. Aspect presented to the receiver station
5. Wavelength
6. Polarization

To make even an intelligent guess as to the relative ease of detecting metal or plywood airplanes by means of radar, or to understand the phase shift that occurs upon reflection, it is well to go deeper into the subject. It is well to think in terms of Maxwell's equations, even though it may be beyond human capability to use them for exact solutions of a given problem. Good design estimates can be made only when they are based on general information as well as upon data obtained from specific instances.

Other Reflection Problems

In general, little can be said about electromagnetic reflections in waveguide without getting into a discussion of electromagnetic propagation. Such a discussion is reserved for later chapters. Here it need only be mentioned that the very justification for waveguide operation is based on reflection, and that all waveguide impedance measurements are best interpreted in terms of standing waves which arise because of the reflection of traveling waves, just as has been described in the discussion of coaxial lines.

As for the reflection of microwave energy from the ground, the practical problem is difficult. The chief alleviating circumstance is that since high-gain antennas are easily constructed for microwave energy, it is often initially possible to restrict the direction of energy propagation so that only a very small amount is reflected from the ground. Although the amount is small, it is nevertheless very seldom that in ground-to-ground communication the reflection energy can be entirely neglected.

The chief difficulty in predicting the effect of ground reflection on a given transmission link, lies in determining the nature of the terrain. Results differ according to whether trees and hills or flat ground is found at the point of reflection. They also differ in accord with a roughness of the ground that is of the same order of magnitude as or larger than, the size of a wavelength of the transmitted energy. Accurate theoretical calculations have been made for calm sea water, since that is a condition that can be observed in many places. The values obtained check very well with experiment, but they are of less value than might be hoped because sea waves that are large compared to microwaves are very commonly experienced. More will be said concerning the allowance which must be made for ground reflections when, in Chapter 11, many of the factors are collected which enter into the successful operation of either a microwave radar or communication system.

Nature of Maxwell's Equations

Maxwell's equations may be considered as very general laws of nature which describe much that is known about electricity and magnetism. From that viewpoint they do not need to be considered as mathematical equations which are derived from something else, but rather they are a wonderfully compact group of postulates that correlate much that mankind has discovered about the subject of electricity and magnetism. Understanding them is a matter of being sufficiently familiar with the mathematical notation to know what the symbols mean, and is not a matter of remembering or inventing mathematical procedures to get from one equation to another. On the other hand, applying Maxwell's equations to a specific problem is different. Then ingenuity and skill are at a great premium. It is possible to solve the simplest electrical problems by the application of Maxwell's equations, although it is usually more expedient to use more specialized rules which are more familiar. These rules, however, can themselves be shown to be a consequence of Maxwell's equations, and in such cases where the rules are only good approximations rather than a rigorous law, that fact will be seen in the derivation.

Maxwell's equations may also be regarded as the culmination of a hundred years of research. The progress of physics and engineering seems always to go forward. First, isolated facts are ingeniously uncovered; next there are many facts that are discovered by many people who were stimulated by the original discoveries; finally there is correlation. With electricity first there were experiments with lode stones, amber rubbed with cloth, static machines, Leyden Jars, etc. These were followed by many contributions from numerous people, until by the time of Michael Faraday (1791-1867), a great mass of uncorrelated experimental information concerning electricity and magnetism was available. Faraday, as the great experimenter of his time, was the genius who did the most to bring together the experimental evidence and make it appear as a correlated whole. He seems to have lacked the necessary mathematical technique to give the whole subject a concise form and that was left for J. Clerk-Maxwell (1831-1879), however, except for Maxwell's contribution of the production of magnetic fields as a result of changing electric displacement fields, Faraday seems to have been one of the first to understand electricity and magnetism as a whole. His understanding, as a matter of fact, was quite sufficient for much of the progress which has been made since his death.

The theory of electricity and magnetism, which neglects the rate of change of the electric displacement field, has often been referred to as the quasi-stationary state theory. It is an approximation which even now is valid in much of today's engineering practice. Maxwell found that the quasi-stationary state solution was not enough to describe all known results. His problem was not only to explain away that difficulty but also to formulate a theory that would include as a part of itself the many useful and well-established rules of Faraday.

Even though Maxwell's equations have stood the test of time, and it is unlikely that they will ever be proven wrong, the process of expanding and generalizing physical theory still continues. During the twentieth century it has been found that ideas of electromagnetic theory were not good enough when dealing with atoms smashed by cyclotrons and other machines designed to examine the inner core of the atom. Modern physicists do not take this to mean that Maxwell's equations are any less valid than they were at the turn of the century, when practically all known data were so well explained; rather, they say that a more general and quantized theory must be worked out that will be valid not only for the macroscopic world but also for the sub-microscopic atom.

Luckily, in the study of microwaves no such fundamental difficulty must be overcome. Maxwell's equations are the final authority for all problems, and there is no need to go beyond them. Because waveguides are in use and more attention is paid to the path traveled by the actual radiation than ordinary radio wavelengths, because circuit elements are often dealt with that are difficult to designate as combinations of L, C, and R, because it is difficult to trace out the path over which charge moves, for these reasons ordinary circuit theory is often insufficient in the study of microwave radio. It may still be a useful guide and analogy, but for a straightforward solution of a problem Maxwell's equations and their accompanying theory must be often considered. In doing so, results inconsistent with calculations at longer wavelengths will not be found; rather in cases where the usual circuit theory is insufficient for all problems, there will arise a more general statement of the laws of nature which govern electromagnetism.

The Equations

The purpose here is to illustrate how a physical picture of the reflection of radio waves may be formed directly in terms of field quantities as defined in a more general electromagnetic theory. In doing this, even in an essentially non-mathematical manner, it is essential that interpretation of the underlying rules be correct.

Seven relations must be specified to describe the basic principles. Four of these are known as Maxwell's equations and owe their rigorous completeness to him. The other three are statements which have to do with the properties of materials; that is, they define electrical resistance, magnetic permeability, and the dielectric constant. These are often called the *constitutive equations*.

Today as these relations are written, it is much easier to see their meaning than it was at the time of Maxwell's death. This is because of the general use which is now made of vector analysis. The existence of such an algebra and the operation of addition and multiplication as it is practiced with vectors have already been discussed. There is no intention of trying to give a complete discussion of vector algebra; indeed only a barely sufficient description of the operations that are used in the bare statement of Maxwell's equations will be given. Yet it is the author's desire to create an appreciation of what they are all about and say enough to justify the actual use made of Maxwell's equations. This shall be done as particular topics are reached and not before. It will be found that vector algebra uses operations that have no counterparts in ordinary algebra. Not only may a vector be added to, subtracted from, or multiplied by, but it also may have a curl or a divergence taken. Disregarding just what the words *curl* and *divergence* mean, the first thing to get in mind is that they indicate that something is to be done to the quantity written after them, just as a plus sign means addition.

Two great advantages are incurred by using vector algebra in writing Maxwell's equations. First, since a vector is more than a number and includes a direction, the number of equations necessary to present the facts is kept to a minimum. Second, vectors do not have to be referred to a particular coordinate system. It is not necessary to set up x, y, and z axes, for example, and then measure everything in terms of distances from those axes. Vector operations, like multiplication and addition, can be performed in accordance with any coordinate system for denoting particular points of space. If an ampere of current flowing along a wire gives rise to a gauss of magnetic field encircling the wire at a given radius, the same thing is meant whether a set of Cartesian coordinates is chosen, in which the current is along the z axis and the magnetic field is measured at a point (x,y,z), or the representation formulated in cylindrical coordinates and the measurement at a point (r, θ, z) made, where r tells the distance from the wire at a distance z along the wire as measured at an angle θ degrees above the horizontal.

This is also the nature of the operators curl and div used in vector algebra. They have a definite physical meaning that can be interpreted in any coordinate system. As Maxwell's equations are normally written no coordinates whatever are in evidence. Only vectors, scalars, and operators appear, and these are all capable of physical explanation quite apart from a particular set of coordinates. For exmple, the calculus operation $\delta D/\delta t$ appears in the first equation written, and signifies the rate at which D changes with time.

When Maxwell's equations are to be used in a problem the operations indicated must be performed, just as in ordinary algebra the operations that are indicated must ultimately be performed. To do this, algebraic expressions are substituted for the symbols indicating vector operations and these substitutions do depend on the coordinates used. The final result, however, is interpreted the same in any event. Coordinate systems are chosen only for convenience. Any problem solvable by the theory can, in principle, be solved in any coordinate system.

The seven equations are:

$$\text{Curl } \mathbf{H} = \frac{1}{c}\frac{\delta \mathbf{D}}{\delta t} + \frac{4\pi J}{c} \tag{1}$$

$$\text{Curl } \mathbf{E} = -\frac{1}{c}\frac{\delta \mathbf{B}}{\delta t} \tag{2}$$

$$\text{Div } \mathbf{B} = 0 \tag{3}$$

$$\text{Div } \mathbf{D} = 4\pi\rho \tag{4}$$

$$\mathbf{B} = \mu\mathbf{H} \tag{5}$$

$$\mathbf{D} = K\mathbf{E} \tag{6}$$

$$J = \sigma\mathbf{E} \tag{7}$$

where $\mathbf{H}$ and $\mathbf{B}$ are measured in oersteds or gauss respectively; $\mathbf{E}$ and $\mathbf{D}$ are in electrostatic volts per cm; J is in electrostatic amperes per square cm; μ is permeability and therefore a measure of the magnetic condition of a material and its characteristics; K is the dielectric constant telling how the medium is subject to polarization; and σ is the conductivity of the substance in electrostatic amperes per electrostatic volt of potential applied between opposite faces of a cubic cm of material; and ρ is charge per unit volume in esu per cubic cm.

Since these relations are an all-inclusive description of the action of macroscopic electricity, any question can be asked about any circuit, and, to the extent the mathematical difficulties can be surmounted the answer shall be found in the equations. Practically, real difficulty may be experienced in formulating the question since it too must be expressed in terms of mathematical symbolism. As a mathematician would say it, the asking of a question consists of specifying the initial and boundary conditions of the problem.

The Reflection Problem

Consider first the important special case in which an electromagnetic wave is traveling through space and meets a conducting surface. A qualitative answer will be given by making physical interpretations of the seven equations just listed. In Fig. 6-15, the initial condition of the problem is illustrated. As it is shown, all the **H** vectors fall in one plane and all the **E** vectors lie in another plane which is perpendicular to the first. This may be looked upon as a simplification for

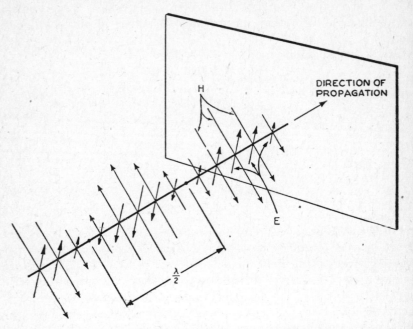

FIG. 6-15. The vector values of **E** and **H** at a certain instant as an electromagnetic wave approaches a reflecting surface but before any reflection has occurred. The whole pattern moves forward in the direction of propagation with a speed which in general equals the velocity of light.

purposes of making the drawing, and shows an example of plane polarization. Further, if a radio beam is produced so that all of the electric vectors are vertical (and all **H** vectors horizontal), the beam is said to be *vertically polarized*. In an unpolarized wave, the directions of the vectors change from time to time in a completely random way, somewhat as is shown in Fig. 6-16(A). Circular polarization means that the vectors rotate together something like the way shown in Fig. 6-16(B). The important thing is that **E** *and* **H** *are always perpendicular to each other.*

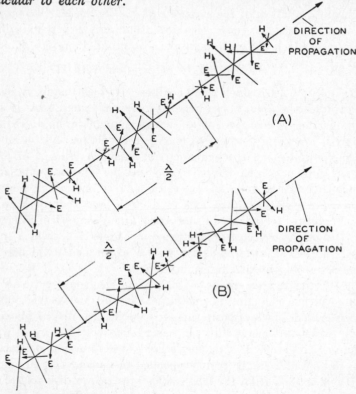

FIG. 6-16. The radiation shown in (A) is unpolarized and that in (B) is circularly polarized.

It may be seen that **E** and **H** are always perpendicular to each other by examining equations 5 and 2. In equation 5, **B** and **H** differ only by a scalar factor of μ and it has been shown that multiplication by a scalar does not change the direction of a vector. Only in non-isotropic mediums does the symbol μ represent something with directional properties. If the permeability of a material is different in different directions, the subject becomes sufficiently complicated to be beyond the scope of this book. In isotropic mediums, equation 5 shows that **B** and **H** have the same direction. In equation 2, the symbol $\frac{\delta B}{\delta t}$ means the time rate of change of **B**, and this is likewise a vector which remains in the same place as **B** and hence **H**. In the case of plane polarization, $\frac{\delta B}{\delta t}$ is a vector directed parallel to **B** and **H**. Now an interpretation of the symbol curl can be made. One property of the curl is that the vector on which it operates is perpendicular to the vector to which the curl operation is equated; therefore, **E** is perpendicular to $\frac{\delta B}{\delta t}$ and consequently perpendicular to **H**.

This equation 2 to which reference has just been made, is the one which explains the operation of transformers and generators. It shows the voltage that is generated by a changing magnetic field. **B** is that property of magnetic field called magnetic induction. As the amount of magnetic induction through a circuit changes (this is $\delta B/\delta t$), a potential (and hence **E** which is potential per cm) is found in the windings. Evidently then the operator curl is one which reconciles the direction of **B** along the axis of a circle and that of **E** around the circle and perpendicular to that axis. This geometrical interpretation of the curl of a vector is illustrated in Fig. 6-17 both as a specific example of this Maxwell equation and as a mathematical operation quite apart from physical interpretation.

Fig. 6-17 illustrates a simple example of an electromagnetic arrangement in which a changing magnetic field causes an electric potential to be generated. Two opposite magnetic poles are placed above and below a horizontal metal disk. In accordance with the usual way of determining direction in a magnetic field (the direction indicated by the north pole of a small freely suspended test magnet), the magnetic field **B** will extend from the north pole through the disk to the south pole. Now if the magnets are simultaneously brought closer and closer to the disk, the strength of this magnetic field will increase and electric fields around circular paths drawn on the disk will be formed. These will cause currents to flow and a heating of the disk will result.

To find the strength of the circular electric field only the rate at which **B** increases must be known. Suppose that this can be measured in terms of gauss per second and the resulting vector number indicated by $\frac{\delta B}{\delta t}$. According to the Maxwell equation (2), it is only necessary to multiply the vector number by $1/c$ (where c is the velocity of light) and a vector is obtained which is the curl of the desired **E** vector. It results in this case that **E** is E_o/r, where E_o is a number proportional to the magnitude of $\dfrac{\delta B}{\delta t}$ and r is the distance out from the center of the disk at which the value of E is desired. Curl is evidently an operator which indicates an operation that is capable of changing a circular field like that of E into a perpendicular but linear field like that of $\dfrac{\delta B}{\delta t}$.

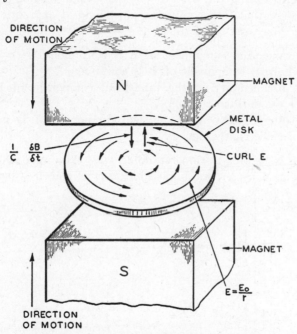

FIG. 6-17. If magnetic poles approach a metallic disk along a line perpendicular to the plane of the disk and if the magnetic field increases at the rate $1/c \times \delta B/\delta t$, then an electric field will exist at every point in the disk and will be so tangentially directed as to urge charge to move around the disk.

Quite a bit has been written in a discussion aimed to justify Fig. 6-15 and explain why it is a picture of an electromagnetic wave approaching a reflecting surface. Poynting's vector, which can be mentally associated with the E and H-fields, shows that the travel is toward the reflector. The initial conditions of the problem of wave reflection have been stated by visualizing the electromagnetic wave as it approaches the surface. The next question concerns the boundary conditions, that is the values of E and H which must exist at the surface. When this has been done, the answer to the question of what happens after the wave reaches the surface becomes comparatively easy.

The Four Conditions

Without restricting the case to any particular medium, Maxwell's equations show that four conditions must hold at any surface of discontinuity. They are:

I The tangential component of **E** is continuous
II The normal component of **B** is continuous
III The discontinuity in the tangential component of **H** is $4\pi/c$ times the surface current
IV The discontinuity in the normal component of **D** is 4π times the surface charge density.

Fig. 6-18 is helpful in understanding why these relations must be true. In Fig. 6-18(A), an impossible case is shown which violates

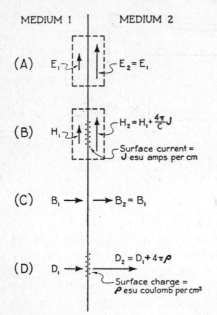

FIG. 6-18. The four fundamental continuity relations of the electromagnetic field quantities are illustrated as they are obtained in the limit.

condition I. E_t (the component of **E** tangent to the interface) is imagined to be larger at an infinitesimal distance into medium 2 than in medium 1 instead of having equal value as condition I demands. According to the interpretation of the operator curl, this would mean that in the dotted region, vectors can exist which are perpendicular to the plane of the paper and which can be identified as curl **E**. By equation (2), curl **E** is equivalent to $-1/c(\delta B/\delta t)$, which is a finite vector representing the time rate of change of magnetic induction in the dotted area. Thus, if the dotted area be imagined to become thinner and approach simply a double line drawn at the boundary, the number of vectors, $-1/c(\delta B/\delta t)$, which may be erected in the area certainly must approach zero. This is possible in the limit only if E_1 and E_2 are equal so they contribute equal but opposite amounts to the curl vectors. Their contributions will be opposite, since the curl vector is thought of as existing between them. They represent tangents to rotations in opposite directions around such a vector as an axis. Consequently, E_1 must equal E_2, and therefore the tangential component of **E** is continuous.

In Fig. 6-18(B) a sketch is shown upon which may be based a similar argument for condition III. This time the vectors perpendicular to the paper are curl **H** or by equation (1), $(1/c)$ $(\delta D/\delta t) +$ $4\pi J/c$. As the dotted area is made thinner, this expression need not approach zero, as did a similar quantity in the curl **E** case, but rather will approach $4\pi J/c$.

To see that II, as illustrated in Fig. 6-18(C), is true, it is necessary only to understand the meaning of the operator div (divergence) as used in equation (3). This equation is simply a mathematical statement of the fact that magnetism arises from magnetic poles which never occur separately but always as a combination of a north and a south pole. A bar magnet six inches long may be said to have a north pole at one end and a south pole at the other. If this magnet is cut into small pieces, no matter how tiny, both poles are still found on each piece. Div **B** $=$ O shows this. Magnetic induction arises from magnetic poles which, however, are never more than infinitesimally separated from opposite poles. Thus, lines of **B** are always continuous for every line of **B** forms a closed loop. Mathematically divergence shows the amount of increase of a vector as it flows through an infinitesimal volume. The statement that Div **B** $=$ O is merely a more general way of stating II.

In a similar way IV can be justified by equation (4), and as is illustrated in Fig. 6-18(D). Here the electric field **D** is one that arises from the presence of charge. Unlike magnetic poles, however, charge can exist on the surface. Thus **D** instead of being continuous at the boundary, will change its magnitude in accordance with whatever surface charge ω is present in a unit area. Equation (4) is illustration of the general case where ρ signifies charge density, whereas in the present case the symbol ω representing surface charge density, is used.

In Fig. 6-19 is illustrated the case of a radio wave approaching a large metallic surface at a right angle. The assumption is made that

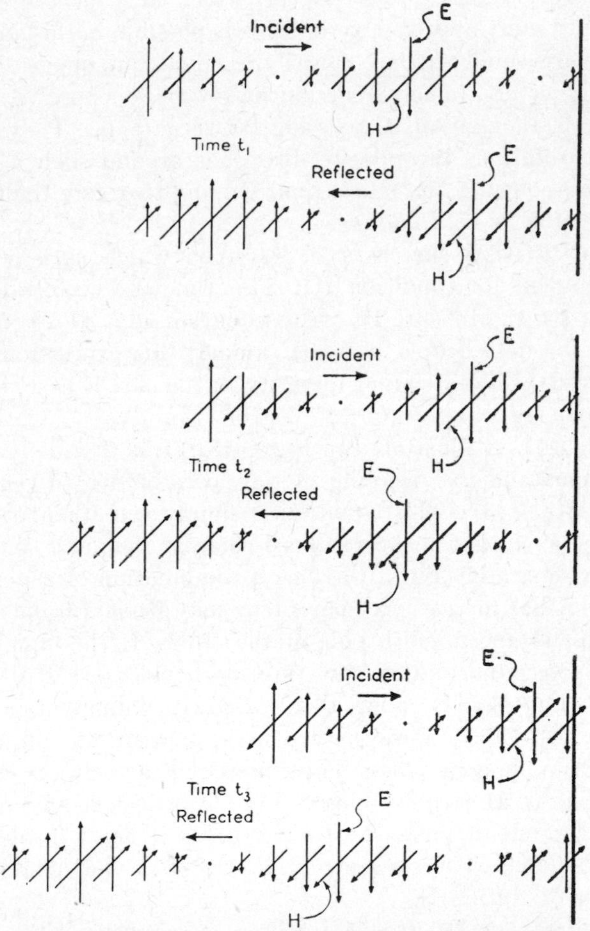

Fig. 6-19. These diagrams represent the manner in which a radio wave is reflected from a large perfectly conducting surface. The **E** vectors are reversed in phase at the surface and the **H** vectors are not.

the metal is a perfect conductor. Then no electric field can exist inside the conductor, since with $\sigma = \infty$, equation (7) would require an infinite current however small the finite magnitude of the electric field. This is impossible, because infinite current would require an infinite amount of energy, which is, of course, absurd. Moreover, it is clear from Maxwell's equations that if **E** is zero everywhere along the surface of the perfect conductor at all times, then **D**, **H**, and **B** must either be zero or constant in value. Thus, the boundary conditions of Fig. 6-19 are very simple. Normal components of **B** and **D** do not exist, and since **E** is zero inside the conductor, it must be zero at the boundary. **H** must also be zero at the boundary except for whatever surface current may flow. These conditions can be satisfied at all times only by postulating a reflected wave of the same amplitude as the incident wave. The surface current generated by **E** can be shown to be just enough to double the value of **H** at the boundary. This means that **H** is reflected without change of phase and **E** with a phase reversal. This is necessary in order that Poynting's vector shall change and show energy flow away from the boundary for the reflected wave. By showing both the **E** and **H** waves at three times, t_1, t_2, and t_3, Fig. 6-19 shows how the existence of the boundary conditions call for such a wave and are satisfied by it. A radio wave approaching a large perfectly conducting surface is reflected without loss.

If the wave approaches at some other angle than perpendicular, the situation is only a little more complicated; Fig. 6-20 illustrates

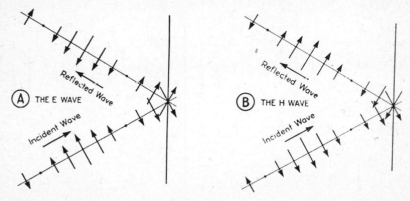

Fig. 6-20. The **E** wave in (A) is reflected with change of phase at a perfect conductor so as to have a net zero tangential component at the surface, but a normal component to the surface charge. The **H** wave is reflected without phase change in (B) with a zero normal component, but a tangential part arising from surface current.

this case. Each vector then has a normal as well as a tangential component. The boundary conditions are satisfied only if the reflected wave makes an equal angle with the surface but in such a phase and at such a position as to satisfy both the normal and tangential conditions. This is so called *specular reflection,* just as is obtained with ordinary light at mirror surfaces.

Fresnel's Equations

As is known from experience, it is by no means necessary to have a perfectly conducting surface in order to get a reasonable amount of reflected energy. It might well be assumed immediately that with

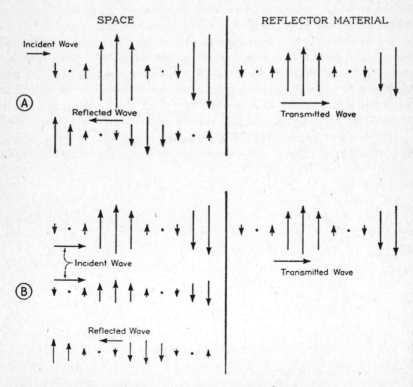

FIG. 6-21. An **E** radio wave approaching a reflector is partially transmitted and partially reflected, as shown in (A). The incident wave is drawn in (B) to show more clearly how the boundary condition is satisfied.

a surface such as wood or a similar material, the reflection efficiency is reduced. **E, H, B,** and **D** may now exist within the material so all the wave is not reflected. Some is transmitted into the reflecting material and either dissipated there or carried on through to still a third medium. The situation at the surface that is necessary to satisfy the boundary conditions and still allow for partial transmission and reflection is illustrated in Fig. 6-21. As shown in Fig. 6-21(A) it looks rather complicated but in Fig. 6-21(B) the original incident wave has been split into two waves, one of which undergoes complete transmission and the other complete reflection. With no residual surface charge or current, it then becomes easy to see that the boundary conditions I through IV have been satisfied.

It would be well now, however, to obtain a method which would show what fraction of the incident energy is reflected and what part transmitted. This will depend upon the physical properties of the reflecting medium. The equations which state this relation for a plane wave approaching the boundary at an arbitrary angle of incidence are known as *Fresnel's equations*. It follows that the reflection coefficient (reflected amplitude divided by incident amplitude) depends not only on the angle of incidence but also on the polarization. Looking back at Fig. 6-15, it is clear that some such dependence might be anticipated. Tilting the wave-train relative to the plate in one direction would give only tangential components of **H** and both normal and tangential components of **E**; in another direction **H** would have both normal and tangential components and **E** would be only tangent to the plate. This causes the boundary conditions to enter into the problem in a different way.

If restrictions are made to approximately normal incidence, however, the situation is not so complicated. For a wave initially traveling in air or vacuum, the reflection coefficient is then given by

$$R = \frac{\sqrt{K} - 1}{\sqrt{K} + 1}$$

where K is the dielectric constant of the target material if the target medium is a dielectric, and $K = 2\pi f J/\sigma$ if the target is a conductor. In order to understand these further, first look back at equation (6). If desired this may be taken as a definition of K. Whenever charge is present in a given volume, an electric field may be observed. That is, a potential change measured in volts per cm may, in general, be observed in the neighborhood of the charge. If the charge giving rise to this field is free charge such as comes from a battery and flows in metals, it is called the electric field **E**. If, on the other hand, the field in part arises from bound charge, the total field is designated as **D**. By bound charge is meant the kind of charge found in insulators. There the electrons are not free to flow throughout the material, but may nevertheless shift their position relative to the positive charge. This shift is called *polarization* and accounts for the fact that the D-field in a material may be larger than the **E**-field.

Dielectric Constant

Now looking at Fig. 6-21, it can be seen why the dielectric constant dictates the reflection coefficient. As the wave approaches the surface, an electric field **E** is obtained at the reflecting medium. This electric field **E** causes a polarization of the reflecting medium in accordance with the dielectric constant, and thus creates a field **D** in the medium. Equation (1) shows that this, along with the current that can flow, influences the value of **H** at the surface. The same sort of argument can be made the opposite way. The approaching **H** wave, gives rise to **B** in the target which, by equation (2), influences the value of **E** at the surface. These two processes work in conjunction, and hence fix the values of **E** and **H** at the boundary, and thus the reflection coefficient.

If the reflector material is really a dielectric, the permeability μ is unity and does not influence the **B** of the reflector material; likewise the current term of equation (1) is negligible because of the very small conductivity, σ. Thus in that case, K alone is the determining property of the material. If the reflector is a conductor, the charge is no longer bound and K loses its meaning. The conductivity, permeability, and frequency then become the determining factors. Sometimes, in order to simplify the statement of Fresnel's equations, reference is made to the dielectric constant of a conductor. This

means that $K = \dfrac{2\pi f J}{\sigma}$ as was previously mentioned. This expression

fits into the Fresnel equation in the same way as K does for dielectrics.

Dielectric constant is probably an unfortunately chosen name for K. Actually K is not at all constant with frequency. Values obtained by optical methods may be very different from those in the usual radio wave, or microwave range. It should also be remembered that many other effects may arise if the calculations do not involve very large surfaces relative to a wavelength.

FOOTNOTES

1. The current of 2 amperes in each of the parallel plates means that a current density of 0.02 ampere per cm of plate width is present. From Ampere's law it may be shown that the magnetic field at any finite distance in front of an infinite sheet of current is given by

$$H = \frac{2\pi}{10} \sigma \text{ oersted}$$

where σ is the current in amperes per cm. Here we are dealing with two sheets of current and a σ value of 0.02. Thus

$$H = \frac{4\pi}{10} (.02) = (.008) \pi \text{ oersted}$$

The use of the expression for an infinite sheet of current in calculating this value does not detract from its accuracy. We use the infinite sheet in order to obtain the magnetic field conveniently; later the size of the plates is limited. In effect, an average value of the magnetic field is therefore obtained.

2. There are 300 practical volts in 1 esu volt; hence, the voltage between the plates is 0.02 esu volt. Since the plates are 2 cm apart, the electric field tension is 0.01 esu volt per cm.

3. Poynting's vector is capable of misinterpretation. For example, if a permanent magnet and the plates of a condenser connected to a battery are so arranged as to produce crossed electric and magnetic fields, no radiation will be incurred. This means that the Poynting vector concept has been incorrectly applied. When such an absurd result is obtained, we can only resort to Maxwell's equations. Poynting's vector is less rigorous than the Maxwell theory and cannot be applied indiscriminately.

4. Consider a wire of 0.1 cm radius and 10 cm long, having a resistance of 5 ohms and carrying 3 amperes. The voltage drop through the wire is 15 volts or 0.05 esu volts. The electric field adjacent to the wire therefore will be 0.05/10 or 0.005 esu volt per cm. The magnetic field at the surface of the wire will have a magnitude of $2i/10r$ or 6 oersted. Poynting's vector into the resistance is

$$P = \frac{c}{4\pi} \frac{E \times H}{10^7} = \frac{45}{2\pi} \text{ watts per square cm}$$

The factor 10^7 is included in the equation in order to convert from the Gaussian system to the practical system. The surface area of the wire is given by $2\pi rl$, namely 2π square cm. Multiplying Poynting's vector by this area, gives

$$Watts \text{ into the resistor} = 2\pi \times \frac{45}{2\pi} = 45 \text{ watts.}$$

This is the same result as calculated by i^2r,

$$i^2r = 9 \times 5 = 45 \text{ watts.}$$

5. Terman, "Radio Engineering", McGraw-Hill, 1937, page 648; R. R. Ramsey and Robert Dreisback, "Radiation and Induction", *Proc. I.R.E.*, vol. 16, p. 1118, Aug. 1928.

6. The energy in an electric field is $KE^2/8\pi$ ergs per cm^3. This may be shown by considering a simple parallel plate condenser. The capacitance of such a condenser is given by

$$C = \frac{KA}{4\pi s}$$

where K is the dielectric constant of the medium between the plates, A is the area of the plates, and s is the plate separation. The energy necessary to charge a condenser to a voltage V is

$$Energy = \frac{1}{2} CV^2$$

Therefore the total energy stored in the space between the condenser plates is

$$Energy = \frac{KAV^2}{8\pi s}$$

Dividing by the volume of the space gives energy per unit volume, as

$$Energy\ per\ unit\ volume = \frac{KAV^2}{8\pi s} \frac{1}{As} = \frac{KV^2}{8\pi s^2}$$

Replacing V/s by $\mathbf{E}$, to which it is equal, gives the desired result.

$$Energy\ per\ unit\ volume = \frac{K\mathbf{E}^2}{8}$$

Similarly the inductance of a solenoid is given by

$$L = \frac{4\pi^2 N^2 \mu r^2}{d}$$

where N is the number of turns, μ the permeability of the core material, r the radius of the solenoid, and d its length. The energy in a solenoid carrying a current is

$$Energy = \frac{1}{2} Li^2 = \mu\ \frac{4\pi Ni}{d}\ \frac{4\pi Ni}{d}\ \frac{dr^2}{8}$$

Remembering that $4\pi Ni/d$ is $\mathbf{H}$, this becomes

$$Energy = \mu\ \mathbf{H}^2 \frac{dr^2}{8}$$

Dividing by the volume of the solenoid as given by $\pi r^2 d$, we have

$$Energy\ per\ unit\ volume = \frac{\mu \mathbf{H}^2}{8\pi}$$

Adding together the magnetic and electric energies, gives the whole expression for energy density in terms of $\mathbf{E}$ and $\mathbf{H}$.

7. "Introduction to Modern Physics" by F. K. Richtmyer, McGraw-Hill Book Company.

8. The test charge must be so small as to cause only a negligible shift of the charge generating the field.

9. $\mathbf{B}$ and $\mathbf{H}$ bear somewhat the same relation to each other as do $\mathbf{E}$ and $\mathbf{D}$. $\mathbf{H}$ represents the magnetic field arising from currents while $\mathbf{B}$, called magnetic induction is the field responsible for inducing voltage by its rate of change. $\mathbf{B}$ is dependent upon the magnetic properties of the medium as well as currents flowing in the neighborhood. In free space $\mathbf{B}$ is equal to $\mathbf{H}$, so the distinction need not be considered.

Chapter 7

WAVEGUIDES

Waveguide and Reactance

IT MAY BE POINTED out with good logic that every transmission line which carries alternating-current power is really a waveguide. As mentioned in a previous chapter, energy may well be considered as moving along a coaxial line or a parallel-wire line in the form of a wave. Whether the waves are thought of as electromagnetic field quantities or simple sinusoidal distributions of current and voltage, the picture is the same. A transmission line is essentially like a track which guides the energy wave along a certain direction. Common usage, however, dictates that the term "waveguide" be restricted to indicate what might more completely be called hollow-pipe waveguide or at least a waveguide in which there are not two distinct conductors.

Because a coaxial line as well as an ordinary conductor pair is often treated in a way that does not particularly emphasize the propagation of electromagnetic waves, the waveguide feature of their operation is not stressed in naming them. When a piece of cylindrical or rectangular hollow pipe is used as a transmission line the situation is different. It then becomes very difficult to talk in terms of current and voltage. The idea of a closed circuit is then difficult to trace, and all but impossible to use for quantitative measurements. The electromagnetic-field wave picture becomes the only useful basis for design, and the name waveguide is therefore a very natural one.

Waveguides are used at microwave frequencies for two reasons. First, they are often easier to fabricate than are coaxial lines and, second, they can often be made to have less attenuation. Coaxial line requires that a center conductor be supported somehow in the center of a cylinder. If solid dielectrics are used, leakage is always present to some extent, and over distances of more than a foot or so that leakage increases to such an extent that it becomes quite serious. It is true, as was previously pointed out, that stub supports can be made and that such supports will minimize leakage loss but, especially

127

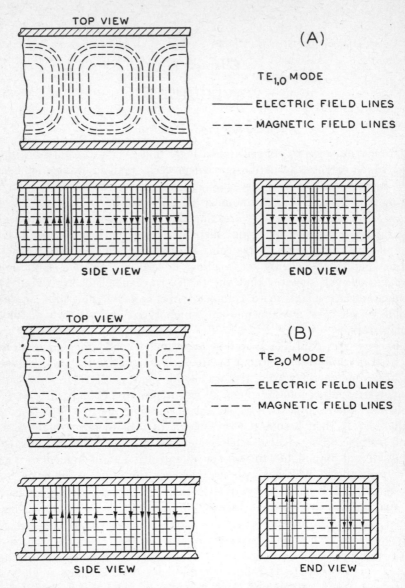

FIG. 7-1. Two modes in rectangular waveguide: in (A) is shown the $TE_{1,0}$ mode and in (B) the $TE_{2,0}$ mode.

when bends or more complicated fittings are needed, the fabrication difficulties are very great.

In nearly every case in which open-wire lines or coaxial lines are used, the way in which energy is transported is always the same. A voltage stress exists between the two conductors and this, in conjunction with current or magnetic field, forms a wave which moves from the source to the load. With a waveguide the situation is not necessarily so simple. It is still always true that a particular pattern of electromagnetic field is formed as a wave, and that the pattern moves along the guide with the energy flow, but any one of many sorts of patterns may occur in a given piece of apparatus. It is said that a waveguide may operate in any one of many modes. A particular mode can be chosen by the use of proper waveguide dimensions and by a proper choice of the mechanism used to launch the waves into the waveguide. Fig. 7-1 illustrates two possible modes of transmission in a rectangular waveguide. End views only of three other modes are shown in Fig. 7-2.

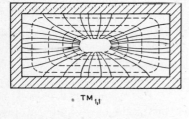

TM$_{1,1}$

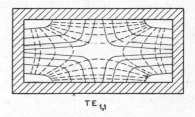

TE$_{1,1}$

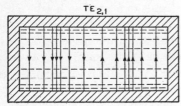

TE$_{2,1}$

Fig. 7-2. End views of $TM_{1,1}$, $TE_{1,1}$, and $TE_{2,1}$ modes in rectangular waveguide.

The terminology used to distinguish the various waveguide modes (such as $TE_{1,0}$ etc.) is rather complicated in appearance but not at all hard to understand, once a visualization of a few sample modes has been accomplished. In general, one or the other of the fields (electric or magnetic) will be found to have no component along the length of the waveguide. When the electric field is such that it is the one which lies entirely in planes lying across the waveguide (the magnetic lines then extend in part along the length of the guide), the mode is said to be a *transverse electric mode, TE*. On the other hand, when the magnetic field is the one which has only crosswise components, the mode is designated as *transverse magnetic, TM*. It will also be noticed, particularly by looking at end views of the waveguide patterns, that along the wider edge of the end-view a pattern exists, which is complete only if the line density and direction varies along the wider edge to a point where it is ready to start over again. The first subscript number tells the number of half-cycles of pattern which exist along the wide edge; the second number describes the same thing for the narrow edge. Some writers reverse this usage, so that caution should be exercised as to which notation is employed.

Generally speaking, it is not desirable to excite more than one mode in a waveguide. The design of fittings to pass energy in one mode makes it impossible for those same fittings to act efficiently for other modes. Thus in rectangular waveguide, one mode (the $TE_{1,0}$ mode) is generally superior to all others. Such waveguides can easily be designed so that only the $TE_{1,0}$ mode is possible without very rapid attenuation. To do this, the narrow dimension should be less than one-half wavelength, while the wide dimension should be greater than a half wavelength but less than a whole wavelength. The use of such a mode (often called the *fundamental mode*) makes it rather certain that no unwanted modes will be present to drain energy from the system. For this reason the $TE_{1,0}$ mode is almost universally used for rectangular waveguide transmission.

A waveguide transmission line may be made of cylindrical pipe as well as rectangular; in fact, other shapes can also be used. Elliptical pipe, for example, has been investigated quite thoroughly. From a fabrication standpoint only the cylindrical waveguide is as easy to make as is rectangular pipe. More will be said about the cylindrical waveguide later, but, except for special applications, it is not very much used. The fields are somewhat more difficult to measure and even to visualize and, what is more important, the circular cross-section gives no orientation reference for the transverse part of the field pattern. The pattern is apt to rotate during transmission and thus lose energy to other modes.

Phase Angle

No matter how complicated the wave pattern in a waveguide may be, it is still a wave and its strength (all components) varies sinusoidally with time and with distance along the transmission path. The electric-field pattern may lead or lag the magnetic wave and give rise to an effect which may be described as analogous to inductance or capacitance. To describe this, first re-examine lumped constants so as to review the phase effects of L and C. Reference will be made again to coaxial line so that the pictures will be simple. Finally there will be described how a waveguide diaphragm can act either as an inductance or a capacitance shunted across the waveguide.

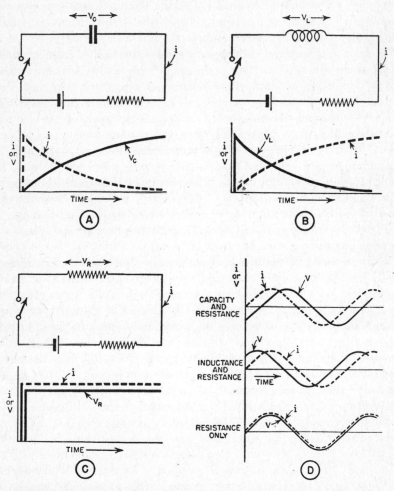

Fig. 7-3. The various phase differences between current and voltage for different circuit elements.

Fig. 7-3 illustrates the way in which current and voltage appear in and across circuit elements as a function of time. If the element is a capacity, then current must first flow and the charge must be carried to the capacitor before a voltage can appear there. Thus, with a capacity, the current leads the voltage. In Fig. 7-3(A) the case is shown for a d-c source connected through a switch to a capacitor. At the instant just before the switch is closed, both i and v are zero. Thus, when current and voltage are plotted against time, both are zero until the switch is closed. When the circuit is completed, a current begins to flow, and as time passes, this current becomes smaller until, when the condenser is completely charged, the current is zero. The voltage across the condenser, on the other hand, cannot appear until a current has carried a charge to the condenser, and cannot reach its full value until the condenser is completely charged.

Fig. 7-3(B) shows the same sort of arrangement for an inductance. Here the voltage depends upon the rate of change of the current. This rate of change is greatest when the current first starts to flow. Thus, with an inductance, the voltage leads the current because its maximum comes first and it approaches zero when the current has built up to its maximum value. With resistance there is neither leading nor lagging; when the switch is closed both voltage and current instantaneously attain their final values, as shown in Fig. 7-3(c).

Fig. 7-3(D) shows how this leading or lagging appears when sinusoidal alternating current is used instead of a battery and a switch.

The values of inductance and capacitance, expressed as coefficients of inductance or capacitance and usually given in henrys or farads, are of less concern in microwave transmission along waveguides and coaxial lines than are the more direct quantities of inductive or capacitive reactance. The usefulness of farads and henrys in wired circuits depends upon the fact that over reasonable frequency ranges these quantities are independent of frequency. A given coil may be said to have an inductance of 500 mh whether a frequency of 100 or 200 cycles is used. The coefficient of inductance is really an electrical description of the mechanical arrangement of the coil. With waveguide propagation, however, the frequency is more or less fixed by the shape and size of the waveguide and the transmission mode being used. Over the fairly small percentage range of frequencies allowed in normal designs, impedance is as good a measure of the inductive or capacitive property of a waveguide circuit as required and much more directly useable.

Impedance Matching

Impedance or reactance, moreover, does serve the same function in microwave transmission as in low-frequency work, namely, it is useful as a criterion for matching one line into another. In Fig. 7-4

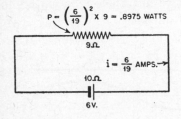

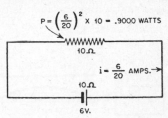

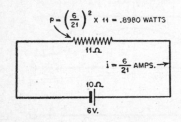

Fig. 7-4. Illustration of impedance matching to obtain maximum energy transfer from source to load.

is drawn a 6-volt battery having an internal resistive impedance of 10 ohms. It is shown connected successively to load resistances of 9, 10, and 11 ohms. Ohm's law gives the current that will flow in each case and i^2r gives the power delivered to the load. A maximum power transfer from the battery to the load is obtained when the impedance of the load is just equal to that of the source. The same is true of microwave impedance; if power is to flow from one waveguide device into another, then a maximum transfer will occur when the impedances of the two are equal. Just as in ordinary alternating-current matching, this equality of impedance implies correctness of phase as well as magnitude. It is this matter of phase which is of particular interest here.

In order to see how inductance and capacitance in the ordinary sense can be interpreted for microwave measurements, where electric and magnetic fields are measured rather than currents and voltages, which are much more difficult for waveguides, first will be examined the case of a coaxial line in which certain facts can be expected. Whether the impedance of a coaxial line is measured in terms of current and voltage or magnetic and electric field is certainly unimportant. The magnetic field depends directly upon the current, while the electric field is voltage per unit length. Plots of either pair are typical of any standing wave, as is illustrated in the cases shown in Figs. 7-5(A) and 7-5(B). Each loop of the standing wave alternately swings up through its positive values and then through its negative values and while one loop is on the positive side, those adjacent are in a similar position on the negative side of the axis.

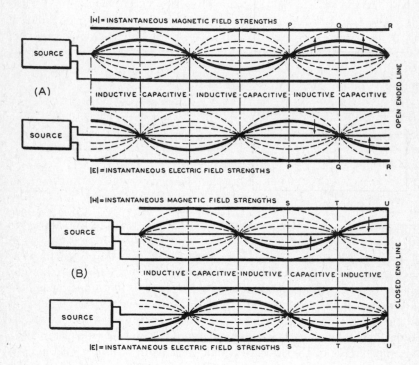

FIG. 7-5. Possible standing-wave patterns for open-ended (A) and short-circuited (B) coaxial lines.

To ask about the impedance of a coaxial line at a given point is to ask about the ratio of the peak or rms values of E to H or of V to i at that point and especially to ask about the time relation of the peak values of the two. Symbolically, impedance Z is given by

$$Z = \frac{V}{i} = \frac{E}{H}.$$

In Fig. 7-5(A) and 7-5(B) is shown a possible standing wave pattern for an open-ended and short-circuited coaxial line respectively. Values of the magnitude (not to be confused with **E** and **H** lines of force) of **E** and **H** are plotted about the center wire as a coordinate axis. Both are shown for various times by the various broken curves and for a particular time by a solid curve. In both Figs. 7-5(A) and 7-5(B), the solid line of **E** occurs at the same instant as the corresponding solid curve of **H**. As time elapses after the particular instant represented by the solid curves, the representation is correct only if the solid curves are expanded or contracted, as shown by the short vertical arrows near the right-hand end of the sketches. Thus, the strength of the magnetic field of Fig. 7-5(A) is first represented by the solid curve, next by the curve of the same polarity throughout but of greater amplitude, next by the solid curve again, next by the curve of the same polarity throughout but of less amplitude, next by a line which is zero everywhere, next by successively larger curves which are on the opposite side of the axis as compared to the solid curve, and so on.

When the instantaneous values of the standing waves are known in the way just described, it is relatively easy to determine whether or not a certain portion of the line has inductive or capacitative properties. The argument shall be traced presently and it shall be found that whenever a pure standing wave is obtained, *alternate quarter wavelengths of the transmission line or waveguide yield a pure inductive reactance while the other alternate quarter wavelengths act as does a pure capacitive reactance.* As should be expected, since a pure standing wave admits of no energy loss, there is no place where the impedance has any resistive component.

Consider any particular point in the quarter wavelength of line between Q and R of Fig. 7-5(A). At the instant represented by the solid curve, **H** (or i), in the upper half of Fig. 7-5(A), is increasing from a positive value to a still more positive value, and **E** (or V) is decreasing in negative value, as indicated by the arrows. When **H** reaches a maximum positive value, **E** will be zero, as shown in the lower half of Fig. 7-5(A) and while **E** then becomes positive, **H** will be returning toward a zero value. Clearly **E** (or V) lags **H** (or i) in the section between Q and R in Fig. 7-5(A), so that this section is capacitive. In the section between P and Q the situation is different. Here as **H** becomes more positive, **E** is already growing less positive and when **H** gets to a maximum value and starts to decrease, **E** has reached the zero level and is ready to start becoming negative. E is here leading H by 90 degrees and the section of the line between P and Q consequently has a pure inductive reactance.

The same sort of argument holds for Fig. 7-5(B) except that it is found there that the quarter-wavelength section TU at the extreme right end of the line, is inductive while the next section back, which is marked as ST, is capacitive. The situation in a shorted line is just the opposite to that in an open line in this respect.

Evidently an open-ended line gives, in the quarter wave adjacent to the open end, the same sort of reactance as a pure capacitance. This is surely not surprising because everyone knows that two parallel wires not connected together, act like the plates of a condenser. The new fact to be remembered is that if the wires are more than a quarter wave long, they may appear to the source as an inductance; they will if they are actually more than a quarter wave long but less than a half wave long. When, in transmission line theory (as applied to waveguide or any other sort of line that is long compared to a wavelength), it is said that a termination is capacitive or inductive, it is meant that the first quarter wavelength back from the termination toward the source is capacitive or inductive as specified. The opposite kind of reactance will be found further back.

It is also reasonable that the final quarter wavelength of a shorted coaxial line should act like an inductance. When less than a quarter wavelength of line is involved, this case is entirely the same as a simple loop of wire which, of course, is an inductance.

The discussion of Fig. 7-5, which has just been given, dealt only with pure standing waves. As was pointed out in the chapter on coaxial lines, a traveling wave is often also present. Such a traveling wave has the effect of making the phase shifts in the various quarter-wave sections become less than 90 degrees but does not change the phase alternation between adjacent quarter-wave sections. In short, if the termination has resistive as well as reactive properties (i.e. if it does not send back a traveling wave of amplitude equal to the incident one), the impedance in the line back toward the source will still be alternately inductive and capacitive over quarter wavelengths but the phase shifts will be less than 90 degrees in either direction, so the impedance will be regarded as a mixture of resistance plus inductance or capacitance, as the case may be.

In a pure standing wave there is never any electric field at the point of maximum magnetic field and never any magnetic field at the point of maximum electric field. The loops (or anti-nodes) of **E** coincide with the nodes of **H** and vice versa. This gives rise to certain ambiguous points as far as phase is concerned. The nodes of **H** (loops of **E**) are points of infinite impedance, while the loops of **H** (nodes of **E**) indicate zero impedance. In the case of either point a definite phase angle cannot be assigned. Any finite distance to one side of either sort of point will yield a pure inductance, while a measurement at any finite distance on the other side will be capacitive.

Measurements

If access is had only to a central section of a uniform line and no specifications of the load or source are given, it is impossible by ordinary measurements to distinguish between pure capacitative and pure inductive terminations. Normally, the only measurement made on a waveguide or coaxial line is that of standing wave ratio. This is usually accomplished by a scheme similar to that shown in Fig. 7-6.

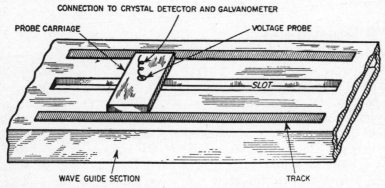

FIG. 7-6. Apparatus for measuring the standing-wave ratio in a waveguide.

Effectively, the apparatus measures the average value of the electric field and, by moving the probe carriage along the waveguide, it allows this measurement to be made as a function of distance along the guide. The *standing wave ratio,* usually abbreviated as swr, is then defined as the ratio of the largest to the smallest measurement of the **average** electric field that may be found in moving the carriage along the guide through a distance of one wavelength. Thus with a short-circuited or open-circuited conductor, such as that shown in Fig. 7-5, where no net energy is transmitted, the swr is infinite. The probe would give a finite reading of electric field at points such as *P*, *R*, or *T* and a zero reading at points like *Q*, *S*, or *U*. At the opposite extreme, where inductive and capacitive effects are entirely tuned out and no reflected wave exists, the electric field is shown as a function of time by curves such as those in Fig. 7-7. At any one time a single sine wave describes

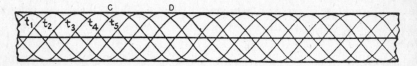

Fig. 7-7. Electric field in a coaxial line with a standing-wave-ratio of unity.

the magnitude of the E-field everywhere in the line. As time elapses this single sine curve moves along the line, as is shown successively by the curves labeled t_1, t_2, t_3, etc. At any two points such as *C* and *D*, there is no distinction between the average values of the electric field.

SWR Characteristics

Thus, swr is a figure of merit of the transmission efficiency of a waveguide or coaxial line. Unity swr indicates perfect transmission; infinite swr shows complete reflection of the energy from a short circuit or open circuit; any intermediate value shows that some energy is being transmitted and some reflected. It is when these intermediate values are obtained that the concepts of inductance and capacitance are helpful. Since, in practice, unity swr is usually impossible to obtain, some capacitive or inductive effect is almost always present. When it is desired to substitute one waveguide device for another in an array where unity swr cannot be obtained, it is necessary to obtain a proper match. Hence, for the same or a better swr in the whole system, the new component must not only be capable of a low swr itself, but also have the same inductive or capacitive property at the point where connection is to be made as did the piece to be replaced.

Fig. 7-8 shows a simple case in which a discontinuity of some sort in a piece of line is such as to give a swr greater than unity. Both in Figs. 7-8(A) and 7-8(B) a swr of about 1.5 is illustrated, but while that in Fig. 7-8(A) is capacitive at the place cut by line *MN*, that in Fig. 7-8(B) is inductive. Comparison with Figs. 7-5(A) and 7-5(B) show this to be true. The energy flowing from left to right up to the junction is shown as comprised of two parts, one of which travels on past the junction into a line with unity swr, and the other part of which is reflected to form the standing wave as shown. It is clear in this particular case that a measurement with swr apparatus can easily distinguish between the two. If the maxima ahead of the junction

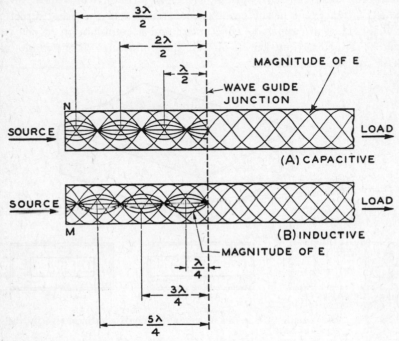

Fig. 7-8. Capacitative and inductive waveguide junctions, each having a swr of 1.5.

come nearer to distances of an odd number of quarter wavelengths from the junction, the reactance is like an inductance at the junction; if they come nearer to an integral number of half-wavelengths, the reactance corresponds to an open-circuit or a capacitance at the junction.

Waveguide Constrictions

As an example of how a waveguide section may be made inductive or capacitative, Fig. 7-9 shows constrictions in a rectangular guide that are appropriate. A waveguide of this sort is usually operated in the $TE_{1,0}$ mode so as to cause the electric field to occur across the small dimension and the magnetic field along the larger one. If this mode is maintained and if the metal diaphragm-like constrictions are very thin in the dimension along the length of the waveguide as compared to a wavelength, then a partial closing of the guide, which completely short-circuits part of the electric field, will appear as an inductive reactance in the guide; a constriction in the other direction will appear as a capacitive reactance; and a combination of the two may be so proportioned as to match the impedance of the guide and cause no reflections at all.

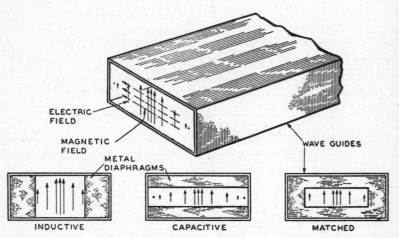

ELECTRIC FIELD

MAGNETIC FIELD

METAL DIAPHRAGMS

WAVE GUIDES

INDUCTIVE CAPACITIVE MATCHED

FIG. 7-9. A waveguide section can be made capacitative or inductive by the use of appropriate constrictions.

If an inductive diaphragm is placed a half-wave beyond the capacitive junction of Fig. 7-8(A), it can be adjusted to create also a swr of 1.5 but one that is out of phase with the capacitive swr of Fig. 7-8(A). The two standing waves will then cancel at points to the left of the junction in Fig. 7-8(A) and the source will cease to receive reflected energy. A similar result may be accomplished by placing a capacitive diaphragm a half wave ahead of the inductive junction of Fig. 7-8(B). An especially noteworthy point, moreover, is that an inductive diaphragm can also correct an inductive mismatch if they are separated by a quarter wave of distance instead of a half wave. In the same way a capacitive diaphragm can correct a capacitive fault. This is because a capacitive or inductive point in a waveguide is really descriptive of only a quarter-wave section and just beyond that point the phase is the opposite.

It is easy to understand the inductive constriction case from the discussion of Fig. 7-5 alone. Just as in that sketch a short circuit of a coaxial line was seen to compare with inductance in the ordinary sense, so here the electric field is partially short-circuited so that any standing wave in the electric field that is caused by reflection must have a node at the constriction, that would characterize inductance. In Fig. 7-9 the short-circuited part of the electric field is shown by drawing vectors on the metal surface of the diaphragm in the position where they would be in the absence of the constriction but where they cannot actually exist when the constriction is in place. These are the portions of the electric field that are short-circuited.

On the other hand, a capacitive constriction does not represent a short-circuit of the electric field, but only raises its intensity by causing the same voltage of the walls of the guide to be distributed over a smaller air gap, so that the number of volts per cm is higher. In a sense, however, such a constriction may be said to be a short-circuit of the magnetic field, in the same way that an open line is a magnetic short, or at least a null. No current can flow near the open ends of the open-circuited line of Fig. 7-5, because it has no place to go and thus a magnetic node in the standing wave is assured. In the waveguide case of a capacitive constriction, eddy currents flow in the constriction and keep part of the traveling magnetic-field wave zero, so capacitive reflections, which are characterized by a node there in the magnetic field, are obtained.

Need for Empirical Data

The complete story of waveguide propagation and the design of terminations, joints, bends, etc. is a difficult one; so difficult in fact that some current practices are still best classed as an art rather than as a science. When direct and complete calculations can be made, they must often be based upon Maxwell's field equations and they give results directly in terms of the E and H field. The whole idea of reactance and impedance is then only an unnecessary step in obtaining the solution. More often, however, the mathematical calculations must be tempered with empirical data, and impedance quantities serve to present the facts to the engineer in a manner analogous to the problems which arise in transmission-line theory.

For example, the equivalent impedance of a piece of very regular rectangular waveguide may be calculated for the mode discussed, to be equal to

$$Z = K \frac{\mathbf{E}}{\mathbf{H}} \frac{b}{a}$$

where K is a constant independent of the dimensions of the guide, $\mathbf{E}$ and $\mathbf{H}$ are the maximum values of the field as obtained at the center of the guide, and b and a are the shorter and longer dimensions of the guide, respectively. Calculations also show that the ratio $\mathbf{E}/\mathbf{H}$ may be expected to be represented by

$$\frac{\mathbf{E}}{\mathbf{H}} = \sqrt{\frac{\mu}{K}} \frac{1}{\sqrt{1 - (\lambda_o/2a)^2}}$$

where μ and K are the permeability and dielectric constant of the medium, and λ_o is the free-space wavelength of the frequency being transmitted. From these two equations it is clear that a perfect match should be obtained between two sizes of rectangular guide by selecting proper values of b and a to give the same Z. Experimentally, this is verified within certain limits, as it also might well be expected to be from considerations of matching diaphragms. Electrically, the insertion of a rectangular matched diaphragm, like that one shown in Fig. 7-9, is equivalent to inserting a very short length of smaller guide.

Practical Limitations

If this criterion for matching different size rectangular guides is examined more closely, however, it will be seen that it must not be followed blindly. It follows from the equations, for example, that if a is only very slightly greater than a half wavelength, $\dfrac{\mathbf{E}}{\mathbf{H}}$ will be very large and hence to obtain a modest value of Z, it will follow that b becomes very small. This means that, in theory, a very thin waveguide can be constructed with any desired impedance. Small changes in the thickness will increase the impedance to any reasonable amount if a is kept near $\lambda_o/2$. With such a guide, however, the necessary fields become very great, and dissipative losses due to corona and the resistance of the walls may make its use prohibitive.

Also, at waveguide junctions, the possibility of coupling to other modes of propagation must not be overlooked. In the straight sections of a waveguide, these unwanted modes will usually be very highly attenuated in a few inches, but a dissipative loss of power may well be associated with that attenuation.

The propagation of electromagnetic waves in hollow pipe is no more a simple subject than many other fields of electrical engineering. The concepts of impedance and reactance cannot be used alone; they express only certain properties of the line in a form which is convenient. The final answer always depends upon the distribution in time and space of the electric and magnetic fields.

Waveguide Impedance

As was pointed out previously, a discussion of waveguide impedance should include a warning that its calculation or measurement is not the whole story. It does not, for example, tell anything about the dielectric breakdown strength which can limit the flow of power through the device, nor need it describe dissipative losses or radiation elsewhere in the circuit. It tells the ratio of the electric to the magnetic field at a certain point in the waveguide, and nothing more. That good use can be made of the concept in making generalizations concerning the matching of elements and the procurement of the optimum operation of an over-all system, is a matter for investigation quite apart from the definition. If the actual values of the electric and magnetic fields are known everywhere in a system at all times, the operation is entirely known; if only the impedance (i.e., the ratio of the field magnitudes) is known, considerably less information is at hand. But it happens that this information is very useful and quite analogous to the concept of impedance as used in wired transmission lines as well as being, in general, much easier to compute or measure.

If the impedance of a certain waveguide that is terminated with a load (such as an antenna) is desired, the values of E and H at the entrance end might be measured as a function of time. Both E and H would presumably be found to vary as approximately pure sine functions of time. If they did not, it would mean that more than one frequency was being fed into the assembly and that more than one mode of the guide was being excited. Separate calculations would then need to be made for each mode. Waveguide impedance is no more independent of frequency than is impedance in the usual sense although, since a given design is usually intended for only a single frequency or at least a fairly narrow band of frequencies, this does not usually have very much effect.

Just as in the case of ordinary wired circuits, waveguide impedance usually implies more than just the ratio of two numbers representing the peak, average, or rms values of the sinusoidally varying fields. The impedance may, as a special case, be pure resistance, or it may be reactive in a way corresponding either to capacitive or to inductive preponderance. What this means in terms of a waveguide may be stated somewhat as follows:

Field-strength Measurement

If at a particular point in a waveguide a small loop is inserted so that a portion of the magnetic field in the guide links the loop but is only negligibly disturbed by its presence, then, as the energy being transported by the waveguide flows past the loop, the linkage varies and a current tends to flow in the loop, as illustrated in Fig. 7-10. This

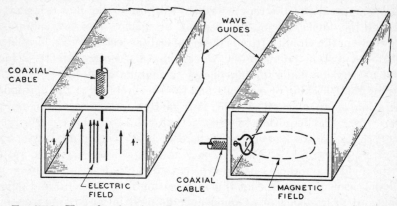

FIG. 7-10. How the electric and magnetic fields in a rectangular waveguide operating in the $TE_{1,0}$ mode, can be measured. The electric field sets up a voltage along the length of the probe (left) and the magnetic field links the loop (right).

current is a measure of the rate of change of the magnetic field and assuming a sine-wave variation, it also measures the strength of the field at a given frequency. It may be rectified to read the average strength of the field. If it were feasible to read the strength of the field directly without detection, it would be found to vary with time as a sine function. That is, if time were marked along the x-axis of a Cartesian coordinate system and the values of the magnetic field at the loop were plotted along that axis but with y-coordinates determined by the field strength in accordance with a suitable scale on the ordinate, a sine curve would result. Positive values of the sine curve might correspond arbitrarily to magnetic flux passing in one direction through the loop and negative values to flux passing through in the other direction. Although it is not generally feasible to make measurements directly for such a plot, average value measurements can be made which indirectly confirm the result.

Alternatively, a small probe can be inserted into the waveguide at the same place along its length as the loop just mentioned. This probe, which is insulated from the guide, can be introduced in such a fashion that its length extends along the electric field. That portion of the probe that is exterior to the waveguide may continue as the center conductor of a coaxial line, the outer shield of which is attached to the waveguide (as shown in Fig. 7-10). Even though the probe is small and extends only a short distance into the guide in order not to influence the operation of the guide appreciably, it will still be subject along its length to a varying electric gradient as electromagnetic waves carry energy past it along the guide. This will manifest itself as a very small flow of energy along the coaxial line in which the probe is terminated. With a suitable arrangement this extracted energy may be measured, and since it was induced into the test probe by the electric field, it is a measure of that field. Thus, the electric field can be plotted against time in Cartesian coordinates and, when that is done, a sine curve again results.

Nature of Waveguide Impedance

With these two sine curves in mind, the impedance of the waveguide system at the point where the probe and loop were located can be defined. If, in proper units, the magnitude of the E-field were 50 times greater than that of the H-field, the impedance is 50 ohms. If the maxima of the two fields occur at the same instant of time, then that 50 ohms is a pure resistive impedance. If the sine curve representing H is ahead of the E curve by an amount equal to a quarter period of the sine wave, the impedance is said to be purely capacitive; if H lags E by a quarter period, the impedance is pure inductance. This is very much like the concept of impedance as applied to ordinary circuits where only voltage and current are involved. Likewise, in a waveguide, pure resistance or pure reactance are limiting cases; actual measurements may show an intermediate phase-shift between the two sine curves.

As in ordinary circuit theory, it is convenient to represent impedance as a vector. To do so, some arbitrary direction such as horizontal and to the right is chosen to represent resistance; then a vector pointing vertically upward might be assigned the meaning of a pure inductance, and one directed vertically downward that of a capacitance. Vectors drawn at intermediate angles represent a mixture of resistance and reactance. The length of the vector will, in all cases, represent the magnitude of the impedance. Thus, a 50-ohm impedance would be a vector drawn 50 units long according to some scale and would point to the right and somewhat upward or downward, depending upon the reactive components, as shown in Fig. 7-11.

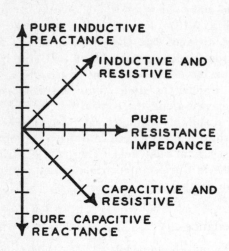

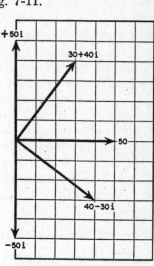

FIG. 7-11. The representation of impedance by vectors.

FIG. 7-12. These vectors are each 50 units long, representing impedances of 50 ohms.

Again, as in ordinary circuit theory, a very compact and convenient way to specify impedance so as to show phase as well as magnitude, is made available by the use of complex numbers. The scheme depends upon the fact that if it is arbitrarily agreed always to draw the impedance vectors in a Cartesian coordinate system with their tails at the origin, then a single point in that system may completely specify an impedance. In terms of complex notation, such a point is written as $A + iB$, where A is the x-coordinate and B is the y-coordinate of the head of the desired impedance vector. In Fig. 7-12 the impedances represented would, reading clockwise, be respectively denoted by complex members, as $+50i$, $30 + 40i$, 50, $40 - 30i$, and $-50i$. All these vectors are 50 units long and, hence, represent impedances whose magnitudes are all 50 ohms.

Selecting a Unit System

As has been pointed out, if it is desired to have impedance values as defined for **E** and **H** result in ohms so as to correspond that much more closely to impedance in wired circuits, it is necessary that proper units be chosen for the measurement of each field. One proper set of units is automatically obtained if the rationalized MKS (meter, kilogram, second) or Giorgi system of units is used. In that system **E** is measured in volts per meter and **H** in amperes per meter. Thus:

$$Impedance = \mathbf{E}/\mathbf{H} = (volts/meters)/(amperes/meters)$$
$$= volt\ meters/ampere\ meters$$
$$= volts/amperes$$

which can be seen immediately from Ohm's Law to be the correct form to give impedance the dimension of ohms. Thus, the impedance of free space may be said to be 376.6 ohms.[1] This means that out in space, after electromagnetic energy has left the antenna, the electric field is always 376.6 times greater than the magnetic field if both are measured in MKS units. To give impedance in terms of gaussian units, a constant must be included; thus,

$$Z = 3 \times 10^8 \frac{\mathbf{E}}{\mathbf{H}}\ ohms$$

where **E** is in esu volts per cm and **H** is in oersteds.

Without carefully considering the properties of the medium, which are usually expressed by permeability and dielectric constant, it can nevertheless be seen that these are reasonable units for **E** and **H** and that they can measure whatever is desired. Electric field is that which occurs between the plates of a condenser. If the plates are 100 volts different in potential then, even though no material (i.e., a perfect vacuum) exists between the plates, it is found convenient to speak of the electric field there. This is so because if a probe is inserted in that space, energy can be extracted under certain conditions. The electric field which is imagined to be present in the absence of all matter is just a measure of the way the 100-volt drop between the plates is divided throughout the space. Volts per meter is a reasonable unit for measuring such a thing.

Similarly, if a charge is moving in free space or, according to Maxwell's equations, if the electric field is changing, a magnetic field is formed. Again it is found convenient to speak of the presence of this field even in a vacuum, because whenever a test magnet is inserted in the space it will usually be subject to a torque which will try to align it with the field. Presumably, the field in any region can always be simulated by allowing a given current to flow through a given length of wire properly located in that region. Hence it is reasonable to measure magnetic fields in terms of amperes per meter.

Orientation of Fields

The first problem in calculating the impedance of a geometric array of conductors which may form a waveguide is to decide how the electric and magnetic fields will be oriented in that array. In doing this, various modes of energy propagation are really being considered. That is, depending upon the feed into the guide and the source frequency, it often develops that a given waveguide assembly will transport energy with the E and H-fields oriented in accordance with two or more schemes (Fig. 7-13). It is then said that propagation in two

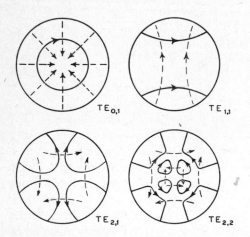

FIG. 7-13. End views of circular waveguide excited in certain modes. The solid lines represent the electric field and the dashed lines the magnetic field.

or more modes is possible. Certain rules may be deduced from Maxwell's equations which serve as a guide in deciding what these modes are by showing certain necessary conditions which must obtain on the inner surfaces of the waveguide. First consider these rules in their most general form.

The rules are valid at any surface of discontinuity of the medium, such as at the surface of a conductor or at a plane which is the boundary between two kinds of dielectric. Restating the rules that were explained in the section on Maxwell's equations, they are: (1) the tangential component of **E** is continuous; (2) the normal component of **B** is continuous, where **B** is defined as the product of **H** and the permeability of the material in which the measurement is made at the time of making the measurement; (3) the tangential component of **H** is discontinuous by an amount equal to the current per unit area flowing in the boundary surface; and (4) the normal component of **D**, which is defined as the product of **E** and the dielectric constant, is discontinuous by an amount equal to the charge per unit area on the surface of discontinuity. These rules, together with a sufficient knowledge of the geometry and properties of the materials plus a knowledge of the radiation properties of any holes in the assembly, are in principle enough to decide the validity of any propagation mode, aside from the attenuation characteristic of its operation. But there is still, in an actual waveguide, the problem of constructing possible modes to be tested by the rules. This part of the job is an art, and only experiments with a given arrangement can prove whether or not unwanted modes will occur at given frequencies. Spurious modes, which are generated somewhere along a waveguide transmission line, can cause serious losses of power, because elsewhere the line is not designed to pass them and they are attenuated out by causing excessive currents to flow and the power to go into heat through I^2R losses.

Field-free Conditions

Very often waveguides are made only of highly conductive metals and use only air as a dielectric. In this case the only surface of discontinuity is that between the air and the metal, which very closely approximates a surface between a vacuum and a perfectly conducting material. A vacuum has a dielectric constant and a permeability which are constant and well known. In the Giorgi system of units, the permeability of a vacuum is $4\pi \times 10^{-7}$ henrys per meter, and the dielectric constant is 8.85×10^{-12} farads per meter. This contrasts with the gaussian system where both μ and K have unity value for a vacuum. A perfectly conducting metal is a medium which can support no electric or changing magnetic fields except perhaps on its surface.

That the interior of such a metal is field-free is clear from Lenz's law; this states that whenever a magnetic field changes, currents are induced in neighboring conductors which oppose that change in the field. Since the metal is resistance-free, these currents completely cancel any change in the field. Steady magnetic fields, such as might arise from permanent magnets, are of no concern; likewise, it is clear that no electric field can exist in a perfect conductor since, by Ohm's law, that would demand infinite current.

Thus, in special cases where only vacuum and perfect conductors are present, the boundary condition rules for constructing propagation modes may be specialized and written somewhat as follows: (1) the tangential component of **E** is zero; (2) the normal components of **B**

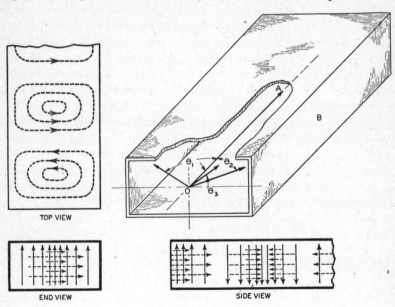

TOP VIEW

END VIEW

SIDE VIEW

Fig. 7-14. Unity swr transmission in a rectangular waveguide by the $T_{1,0}$ mode. Solid lines represent the electric field and the dashed lines the magnetic field.

and **H** are zero; (3) the tangential component of **H** is equal to the current per unit area flowing in the boundary surface; and (4) the normal component of **E** is equal to the charge per unit area on the surface of discontinuity divided by 8.85×10^{-12}. Taken together, these say qualitatively that **E** lines of force may start and end at the metal surfaces and are perpendicular to them. Likewise, magnetic lines of force do not start or stop on the surfaces and, in the limiting case, they touch the surfaces only as tangents.

In Fig. 7-14, a section of a rectangular waveguide is represented as operating in an acceptable mode. In the end, top, and side views the electric and magnetic fields are shown by lines of force. These lines indicate the strength of the field by their spacing and, in accordance with the arrows, they show the field direction at every point through which they pass. The mode shown is one commonly used and is usually called the $TE_{1,0}$ mode. The letters TE refer to the fact that the electric field runs only transversely across the narrow dimension of the waveguide, while the magnetic field extends across the wider dimension and has a longitudinal component as well. The subscripts $1,0$ indicate that in going across the wide dimension, one maximum in the electric field strength will be observed, while in moving across the guide in the narrow direction, the magnetic field is found to be constant and without maxima or minima. It will be observed that this $TE_{1,0}$ mode qualitatively satisfies the boundary conditions which have been quoted; namely, the H field lines curve so as to remain tangent to the wall at contact and the electric field intensity falls off to a zero value at the side walls so as to present no tangential components.

Desired Conditions

It is desired that the energy in the waveguide shown in Fig. 7-14 flow along the guide in the direction of OA. If any energy does flow crosswise in the guide, or at any angle θ from the desired direction, this energy may be absorbed in the walls of the guide, and dissipated. In that case the transmitted wave will be attenuated. It turns out that in the $TE_{1,0}$ mode there is never any energy flow toward the wide sides of the guide and that although energy is at times directed toward the narrow side, it never reaches that surface if operation is at a frequency above the cutoff frequency.

Since Poynting's vector, showing the direction of energy flow, is always mutually perpendicular to both the E and H-fields, it is understandable that no energy will flow in a direction such as θ_3 toward the wider side (toward the bottom as shown in Fig. 7-14) of the guide. In order for it to do so, the E vectors would have to tilt to remain perpendicular to the new direction of propagation, and would thus presumably cause trouble with the boundary conditions.

As for energy flowing to the other walls of the guide, the situation is different. No longitudinal components of **E** are needed; and **H**, except at the center of the guide, does have at least a small component along the guide.

In Fig. 7-15, another top view of a rectangular guide in the $TE_{1,0}$ mode is shown. The electric field is perpendicular to the paper. Vectors representing it are shown either as dots or crosses. The dots indicate a vector coming out of the plane of the paper and the crosses show one going in. The strength of the field is indicated by the density

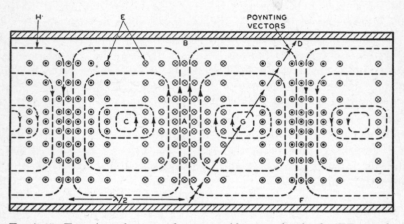

FIG. 7-15. Top view of rectangular waveguide operating in the $TE_{1,0}$ mode with unity swr. Dots and crosses in circles represent the electric field and the magnetic field is represented by the dashed lines.

with which these dots or crosses are drawn. Thus, at the instant shown, the electric field has its maximum value at a point such as A. Starting from the center the intensity then falls off like a sine function, crosswise to the guide, to become zero at points like B, and lengthwise to zero at points like C.

This arrangement of the electric field, along with the magnetic field also shown, moves along the guide and in doing so carries energy with it. For a waveguide operating like the one shown in Fig. 7-15, this is strictly true for wavelengths which are short enough to be below the cutoff frequency. The mathematics of this are moderately complicated but it is, at least, apparent that this is possible. Remembering that the direction of Poynting's vector is obtained by thinking of the direction of motion of a right-hand screw turned so as to rotate the **E** vector into the **H** vector, it is clear that in Fig. 7-15 a wave will be propagated along the length of the waveguide. Considering only the portion of the magnetic field which runs crosswise to the waveguide (vertically as shown in Fig. 7-15), Poynting's vector is everywhere directed from left to right. At a point such as A, the E vector is pointing into the paper and rotating it so as to cause it to line up with H, will be turning it in a direction that would advance a right-hand screw toward the right-hand margin of the paper. The same situation is true at any point in either direction within a quarter wavelength along the guide from a line joining points A and B, if only the component of H crosswise of the guide is considered. Moreover, at points more than a quarter wave (but less than 3/4 wave) away from a line through points A and B, both the E and H-fields are reversed, so Poynting's vector continues to point to the right. Evidently as the phase of E and H is arranged in Fig. 7-15, a pure traveling wave is obtained.

Now actually the H vector has some intensity directed along the length of the waveguide, the only exception being at those points in a plane along the length of the waveguide which is everywhere midway between the surfaces forming the narrow sides of the waveguide. In Fig. 7-15, this plane would be represented by a horizontal line drawn through point C. As a result of such longitudinal components of H, some energy appears to be propagated toward the sidewalls of the waveguide. The net amount reaching the walls is zero, however, because when complete account is taken of time and space variation, it can be shown that the flow toward the wall is just offset by that moving away.

It is difficult to describe completely the situation graphically, but at least an example of the transverse flow can be quoted. Several Poynting's vectors are shown in Fig. 7-15 pointing toward D on one side wall. Those which are shown will not reach D simultaneously and, hence, are not the proper ones to indicate complete cancellation of energy flow to D, but at least they serve to show that Poynting's vectors propagated to D may be of the sort in which the E vector points out of the paper, or another sort in which the E vector heads into the paper but is compensated by a reversed magnetic field. Under proper conditions, an energy flow, such as the one shown as directed toward D, will be just canceled out before reaching D and thus allow a zero tangential electric field there as required by the boundary conditions. When this is true, no energy is present at the wall surface and there is, consequently, no attenuation of the energy flow along the guide.

Cutoff Frequency

In the $TE_{1,0}$ mode the cutoff frequency, above which there is no attenuation, may be determined very simply and to a certain extent can be intuitively verified. The shortest route by which a point such as D on the side wall of the waveguide shown in Fig. 7-15 can feel the effect of waves propagated from a series of points across the guide is along a transverse line like an imaginary one drawn from D to F. In the case shown point D is subject to possible energy flow along the path traced out by the series of Poynting vectors. As has already been indicated, however, these vary in magnitude and have zero value right at D. When the whole pattern of fields has moved along so that a point like G has almost reached a point opposite D, a new series of Poynting vectors directed toward point D would extend from point F to point D. In other words, as time elapses, the vectors directed toward point D revolve around D but if there is to be no attenuation, they must do this while still varying in magnitude along their path so as to keep a zero value at D. If the distance DF (the width of the guide) is equal to or greater than a half wavelength, then the waves directed toward D at the proper instant from points along the line DF can have magnitudes which vary like a sine wave loop and hence present a zero value to point D. If the waveguide width is less than a half wave, at least when the series of Poynting vectors extends along line DF, some net energy flow to D does take place. Complete cancellation of energy flow into the walls of the guide takes place even if the width of the waveguide is greater than a half wavelength because of the peculiar distribution and motion of the field strength values. On the other hand, wavelengths any amount longer than twice the guide width cause energy to be carried to the side walls and, in attempting to violate the boundary conditions, that energy is dissipated.

The cutoff frequency of a rectangular waveguide in the $TE_{1,0}$ mode is therefore specified by $\lambda_o = 2b$, where λ_o is the wavelength in free space, and b is the wider dimension of the guide. At all longer wavelengths some attenuation is experienced. Except for complications which may arise in order to avoid higher order modes when $\lambda_o < b$, all shorter wavelengths are readily passed. A waveguide is analogous to a high-pass filter in this respect.

Specific Impedance

Consider now the impedance of the $TE_{1,0}$ mode in a rectangular waveguide. A first-order approximation will be quoted by assuming that the longitudinal components of the magnetic field may be neglected and the propagation considered to move with a velocity like that in free space. In that case a result is obtained [2] that is the same as the impedance of free space, namely

$$Z = \sqrt{\frac{\mu}{K}}$$

in MKS units.

In the actual case of the $TE_{1,0}$ mode in a rectangular waveguide, the H-field is somewhat larger. The correction factor due to a stronger magnetic field to account for the longitudinal component or to a lower velocity of propagation, is

$$\frac{1}{\sqrt{1 - (\lambda_0/2b)^2}}$$

Thus the specific impedance is

$$\frac{\sqrt{\mu/K}}{\sqrt{1 - (\lambda_0/2b)^2}}$$

It is interesting to note that this expression is independent of the narrow dimension of the waveguide. This corresponds to the fact that no energy flows crosswise of the pipe in that direction as has been pointed out. In the other dimension of the guide there is a crosswise energy flow (which may cancel out at the surfaces) so the impedance is affected.

This impedance is said to be a *specific impedance,* analogous to a notation used in acoustics, because still another condition must be added before an overall impedance applicable to the joining of two waveguide sections of different size can be written down. The condition is that when flow takes place from a guide of one size to that of another, as shown in Fig. 7-16, it is a sort of total amount of electric and magnetic flux which must join at the junction if there is to be no reflection with an attendant standing wave to indicate a mismatch. For example, if energy is flowing from the large pipe into the smaller one, the field strengths in the large pipe are modified near the junction, because part of the large waveguide is closed off. To join the fields smoothly between the two pieces, this must be taken into account.

Another way of describing what is desired is to say that the charge and current on the wider wall of the guide must join smoothly at the junction since doing this will automatically average the fields in the right way.

Now, **E** alone does not specify the amount of charge present on the wall of the waveguide since a given **E** may be obtained by a little charge on closely-spaced plates, or by more charge on plates further

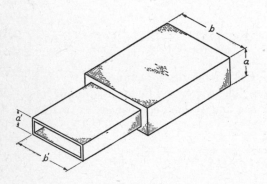

Fig. 7-16. Junction between two sizes of rectangular waveguide.

apart. The quantity in which interest is focused is a**E**, where a is the narrow dimension of the guide. Likewise, it is b**H** that requires the currents to be continuous at the junction. Thus finally, the impedance of a rectangular waveguide in the $TE_{1,0}$ mode may be given as

$$\frac{a\mathbf{E}}{b\mathbf{H}} = \frac{\dfrac{a}{b} \quad \dfrac{\mu}{K}}{\sqrt{1 - \left(\dfrac{\lambda_0}{2b}\right)^2}}$$

This impedance is often called the *current impedance* since it is the specification necessary to cause the current flowing in the wide side of the guide to be continuous.

Wave Guide Junctions and Terminations

The most difficult part of the design of any waveguide system is that of constructing proper terminations, bends, and junctions between sections. The requirements that have to be met by such parts are numerous, and even visualizing the way in which the currents flow and in which the electric and magnetic fields are oriented, may be far from easy. The present discussion is by no means exhaustive as

to the results achievable, nor is it a listing of fittings and junctions
most commonly used; instead, it is an examination of various approaches which are best suited to lead to optimum designs, plus a discussion of certain phenomena that are common to many waveguide
terminations.

To see how difficult the situation may be, first examine the problem
of T-joints. The cross-section of a waveguide may be circular, elliptical, or rectangular in shape; for that matter, there are undoubtedly
even more complicated shapes which will support a traveling electromagnetic wave without great attenuation. A rectangular waveguide is
often chosen because it is relatively easy to manufacture to accurate
dimensions, and also because its operation is the simplest to understand and denote by algebraic equations. The possibilities of making
fittings, such as T-joints, for more complicated types of guides have
not yet been explored very thoroughly.

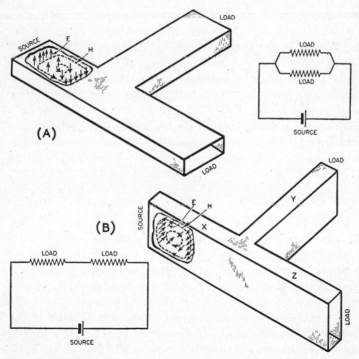

FIG. 7-17. Shunt (A) and series (B) waveguide-connected loads
across a single source.

T-joints in Waveguides

As shown in Fig. 7-17, there are at least two ways of joining a rectangular waveguide to form a T. In Fig. 7-17(A), the wider sides lie in a single plane while, in Fig. 7-17(B) the shorter sides of the rectangular cross-sections are continuous in one plane. If sources and loads are connected to these junctions as shown, then for operation of these guides in the $TE_{1,0}$ mode, the cases are roughly analogous to the series and shunt connection of two loads across a single source.

In Fig. 7-17(A), it is clear that the electric field does not need to change direction at the junction, and that its value there is the value impressed across the entrance to the two legs leading to the loads. With the magnetic field, however, the longitudinal component of the source leg becomes the transverse component in one load leg and remains a longitudinal component in the other. This is like a wired circuit of two loads in parallel, where the voltage across the loads must be the same although the currents may differ.

Similarly, in Fig. 7-17(B), the transverse component of the magnetic field is common to both load legs and the electric field has to change in direction to be propagated to one of the loads. This is similar to two wired loads in series with a source. There the current to each load is the same but the voltages across the loads may be different. Unfortunately, however, this is about where the similarities end. If the impedances of the two loads are known, it may be possible to combine them in such fashion as to predict the desired impedance of the source to fair accuracy, but the method of combination is not the same as with wired circuits and, moreover, it is rather complicated.

Electric Field Values

In Fig. 7-18 the series-connected T is shown again. The labels X, Y, and Z will correlate this view with the one shown in Fig. 7-17(B). If the dimensions of the guide are such that only the $TE_{1,0}$ mode of propagation can be transmitted without appreciable attenuation and all other modes are rapidly attenuated, then, at a distance of several wavelengths away from the junction, the electric field will have instantaneous values as shown. This will be true if the width of the guide (dimension into the paper in Fig. 7-18) is between one-half and one wavelength, and if the height of the guide is less than that width. Under such conditions, the energy propagation which is of interest, is accomplished by the motion along the guide of a sinusoidally varying electric field like the one shown.

When the wave carrying energy from the source reaches the junction, the electric field is distorted, because there is no top surface to the guide which can hold a charge at the terminations of the electric lines of force. Thus, in an overly-simplified illustration, the electric lines are forced to terminate at or near the corner of the junction as shown in Fig. 7-18. This provides a proper component of the electric field for propagation up into the vertical leg of the T but also forces a

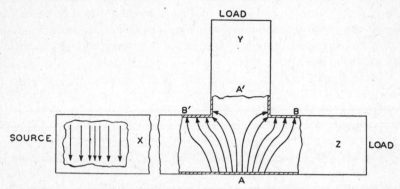

FIG. 7-18. A simplified illustration of a series T waveguide junction, showing how the electric field is distorted at the junction.

high electric field strength to appear at the corners. Consequently, these corners are subject to the periodic presence of high charge densities which cause a certain amount of dissipative power loss.

The electric field shown at the junction in Fig. 7-18 is overly simplified for at least two reasons. In the first place, the traveling wave from the source is, in general, not the only one present; there may be waves reflected from the loads and from each connection of a waveguide with the junction. Also, the irregularities in the field at the junction will cause the excitation of higher modes in any or all of the connected waveguides; the fact that these higher modes are rapidly attenuated and do not extend far into the waveguides does not lessen their presence at the junction or prevent energy loss in them. With these complications it is easy to see that the problem is a difficult one to solve in a purely theoretical manner. As always, the need is to satisfy Maxwell's equations at all boundaries for each possible mode, and to add up the field components resulting from each mode, in order to give a complete solution of the problem.

Impedance Determination

Once such a solution is obtained either theoretically or empirically, it is most convenient to express it in terms of impedance. That is, graphs or algebraic expressions connecting the desired impedance of any two of the legs and that of the third are needed, in order to show the relation which will cause energy to be transferred through the junction most efficiently. To follow a standard method, it is necessary to choose points at which the impedance is to be evaluated. It is convenient to make the measurement for both of the horizontal guides of Fig. 7-18 at a cross-section indicated by AA' or its equivalent (impedances in transmission lines repeat every half wavelength); for the vertical waveguide, the impedance may be computed or measured at BB'.

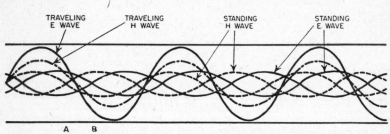

Fig. 7-19. The curves represent the field strength in a waveguide by their distances above and below an imaginary center line. As a function of time, the traveling waves move to the right; the standing waves assume successive values between the extremes shown.

Reference to Fig. 7-19 makes it clear that, in general, the impedance of a waveguide line depends upon the position at which the measurement is made. The component of the field due to standing wave alone represents an E/H value or impedance that varies from infinity at a point like A to zero at a point like B. (This was explained more thoroughly in an earlier section.) Superimposing E and H values from the traveling wave on this standing wave modifies the ratio but does not remove the dependence of impedance on distance along the line. This situation is similar to that which prevails in other electrically long transmission lines and is the reason why matching criteria for a device like a T junction must specify the impedance of each leg at a particular point. Any other point which is an integral number of half wavelengths away from the given point and back into the leg in question will give the same measurement of impedance. For that matter, if the wavelength is known and the impedance at any given point on the wave is measured, it is easy to calculate the impedance at any other point. Charts for making such calculations are commonly used.

Open-Ended Waveguides

Mechanically, the simplest termination that can be imagined for a waveguide, is none at all. Because of its very simplicity there is considerable interest in what happens when a long waveguide the far end of which is well removed from other obstructions, is left with just an open end. Qualitatively, some energy is radiated and some is reflected back into the guide. Moreover, of that which is radiated, some moves straight ahead, some appears as side lobes, and a considerable amount is radiated backward along the outside of the guide.

In Fig. 7-20(A) the electric and magnetic fields are shown, which as a first approximation may be expected at the open end of a rectan-

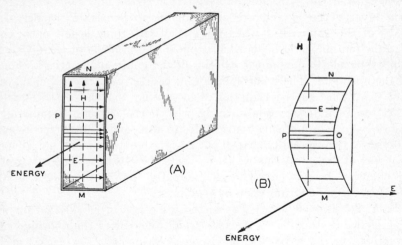

Fig. 7-20. Instantaneous values of **E** and **H** fields at the exit of an open-ended waveguide operating in the $TE_{1,0}$ mode.

gular waveguide that is operating in the $TE_{1,0}$ mode. The electric field which exists across the narrow dimension, has maximum intensity at the center and shades off to zero at walls M and N. The magnetic field which is perpendicular to the electric field, varies in the MN direction in the same way as does the electric field. Thus, since the energy flow in an electromagnetic field depends upon **E** and **H**, it is expected that the energy flow out of the guide as radiation should be given in strength by a function something like the one drawn in the three dimensional plot of Fig. 7-20(B). It is desired to find how this energy proceeds out into space.

Huygen's principle at first seems to offer a method of solution, for it states that it is only necessary to imagine the electromagnetic wave at the end of the waveguide to be replaced by an array of point sources which vary in strength in accord with the plot of Fig. 7-20(B); to construct spherical waves about each of these sources; and to add these waves in proper strength at various points in space so as to determine the pattern of the radiation. This type of calculation, however, neglects radiation which arises from currents flowing in the outer surface of the waveguide, and although it approximates the forward radiation, it does not predict the backward component, which is experimentally observed and which is nearly as strong as the forward component when the waveguide is operated near cutoff.

Because of the skin-effect, waveguide currents flow only in a very thin layer of metal and are quite unable to penetrate through the walls of the guide. But when the end of the guide is left open, the electric and magnetic fields which appear at the plane of the opening, cause currents to flow in the exterior of the guide in the neighborhood of the open end. These currents are, of course, very rapidly changing and contribute to the radiation field around the end of the guide. This reason indicates qualitatively why horns or cone terminations are so helpful in matching waveguides to free space. As in the acoustical case, very specially shaped horns give the best results, but almost any sort of flange or cone which prevents these exterior currents from propagating energy backward will greatly improve the desirability of the waveguide termination as a radiator.

S. A. Schelkunoff has demonstrated a method of calculation for an open-ended rectangular waveguide which overcomes the difficulty encountered in the naive use of Huygen's principle. The argument is based upon the use of a so-called equivalence theorem. A sheet of electric current and a sheet of magnetic current are imagined to be flowing in the plane of the waveguide opening and over the outer surface of the guide. If such currents are adjusted so as to just cancel out both the aperture fields and the outer surface currents which are present when the guide is radiating, then the cancellation completely stops any flow of energy from the guide. If no energy is fed into the source end of the guide, these simulated currents must duplicate the radiation field except for a reversal of sign. Maxwell's equations are sufficient to calculate the field arising from this equivalent current distribution. The great advantage accruing from such an equivalent type of calculation lies in the fact that the current-sheet distribution does not have to be one that is physically realizable. It may be as imaginative as desired as long as it does provide the necessary cancellation and lend itself to use in the field calculation. It may allow these calculations to be simpler than would the actual currents in the interior of the waveguide, which may not be accurately known and are difficult to compute or measure.

Design Considerations

Reflections back inside the waveguide occur not only at an open end, but in general are found wherever there is any sudden discontinuity such as a change in shape or size or a change in the dielectric inside the guide. Only by very careful design is it possible to minimize these backward reflections. When space is available, it is therefore often advisable to avoid sharp discontinuities and to use tapered sections to connect waveguides of different size, or to use bends of not too small a radius of curvature to replace right-angle junctions.

To see qualitatively why a tapered section like that shown in Fig. 7-21 is superior to a sudden change in cross-section, it is only necessary to realize that the wedge-shaped connecting piece will propagate

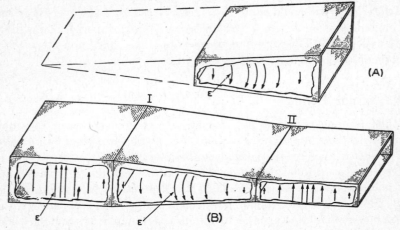

FIG. 7-21. Tapered sections to connect waveguides of different sizes.

approximately cylindrical electric waves without much attenuation, and that the reflections at the entrance and exit to the tapered connector can be negligible because the discontinuities in the waveguide size can be kept small. In Fig. 7-21 (A) an exaggerated wedge-shaped section is shown to indicate that cylindrical waves are natural for such a piece. The broken lines indicate that if the wedge were continued, it would converge to a line. If this line were a wave source, then cylindrical waves might be expected to emerge from it, just as circular waves spread out about a pebble dropped into a quiet pool of water. A more practical tapered connector, as shown in Fig. 7-21 (B), is two or more wavelengths long for frequencies which allow the guides shown to operate in the $TE_{1,0}$ mode. The discontinuities shown at cross-sectional surfaces I and II are so mild as to cause little reflection.

If energy traverses the system from left to right, there will be at the boundary I incident and reflected plane waves to the left, and incident and reflected cylindrical waves to the right. At the boundary II incident and reflected cylindrical electric waves will be to the left and a transmitted plane wave to the right. It is not too difficult to express these waves mathematically and to match them at the surfaces to allow for continuity of energy flow. Such a calculation can yield the amount of reflected power back into the waveguide as a function of the ratio of the waveguide sizes and the length of the tapered line. The result is in agreement with experiment, and shows that, for all usual cases, a tapered section that is more than two or three wavelengths long, will yield quite satisfactory results. Moreover, it is certain in any event, that a sufficiently gradually tapered line will be non-reflecting. This applies to coaxial lines and non-rectangular waveguides, as well as to the case discussed.

Waveguide Bends

The arguments concerning bends in waveguides are in the main similar to those for tapered sections, except that a change in direction of the electric or magnetic field is also involved, just as it was in the discussion of T-junctions. The change here, however, is gradual, and is not abrupt as was the case for the T-junction. The creation and attenuation of higher modes is not at all a serious problem. In Fig. 7-22 are shown two types of bends in a rectangular waveguide which are often respectively referred to as E- and H-bends. The assumption is that these pieces are to be employed at such a frequency that only the $TE_{1,0}$ mode can be transmitted without rapid attenuation. That is, it is assumed that the wavelength of the energy in free space will be less than twice the wider dimension of the guide, but not so little as to be less than or equal to that dimension. Under these conditions the electric field vectors will be oriented approximately as shown in Fig. 7-22. With the E-bend the electric vector is forced to change

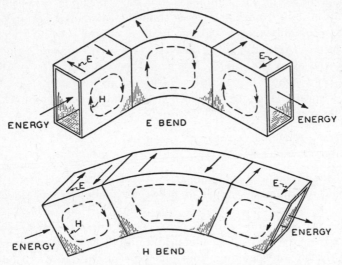

Fig. 7-22. E and H bends in a waveguide.

its angle while, with the H-bend, it is not. In the H-bend, it is the transverse component of the H-field which must turn as it proceeds along the waveguide.

If the bent portion of either of the guides shown in Fig. 7-22 is considered as a section of a waveguide bend which continues around to form a complete 360° turn, so as to conform to a rectangular toroid, it is possible to show that, for either type of bend, the attenuation in the toroid section itself can be as small as in a straight section of waveguide. For example, in the case of the E-bend, the toroid section of the waveguide serves only to cut out a portion of a radial field, the center of which is at the center of curvature of the bend. Since the walls of the waveguide partition off this section by virtue of conductors placed normal to the field, at least the boundary condition of the electric field is adequately met.

Algebraic expressions for the waves in the bent section can be written and they can be matched up to the plane waves in the straight sections, paying due attention to the higher modes. Out of such calculations can be obtained expressions for the amount of reflected energy to be expected at the discontinuities where the two types of guide are joined. It turns out that the loss due to such bend junctions are fairly negligible even if the radius of curvature is only a few times as great as the wider dimension of the waveguide. Experimental results are usually somewhat worse than the calculated performances. This is presumably due to the mechanical difficulty of making truly smooth bends. Actually, some reflections do occur at points along the bend as well as at the joints. But even then the loss is so small that bending a waveguide is generally considered an easy and efficient way to turn a corner. This applies both to E- and H-bends and to bends in circular waveguides as well.

Junctions

When the problem is encountered of constructing junctions between waveguides of different shapes or between a hollow waveguide and a coaxial line, a great many fairly complicated arrangements are possible. So far as guide-to-guide connections are concerned, the procedure is usually only of academic interest because there is seldom a valid reason for changing from one type of waveguide to another. When there is a reason, the change can be made by the use of sections which gradually change from one shape to another and by the use of matching diaphragms which have already been described.

Junctions between coaxial lines and hollow waveguides are much more frequently used. It is often more convenient to bring the energy out of a vacuum-tube generating device with coaxial fittings than with a hollow waveguide because the coaxial line is smaller. On the other hand, for transmission over distances greater than a foot or so, a hollow guide is preferred on the basis that the losses can be made smaller.

In Fig. 7-23 is shown a schematic representation of one method of introducing a signal from a coaxial line into a waveguide. The left-hand end of the waveguide and the upper end of the coaxial line are closed off or shorted. Here, the short-circuits are shown as being adjustable to indicate that the impedance of the waveguide and the coaxial line may be matched within certain limits by proper adjustment. Once the characteristics of the waveguide and coaxial line are known, these adjustments can, of course, be fixed.

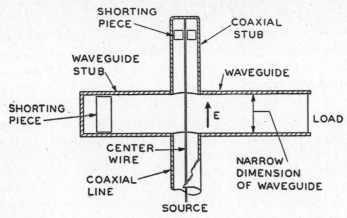

FIG. 7-23. A transition junction from coaxial line to waveguide.

The waveguide in Fig. 7-23 is assumed to be proportioned so that only the $TE_{1,0}$ mode can be propagated without great attenuation, and is represented as being seen from the narrower side of the rectangular guide. Thus, it is wanted that energy from the coaxial line shall set up an electric field in the waveguide which is oriented as has been shown. Qualitatively, this seems to be just what is to be expected from the way the coaxial center wire is inserted. Voltage waves between the two conductors of the coaxial line must appear between the center wire and the waveguide walls when the waveguide is reached. Currents in the center wire at the waveguide likewise create the right sort of magnetic field.

The main problem is that of tuning the two stubs. Energy coming up the coaxial line to the waveguide will also energize the coaxial stub section; energy reflected from the shorted coaxial end must return without loss, so as to keep the net energy flow into the stub at zero and yet not pass backward along the line to the generator. Likewise, energy radiated from the coaxial center-wire antenna into the waveguide must be reflected from the waveguide short-circuit and proceed to the load without causing such an interference at the antenna wire as will prevent further energy radiation. In brief, this means matching the coaxial line impedance to that of the waveguide. As far as the resistive components of the impedances are concerned, it turns out that, in a junction like the one shown in Fig. 7-23, the waveguide can be matched to any coaxial input, the resistance of which is less than twice the characteristic impedance of the waveguide. This adjustment consists of moving the coaxial wire of Fig. 7-23 off center in the waveguide in a direction into or out of the paper. Adjustment of the coaxial stub allows the coaxial line to be tuned to any reactance.

Analytical Methods

The method of making a theoretical study of this type of coaxial antenna in a waveguide is rather interesting. As has just been said, the reactive component of the coaxial line impedance can be anything that is desired; the resistive impedance depends entirely upon the lateral placement of the coaxial line in the waveguide stub. Apparently, then, the job of theoretical analysis is one of finding how fields spread out from a voltage which periodically appears along a wire running across the inside of the guide.

J. C. Slater has solved this problem for a dipole radiator by using a method of images. Fig. 7-24 serves to show how he proceeded. The

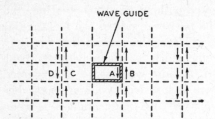

WAVE GUIDE

Fig. 7-24. Image array to simulate field in a rectangular waveguide arising from excitation by a single electric dipole.

rectangle shown by heavy lines represents a cross-section of a rectangular waveguide at the point where an electric dipole has been inserted. The vector shown at point A inside the waveguide is an instantaneous value of an electric field caused by the charge in that dipole. This field varies continually with a frequency equal to that of the energy under consideration and, in conjunction with an accompanying magnetic field, radiates toward both side walls of the guide as well as along the length of the guide. The energy reaching the side of the guide is reflected. Now, if for a moment the right-hand side of the guide is imagined removed and a second dipole placed at B, first-order reflections are simulated by that image source. Anywhere along the line where the right wall formerly existed there is now zero energy, because the source and image B just cause complete interference there; in other words, such a simulated arrangement satisfies the same boundary conditions as does an actual wall.

Likewise, it at first seems that the left wall of the waveguide could be removed and all of the reflections from it simulated by assuming another image source at C. This is possible insofar as first reflections go; however, in removing that second wall, provision also must be made for reflections from the image source installed at B. This requires a second image at D, and so on. Consequently a whole array of image sources is required to simulate the actual radiation field with the walls of the waveguide in place. Because of its regularity, this is fairly easy to represent mathematically. The line of sources presents the same problem as does an infinite optical diffraction grating and allows an easy computation of the radiation distribution to be made. Once it is known for an unobstructed waveguide, one end can be closed and the reflected wave from the end added to get the actual situation, analogous to the junction of Fig. 7-23.

FOOTNOTES

1. The impedance of free space is given by

$$Z = \sqrt{\frac{\mu}{K}}$$

where in MKS units μ is $4\pi \times 10^{-7}$ henry per meter and K is 8.85×10^{-12} farad per meter. In the MKS system, μ and K have dimensions such that Z results in ohms.

2. If at some point on the boundary surface of the wider side of the guide and using MKS units, the electric field at some instant is E_1 then in accordance with boundary condition 4, a charge must be present on that surface with a density equal to $KE_1 = 8.85 \times 10^{-12} E_1$, where E_1 is in volts per meter. The charge, in accordance with the present approximation, then moves along the guide with the velocity of light given by $c = 3 \times 10^8$ meters per second and hence, corresponds to a current density of $3 \times 8.85 \times 10^{-12} \times 10^8 E_1 = cKE_1$. By the boundary condition of rule 3, it follows that the magnetic field at that point must be $H_1 = cKE_1$ and the impedance given by $E_1/H_1 = 1/Kc$. Because it is well known that

$$c = \frac{1}{\sqrt{K\mu}}$$

it may be stated equally well that the impedance of free space is given by

$$\sqrt{\mu/K}.$$

Chapter 8

RESONANT CAVITIES

RESONANT CAVITIES are devices which may be used with microwaves to serve the same purposes as do resonant circuits at ordinary radio frequencies. For example, in an ordinary Hartley oscillator, the resonant tank circuit containing lumped values of inductance, capacitance, and resistance accomplishes at least three things: it fixes the frequency at which the oscillation is to take place; it provides a storage place in which r-f energy can initially accumulate and build up to a high voltage for effective transfer to the load; and in conjunction with the circuits of the oscillator, it provides feedback to the grid in proper phase and impedance so that the oscillation will be maintained.

The tasks accomplished by a resonant cavity are, in general, analogous to these three things. In fact, the similarities of purpose and action of resonant cavities and resonant circuits are so strong that much of the same terminology is used in describing both of them. Quantities specifying frequency, energy storage, and impedance have much the same meanings when applied to either kind of device. There are some very fundamental differences, however, and caution must be exercised to see that the analogies are not carried so far as to mask the advantages of cavity resonators.

In order to enter the discussion of this chapter, the action of a resonant circuit in a Hartley oscillator will first be described, and the various design constants of a resonant circuit will be reviewed as they are normally used in such an arrangement.

Frequency Determination in Resonant Circuits

The action of the Hartley oscillator shown in Fig. 8-1 is qualitatively easy to understand by talking about charge and current alone. Charge flows from plate m of the lumped capacitance around through the inductance L. After accumulating on plate n of the condenser C, it is urged by the crowded condition there and by the field around the inductance, to reverse itself and flow back through the inductance to

170

the other plate. Having done so, it again reverses direction **and, in** general, each time the condenser becomes the recipient of most of the charge, the direction of flow is reversed so that a continual oscillation is indicated. Furthermore, the plate circuit of the oscillator vacuum tube is regulated by the grid in such a way that the charge is given an added impetus at just the proper point in each cycle. The starting up of the oscillator causes the charge to oscillate initially back and forth with greater and greater strength. It is like pushing a child's swing. The swing is a mechanical resonant device, and small pushes

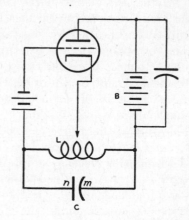

FIG. 8-1. A wired resonant circuit as used in a Hartley oscillator, the resonant frequency of which depends on the values of the lumped inductance L and capacity C.

at the proper point in each cycle produce greater and greater amplitudes. The amplitude of the oscillation stops increasing only when a load (intentional or accidental) appears and drains off energy as fast as the vacuum tube can supply it. This condition is automatically found as the voltage of the resonant circuit increases, because that increase also causes the amount of power flowing into the external load to get larger, and somewhere on the scale of increasing oscillation strength it becomes equal to the power from the vacuum tube.

Depending upon the size of the condenser used in the tank circuit of a Hartley oscillator, it takes more or less time for enough charge to collect, so that a given voltage is present which urges the discharging process to begin. Depending upon the size of the inductance there is more or less magnetic field which, in changing, has more or less effect in causing each period of current flow to persist. These factors determine the frequency of oscillation. If the time necessary to make one complete oscillation is one-millionth of a second, then the radio frequency generated is one megacycle, since the charge in the tank circuit can make one million round trips in a second. It is well known that the resonant frequency of a lumped constant resonant circuit is given by

$$f = \frac{1}{2\pi\sqrt{LC}}.$$

In a Hartley oscillator, the strength of the oscillation in the tank circuit is limited not only by how much energy is fed into the oscillation by the vacuum tube, but also by the ability of the resonant circuit to store the energy it receives. This factor is expressed by Q, which is a sort of reciprocal measure of the friction of the oscillator circuit. When the Hartley oscillator is first turned on, only a small amount of charge travels back and forth from condenser plate to condenser plate. As cycles elapse and additional energy is admitted to the tank circuit by the tube, the oscillating current grows and it would continue to do so indefinitely if it were not for losses in the resonant circuit itself, and from it into the load. The Q of the circuit is a measure of the degree of freedom from such losses.

Thus, in an entirely loss-less circuit where the oscillations might indeed eventually become infinite in strength, the Q would be said to be infinite. In practical oscillators of the Hartley type, a Q of 50 or 100 is often encountered. On the other hand, with resonant cavities, unloaded Q's running into the thousands may be obtained. In the Hartley circuit shown in Fig. 8-1 all possible losses from the tank circuit may be simulated by inserting a resistance R in series with the inductance and capacitance. If this is done the Q of the circuit may be written as

$$Q = \frac{\sqrt{L/C}}{R}.$$

The quantity $\sqrt{L/C}$ is proportional to the energy stored by the circuit. The quantity R is proportional to the energy lost from the circuit in a cycle.[1] A definition of Q for cavities will be given later and then the equivalence of the definitions for the two cases will become clear.

The third item to be mentioned in conjunction with the operation of a wired resonant tank circuit in a Hartley oscillator has to do with supplying energy to start, and then to maintain, the back-and-forth flow of charge. In order for the oscillation to be built up in the first place, energy must be fed into the tank circuit from the battery B, of Fig. 8-1, at just the proper time in each cycle. This is accomplished by letting the oscillation itself affect the grid of the tube in such a way as to apply voltage across a portion of the inductance at just the right moment in each cycle.

By noticing the mid-position of the cathode connection to the coil, it is clear that the grid is 180 degrees out of phase with the plate, so that the tube does supply energy to the tank circuit in a proper phase. Furthermore, it is clear that shifting the position of the tap will change the ratio of grid and plate voltages, while maintaining the same sum. It is also possible to change the total voltage across the coil by changing the ratio of L to C. If a large L and a small C are used, high voltage and small currents will be obtained. Because of the large value of inductance, even a slow current increase will generate a large voltage. Such a condition is one of high impedance and very often gives the best efficiency. If a small L and large C are used, the resonant circuit is one which operates at low impedance. Rather large currents will be required to carry enough charge to a large condenser so as to raise its potential only a moderate amount. This condition, in practice, may often give the greatest freedom from harmonics.

All of this amounts to saying that the impedance of a wired resonant circuit like the one of Fig. 8-1, must be considered in conjunction with the impedance of the grid and plate circuits. The resonant circuit of the tank circuit might, for example, be correct with any values of L and C which satisfy the relation

$$f = \frac{1}{2\pi\sqrt{LC}}$$

To determine L and C completely, a quantity

$$Z = \sqrt{L/C}$$

must also be recognized.

Cavity Development

A common scheme of introducing the cavity type of construction of resonators is to show how one type of cavity can be developed from a resonant circuit. Suppose one starts with a single loop of wire and a condenser, as is shown in Fig. 8-2(A). The resonant frequency of such an arrangement will be fairly high but, in the proportions shown, it will not be as high as are true microwave frequencies. As the size of the loop is decreased in order to raise the frequency further, the losses become excessive and the loop practically vanishes before the true microwave region can be reached. Another way of reducing the inductance of the loop shown in Fig. 8-2(A) is to add other loops in parallel with the one shown. In the limit this may result in an ar-

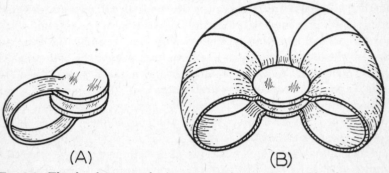

(A)   (B)

Fig. 8-2. The development of a resonant cavity can be considered as starting with a single turn of wire and a condenser, as in (A), and putting turns in parallel until a completely enclosed volume results, as in (B); this is called a rhumbatron cavity.

rangement like the one shown in Fig. 8-2(B) or finally in a completely enclosed volume. A cavity of this doughnut-shaped type has a special name; it is called a *rhumbatron cavity*.

For at least two reasons the discussion of cavity development from a loop and a condenser must not be taken too seriously. In the first place, the roles of inductance and capacitance are not so neatly divided as the cavity development picture tacitly assumes. Capacitance effects occur between various parts of the loop, as well as between the plates which were initially labeled as a condenser. Such effects are important enough, so that calculations which do not recognize them are generally worthless. The fact of the matter is, aside from using the terms to denote the phase of the electric field as compared to the magnetic field, the concepts of inductance and capacitance have no value in microwave calculations.

Secondly, it must be clearly understood that resonant cavities are much more versatile devices than the development argument seems to indicate. They are by no means restricted to the rhumbatron shape, nor do they always involve current flows which appear to correspond to the charging and discharging of a condenser through an inductance.

In the present discussion, it has been decided to introduce the resonant cavity as the microwave counterpart of the resonant circuit, and the properties of a resonant circuit in conjunction with a Hartley oscillator have been spoken of particularly. Both of these things have been done only as a matter of convenience. In addition to giving a further description of the method of cavity design and operation, other types of cavities and the variety of uses to which cavities can be put must be illustrated. In general, resonant circuits are not useful at microwave frequencies because of excessive radiation. This is much the same sort of situation as the one that was discussed in explaining why open-wire lines were not possible for microwaves. On the other hand, resonant cavities are not used much outside of the microwave spectrum because their bulk then becomes too great.

Cavity Forms

Three general types of resonant cavities may easily be distinguished in terms of their general physical construction. A *coaxial resonator* is one in which coaxial conductors are used. A *waveguide cavity* is one in which the hollow volume may be thought of as a waveguide section closed off at both ends. The third is the *rhumbatron* or *reentrant type*, which has already been mentioned.

It is particularly easy to understand the operation of a *coaxial type* of resonant cavity, because it may be explained in terms involving only current and voltage. Such cavities are used to support the inner conductor of a coaxial line and are then referred to as *stub supports*. Such devices have already been mentioned in the discussion of coaxial lines.

Coaxial resonant cavities also possess an advantage when used in conjunction with measuring apparatus, inasmuch as the velocity of propagation in a coaxial line is, over broad limits, independent of frequency. This means that the phase velocity (velocity with which a wave-front moves along the line) in a coaxial resonant cavity may be assumed to be equal to the velocity of light, and also that measured wavelengths correspond to actual free-space wavelengths.

In Fig. 8-3 a tunable coaxial cavity is shown arranged so as to be excited by energy tapped off a circular waveguide transmitting in the $TM_{0,1}$ mode. A galvanometer and crystal are arranged to measure the energy content of the resonator and thus indicate when resonance is obtained.

As the electric field configuration sketched in the waveguide of Fig. 8-3 moves along from left to right, the probe-like extension of the center wire of the coaxial line finds itself parallel to an electric field of varying strength and direction. For example, when point A of the field configuration in the waveguide is at the coaxial line, the coaxial probe finds itself charged positively at the tip.

This follows from the very definition of an electric field, which says that lines of electric force point in the direction that a free positive charge is urged. Since any metal always contains free negative charges, the motion of a positive charge to the end of the probe is equivalent to the flow of a negative (electron) charge into the coaxial line. At a later time, the traveling wave in the circular waveguide

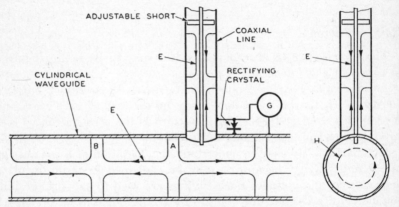

FIG. 8-3. Use of a coaxial resonant cavity to measure the wavelength in free space of energy traveling along a cylindrical waveguide in the $TM_{0,1}$ mode.

causes a point such as B to affect the coaxial line. The opposite situation is then in force and a positive surge of current is sent up the coaxial line, and this is equivalent to a flow of electrons to the tip of the probe. This procedure continues and varies sinusoidally, so an alternating current is urged to flow in the coaxial line at a frequency equal to that of the energy in the waveguide.

Continuing to refer to Fig. 8-3 it can now be seen why an adjustment of the length of the coaxial line can cause it to act as a resonant cavity. The upward flow of charge of one sign in the center conductor is equivalent to the downward flow of charge of the other sign. As a matter of fact, it is known that electricity in metals is actually almost entirely a matter of the motion of negative electrons. Positive ions have a much lower mobility and do not ordinarily contribute to electric currents. The mention of the flow of positive charge is only a convenient and harmless fiction based on long usage and has the same meaning as a flow of electrons going the other way. Uncharged bodies contain large but equal amounts of positive and negative charge; taking away negative charge is in every way the same as adding positive charge.

Thus, between the time the field configuration marked A is at the coaxial line and the later time when B arrives there, if the negative charge sent up into the line by the presence of field A can travel to the closed end and, finding things crowded there, be reflected back along the line so as to arrive at the probe end simultaneously with field B of the guide, then a very special situation exists in which the field lines A cooperate to generate the same alternating current as those of the lines marked as B. With this type of cooperation, large currents are built up in the coaxial line and the conditions of abnormal energy distribution, which are always characteristic of resonance, are obtained.

Waveguide Cavities

Calculations are usually made for three kinds of hollow non-reentrant cavities. They are those which have the shapes of spheres, cylinders, or rectangular prisms. The properties of these types are easily computed from Maxwell's equations in terms of well-known functions. The only assumption is that of perfect geometry, which can be approached by accurate machine work, and also the data obtained from certain physical measurements of materials, such as skin depth, which are now fairly well known for good conductors. Of these shapes, the cylinder and the rectangular prism are the easiest to understand because, except for certain degenerative modes, they may be interpreted as pieces of cylindrical or rectangular waveguides closed off at both ends. Energy in such a piece of waveguide then travels back and forth, being successively reflected at each end. If the time of travel is such as to synchronize itself with the energy fed into the cavity, resonance takes place.

Reference to Fig. 8-4 will aid in explaining how a resonant cavity may in certain cases be interpreted as a piece of waveguide in which energy travels back and forth along the length of the waveguide while undergoing reflection each time it reaches an end. In Figs. 8-4(A) and 8-4(B) a traveling wave in a rectangular waveguide is shown. In accord with the rules for determining Poynting's vector, it can be

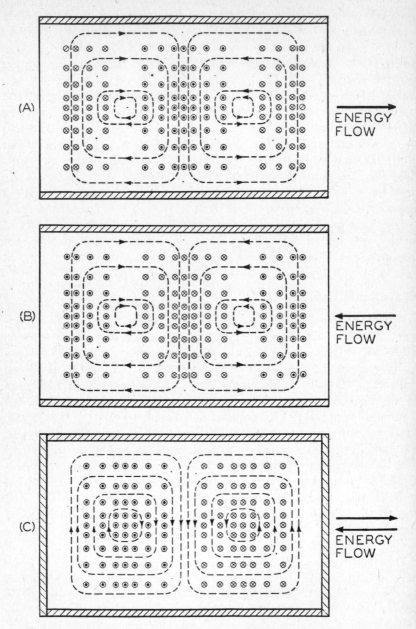

Fig. 8-4. Cross-section views, looking through the wider dimension, of three pieces of rectangular waveguide operating in the $TE_{0,1}$ mode.

seen that the first case Fig. 8-4(A) is one in which the wave is traveling to the right, while in the second case Fig. 8-4(B) the flow is to
the left. Now, if as in Fig. 8-4(C), the ends of such a piece of waveguide are closed off, the traveling waves are reflected and caused to
travel simultaneously in both directions. This reversal of flow might,
in principle, be accomplished by reversing the direction of either, but
not both, the **E** or **H** lines. In the case of the closed-off end, the
reflection must be due to the reversal of the **E** lines. This point has
been discussed before in Chapter 6. Briefly, the reason is that the **E**
lines must have zero magnitude tangent to the end plates, and this is
possible only if **E** undergoes a change of phase upon reflection.

If a section of waveguide any number of half wavelengths long
(the case of Fig. 8-4 is for two half waves of length) is sealed off at
both ends, the traveling waves moving in opposite directions give a
net field in the section, which is a standing wave like the one shown
in Fig. 8-4(C). It will be noted that the sketches of Fig. 8-4 are called
instantaneous views of the fields. As the two traveling waves combine,
the amplitude of the standing wave will change (i.e., the strength of all
the field lines shown will change) and will periodically reverse direction together. The correct picture of a resonant waveguide cavity
of the sort shown in Fig. 8-4(C) is therefore one in which the field
is always either as shown or else completely reversed, and which
varies in strength in a manner that is a sinusoidal function of time.

It is of some interest to picture the operation of this kind of cavity
in terms of electric currents because it then becomes immediately clear
that the ordinary ideas of inductance and capacitance are not applicable. The current paths are illustrated in Fig. 8-5, where it is shown
that the currents originate on the wide face of the waveguide and flow
around and across one or the other of the narrow sides so as to end
up on the other wide face. The current paths are shown as they exist
during one half-cycle. During the next half-cycle all the arrows will
be reversed since, as is true of any alternating current, the flow is first
in one direction and then in the other. The charge which enters into
the current flow comes from various points across the wide face of the
waveguide, but more arises per unit area at points near the center
of the wide face. The instantaneous charge distribution across the
wide face is sinusoidal with the greatest concentration at the center.
As the current flows along any one of the paths shown, it therefore
increases in strength to a maximum and constant value along the narrow dimension surface. The currents also have a sinusoidal variation

in strength along the length of the half-wave section of waveguide, being strongest at the center and of zero value at the ends.

Although the rectangular waveguide case has been discussed, so as to use the same waveguide mode as has been previously described in the most detail, the cylindrical shape is more often used in practice. The reason is entirely a practical one. The cylindrical shape is most often used because radial dimensions can be accurately held by careful machining on a lathe. The spherical cavity is the most difficult

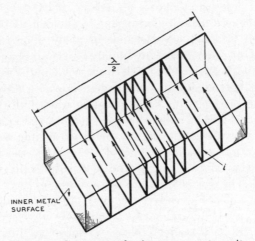

Fig. 8-5. Current paths in a resonant cavity consisting of a half wavelength section of a rectangular waveguide operating in the $TE_{0,1}$ mode. The drawing represents the inner surface of such a cavity and is drawn as being transparent so as to allow the current lines to be seen in their entirety.

of all to manufacture and, since it is not known to have any real superiority, it is seldom, if ever, used. More must be said of cylindrical types and of other modes of operation, but to do so it will help to restate the system of mode identification and describe how it is extended to cover all cavity modes.

Mode Nomenclature

A complete nomenclature specifying all TE and TM modes in waveguide resonant cavities requires three subscripts, such as TM_{ijk} or TE_{lmn}. In each case one subscript is assigned to each of the three pertinent dimensions and gives the number of half-wave (full-wave in one case) periods contained in that dimension. Zero values of a subscript indicate that the electric and magnetic fields are constant in that dimension.

The last subscript, that is k or n, is usually assigned to the lengthwise dimension of the waveguide, and the other two subscripts describe the wave just as they do in a waveguide transmission line. For example, in the rectangular cavity of Fig. 8-4(C), the waveguide mode is described as the TE_{01} mode. The cavity mode is described as the TE_{012} mode. The last subscript says that two half wavelengths are contained in the length; the first subscript says that both the fields are of uniform strength as measured instantaneously at any set of points equidistant from the narrow side wall but in a plane perpendicular to the length of the waveguide; the second subscript says that a variation along the wider dimension of the guide corresponding to one-half period, is found.

The resonant modes of a particular cavity which correspond to the lowest possible frequencies, are invariably of particular interest and are often labeled as simply an E_o or H_o mode, depending upon whether reference is being made to the lowest TM or TE mode. Fig. 8-6 shows

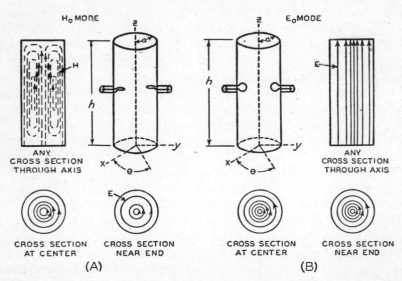

FIG. 8-6. Cylindrical resonant cavities operating in the H_o and E_o modes. The cross-section views show instantaneous standing wave orientations of the **E** and **H** vectors. Both cases have fields independent of the angle θ. In the E_o resonator, the field is also independent of **Z**.

these fundamental modes, as they are called, for a cylindrical cavity. These two modes are the lowest of an infinite number of frequencies at which such cavities can be made to resonate.

Sometimes even higher order modes are marked with the letters E or H along with their appropriate subscripts. E-labeled modes are those modes in which the electric field has a component parallel to the axis. They are identical to the so-called TM modes, meaning those modes in which only transverse components of the magnetic field occur.

In the same way, H modes, which have magnetic fields with components running lengthwise of the cylinder, are also referred to as TE (transverse electric) modes. As has been said before, both the E and H modes possible in a cylindrical cavity are infinite in number. Subscripts are usually used to indicate a particular mode. Thus, the E_o and H_o modes are the lowest frequency modes in which the cavity will resonate in the E or H modes respectively.

For example, as is indicated in Fig. 8-6(B) it will be noticed that the diameter of the cavity for E_o operation is equal to one-half wavelength. In traveling along the diameter of the cavity, the path goes from a zero electric field at the left edge through a maximum at the center and back to zero again at the right edge as in any travel over a half wavelength. The diameter might equally well be a whole wavelength or, for that matter, any integral number of half wavelengths. If it were two or more half wavelengths long, there would be a higher E mode of operation.

As a matter of fact, there may be higher E modes for other reasons too. They may exist because of a higher number of half wavelengths, which are required to fit into the length of the cavity or around the axis in an angular array in accord with the angle θ. Several examples of various modes in cylindrical cavities are shown in Fig. 8-7. Each is labeled with appropriate subscripts, including the letter x which is the last subscript in all cases. The first subscript will be seen to denote the number of full periods of variation around the circumference; the second subscript indicates the number of half-period variations along a diameter, and the third subscript shows the number of half wavelengths over which the waveguide extends. In Fig. 8-7 the length is not shown so this last subscript is of course undetermined.

The E_o and H_o modes of Fig. 8-6 are more completely described as TM_{010} and TE_{011} modes since both have fields that are constant with angle, one-half wavelength wide along a diameter, and in the E_o

case, constant along the axis but in the H_o case also one-half wavelength long in that dimension.

It is more difficult to sketch or describe in words the various modes of a cylindrical cavity than it is to understand once the general idea is grasped. Since designs are rarely, if ever, made for use in any but the very lowest modes, it is really only necessary to understand that higher frequency resonances are possible.

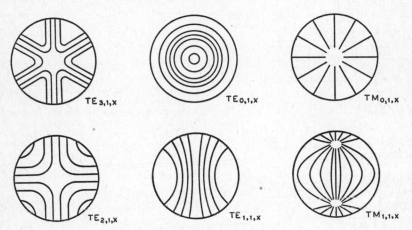

Fig. 8-7. Electric field configuration in several cylindrical waveguide modes.

One other point of information, however, should be included for the sake of completeness. It has to do with the harmonic arrangement of the various resonant frequencies. It might be thought, for example, that since higher modes are always created by halving or otherwise dividing the wavelength by integral numbers, it would follow that higher resonant frequencies would occur at multiples of the frequency which resonates the lowest mode. This is not true, because, unlike the coaxial line, the phase velocity of radiation in a hollow waveguide is dependent upon frequency. Thus when the wavelength is halved, the frequency is not doubled.[2] As a matter of fact, it turns out that the frequency progression for both E and H modes is given by expressions containing the roots of a Bessel Function.

Coupling

Three general methods of coupling to a resonant cavity, so as either to excite it from a source or couple it to a load, may be distinguished. They may be called *probe coupling, loop coupling,* and *slot coupling.* The first two have already been mentioned in conjunction with waveguide transmission lines and are illustrated in Fig. 8-8. The probe is always inserted so as to lie parallel to the electric field, while the loop is always arranged so that magnetic flux can pass through it. It is in principle possible to compute the impedance of

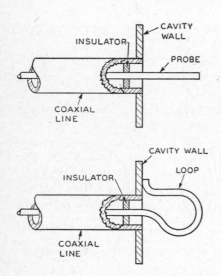

FIG. 8-8. Two methods of coupling to a resonant cavity so as to excite it from a source or couple it to a load. The probe in the upper sketch, is inserted so that it lies parallel to the electric field, while the loop, shown in the lower drawing, is always arranged so that the magnetic flux passes through it.

coupling loops and probes. The only assumptions necessary are that the loops are entirely in the cavity and of known geometry, or that the probe length is known as well as its position. Such calculations, however, are usually not made because of various practical considerations, and because empirical adjustment is frequently more satisfactory.

Slot coupling to a resonant cavity is achieved by cutting a slot in the side wall so that the current paths are interrupted. If the slot is thin enough, the action of the cavity will not be too greatly upset by its presence, and yet the interruption of the current lines will mean that a voltage appears across the width of the slot and hence causes the slot to radiate into space or into a waveguide transmission line which may be connected at that point. If such a waveguide is connected to the cavity and fed externally so as to produce a voltage across the slot, the same system may cause the cavity to be excited.

Resonant Frequency

In a wired resonant circuit, the resonant frequency is determined by the values of L and C which, in turn, specify the physical construction of those elements. In the case of resonant cavities, on the other hand, the resonant frequency may be directly interpreted as a requirement concerned with the cavity dimensions. In general, the dimensions of a resonant cavity must be chosen so as to be equivalent to an integral number of half wavelengths. To discuss the matter in more detail, specific examples may be considered.

Coaxial Cavities. In conjunction with Fig. 8-3, a physical picture of coaxial cavity operation has already been presented. Electrical charge was described as traveling up the coaxial line, and back again after reflection, in just the right amount of time so as to reinforce a flow of charge of the opposite polarity which is then urged to move up the line. From this it may be deduced that the resonant frequency f is dependent only upon the length of the coaxial line. Since in Fig. 8-3, the negative charge which was spoken of as traveling the length of the line and back, must do so while a half wavelength of energy moves past the coaxial line entrance, it is clear that the coaxial piece should be of a length over which charge can travel back and forth in a time equal to one-half cycle, or one way in a time equal to one-quarter cycle. Since the velocity with which energy travels in a coaxial line is that of light, this is equivalent to saying that the resonant frequency of a coaxial resonator is $c/4L$, where L is the length of the line. The electrical energy moves c cm per second and needs to go $4L$ cm for each cycle. The number of complete trips per second, the frequency, is thus

$$f = \frac{c}{4L}$$

H_o Mode in a Cylindrical Cavity. From what was said in reference to Fig. 8-6 it is clear that resonance is obtained when the length of the cavity (dimension h in Fig. 8-6(A)) is equal to an integral number of half wavelengths of the radiation inside the cavity. This wavelength in the guide is given by

$$\lambda_g = \frac{\lambda}{\sqrt{1 - (\lambda/\lambda_c)^2}}$$

where λ is the free space wavelength and λ_c is the longest wavelength that can be propagated in the waveguide. The free space wavelength may be calculated by $\lambda = c/f$, where c is the velocity of light. The cut-off wavelength, λ_c, for the H_o mode may be found by

$$\lambda_c = 1.64a$$

where a is the radius of the cylinder, chosen arbitrarily within the range where H_o propagation of the desired frequency is possible. With these calculations, λ_g can be found and, having done so, the only need is to dimension the length of the cylinder equal to $\lambda_g/2$ in order to obtain an H_o resonant cavity at frequency f.

E$_o$ Mode in a Cylindrical Cavity. The E_o mode of a cylindrical resonator is of particular interest because its resonant frequency is dependent upon only one dimension, the radius. As is indicated by the more elaborate nomenclature TM_{010}, it has constant field strength in two dimensions. The mode is said to be fully degenerate, because only one dimension influences the resonant frequency. The other two dimensions are not required to fit any particular number of half or whole periods of variation, and hence may have any dimensions. The E_o mode resonates because of a periodic variation in the radial field which is always identical throughout the length of the cylinder. The E_o mode has a slightly lower Q than the H_o mode and demands a higher frequency, but has some design advantages. In E_o mode, the resonant frequency f_n and the radius a of the cylinder are connected by the equation

$$f_n = \frac{c}{2.61a}$$

Q

The most general definition of Q is

$$Q = 2\pi \, \frac{energy \ stored}{energy \ loss \ per \ cycle}$$

This quantity imposes a limitation on the extent to which an oscillation will build up in a resonant cavity. A low Q may result from anything that drains energy away from the cavity in question. As soon as this drain is equal to the rate at which energy is fed into the cavity, the energy density in the tube has reached its maximum value. The Q of a cavity is, in practice, always less than infinity because the material of which it is made is not a perfect conductor.

Actually, however, this is not usually the most important limiting factor. Rather, irregularities which are departures from the proper dimensions and symmetry, plus losses that are necessary into the coupling loops or probes which extract energy from the cavity, are more important. Because the load on the cavity often has a large effect, it is common to speak of the loaded and unloaded Q for a resonant cavity, in the same way that is done for resonant circuits containing lumped inductance and capacitance.

The unloaded Q of a perfect cylindrical resonator operating in the E_o mode is given by

$$Q = \frac{ah}{\delta\,(a+h)}$$

where δ is the skin-depth penetration of the microwave frequency being used.

The calculation of Q for H_o resonant cylindrical cavities is straightforward, although it does involve a very complicated algebraic equation. It is sufficient to say that the calculated Q is invariably very high (many thousands) and is not generally realized in practice because of loading and inaccurate construction.

The unloaded Q of klystron-rhumbatron resonators is of the order of 10,000. When loaded under typical adjustment conditions, this is reduced to the order of 1000. The actual Q employed in various tubes depends, among other things, upon band-width considerations.

Extreme Q Values

An example of the very large values of Q which may be obtained with cavities under special conditions is afforded by the *echo-box* (see Chapter 9 on antennas). Here a fairly large hollow metal cube made of sheet copper (about 18 inches on a side for 10,000 mc) is fitted with a parabolic-reflector antenna which has a feed that is coupled to the electromagnetic fields which may exist within the box. Such an echo-box is normally used to test radar systems. A pulse of energy is fed into the box from the radar transmitter. The very high field strengths which accompany the transmitted radar pulse, are accepted by the echo-box antenna, and the energy is fed into the box where it takes the form of a three-dimensional standing-wave. Since the echo-box is placed relatively close to the radar set, ample energy is available to excite the electromagnetic fields inside the box. Once they are excited, however, they do not die out very rapidly; consequently, the echo-box continues to radiate a small amount of energy for some time after it is excited. The re-radiation serves well as a calibrated echo signal for the radar receiver. It is only necessary to locate an echo-box at a prescribed distance in front of a radar set in order to get an echo signal which persists long enough to be readily identified, and which gives a standard of operation that can be repeated from day to day.

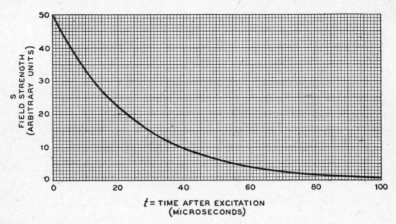

FIG. 8-9. The field strength in an echo-box plotted against time after excitation.

Fig. 8-9 shows a plot of field strength in an echo-box as a function of time under such circumstances. It is known that the curve has a form which may be expressed by

$$S = A\epsilon^{-kt}$$

If two points on the curve can be measured such as $S = 50$ when $t = 0$ and $S = 1$ when $t = 100$ microseconds, the equation may be given numerical constants and written as [3]

$$S = 50\epsilon^{-(0.039)t}$$

where t is in microseconds.

From this the time constant of the discharge of energy from the cavity may be determined. It is defined as the time in which the field strength drops down to $1/\epsilon$ of its original value. To find this from the equation just given, the value of t is found when S is equal to $50\epsilon^{-1}$. Representing this time constant as T microseconds it is apparent that $T = 1/0.039 = 25$ microseconds.

It is well known, although complicated to prove, that

$$Q = 2\pi fT.$$

Hence, if under the circumstances mentioned, the frequency is 10,000 mc, the Q of the echo-box is

$$Q = 2\pi 10,000 \times (0.039) = 2,450$$

which is much higher than is normally achieved in any other electrical arrangement.

Shunt Resistance

In order to describe the energy losses from a cavity, it is customary to speak of a quantity called *shunt resistance*. The shunt resistance of a resonator may be compared to the resistance represented by a parallel L and C circuit at resonance. Parallel resonant circuits have an infinite impedance if no dissipation of energy takes place. Thus a very high shunt resistance means that the cavity has very little loss and also a high Q. In a coaxial resonant cavity a ratio of outer to inner diameter of 9.2 gives the greatest shunt resistance. Changing the ratio must mean changing the size of the inner conductor since the overall size of the line is limited by the frequency that it is wished to transmit, as well as by convenience. A larger ratio than 9.2 makes the center conductor have too much resistance, while a smaller ratio means reducing the space between the conductors and hence having a stronger electric and magnetic field to transport the energy. This last implies that larger currents must flow and these of course give rise to greater resistance losses.

The distinction between Q and shunt resistance is clear when Q is defined as

$$Q = 2\pi \frac{energy\ stored}{energy\ loss\ per\ cycle}$$

Both Q and shunt resistance describe the losses in a resonator but Q is also concerned with something else. Generally speaking, the Q and the shunt resistance rise and fall together but, at least in principle, one can imagine a large Q and a small shunt resistance in a cavity which has considerable loss but also huge storage ability. One can also imagine small Q and large shunt resistance. That would be the case in a cavity that had little loss but also negligible storage ability.

Energy Storage

The Q of a cavity alone is not sufficient to describe the storage ability of a cavity. Q tells only of the ratio of energy stored to energy lost, and increasing the size of the cavity can increase its storage ability without increasing its Q. Thus a cavity of 1,000 Q will have a storage ability that is limited by its Q, but two identical cavities, each having a Q of 1000 and connected in parallel, will store twice as much energy even though the Q of the combination is the same as the Q of either one. The unloaded Q of two identical cavities connected in parallel will be the same as either one considered individually, because putting them together not only doubles the energy stored but also the loss. Each one has the same loss as before.

A multiple cavity arrangement can be simulated by using a waveguide cavity that is several wavelengths long. It may be thought of as consisting of several cavities each of which is one wavelength long and which are connected end to end. The fact that each but the first of such a series of cavities, is fed through some of the others is unimportant, and the whole group performs just as if each cavity were supplied with an individual feed and all such feeds were connected in parallel. A piece of waveguide exactly 10 wavelengths long and closed at both ends is a resonant cavity of high storage ability although not necessarily of high Q.

The Q of the device of Fig. 8-3 is limited by the energy drain of the crystal and galvanometer as well as by the intrinsic shunt resistance of the resonator. The greatest unloaded Q of a coaxial resonator is obtained when the ratio of the dimensions of the outer and inner conductors is 3.6. (The origin of this number has already been described in an early chapter on coaxial lines.) The ratio for optimum shunt resistance is not the same as for optimum Q. A compromise must be made, depending upon which is the more important in a particular application.

Volume Dependence of Q

It has just been pointed out that merely increasing the length of a waveguide cavity will not, in a first approximation, change the cavity Q. This is an example of a situation in which doubling or tripling the volume of the cavity does not by any means double or triple the Q. Opposed to this, however, is the general fact that the larger the cavity the greater will be the resulting Q, assuming, of course, that equivalent perfection of construction is obtained in both cases.

All of this may be stated for an average cavity (more or less inde-

pendent of the particular mode of operation that is chosen) by saying
that the unloaded Q of a perfect cavity is approximately proportional
to the ratio of volume to surface area. Such a dependence is certainly
to be expected, since the volume is the space in which the energy is
stored and the surface is the place in which it is lost.

Impedance

If the power losses in the coaxial line of Fig. 8-3 are negligible,
the phase of the input impedance is determined when the resonant
frequency is arranged. The standing-wave pattern in such a resonant
quarter-wave line is shown in Fig. 8-10. It is the case of a quarter-
wave line shorted at the remote end and voltage fed. By noting the

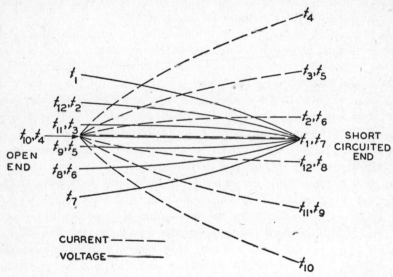

FIG. 8-10. The standing-wave pattern in a quarter-wave line short-circuited at the remote end and fed by a sinusoidal voltage at the open end.

sequence of the time indexes (t_1, t_2, etc.) on the voltage (solid) and
current (dashed) curves, it can be seen that the voltage in the quarter-
wave section leads the current by 90 degrees. Thus in the order shown,
the voltage curves are correct at successive points in time so that the
pattern starts at maximum positive values, falls through zero to a
negative maximum, and returns. The same thing happens to the current lines except that they are a quarter cycle behind and do not

reach a zero value until the voltage curves have already taken on maximum negative values. Remembering that by phase is meant the time relation between the variation of current and voltage, it is clear that this shows that current and voltage are 90 degrees out of phase, and specifically that in this quarter-wave section, the impedance is like that of a pure inductance. The only questionable point is the one located exactly at the open end. Here the impedance is infinite and the phase is indeterminate. If one was to pretend that the curves extended on beyond the open end, it would be found that the phase was exactly reversed in that region. The current curves would have crossed the axis and would, therefore, be changed by 180 degrees as compared to their phase on the right-hand side of the open end. This says that in a shorted line (or open-ended line for that matter) the phase is pure inductance and then pure capacitance in alternate quarter wavelengths. This assumes no losses at all.

In the actual case of Fig. 8-3, some loss (at least into the galvanometer) must be present. This causes the impedance at the open end of the coaxial line (i.e., where it joins the waveguide) to have a value that is less than infinite. The phase still makes a sudden change from the inductive side to the capacitative side, however, and if the losses are kept small, the situation described for a loss-less coaxial line remains a good approximation. The possible adjustments of the apparatus of Fig. 8-3 which can affect the amount of disturbance in the waveguide because of presence of the coaxial stub, are the length of the coaxial probe and the sizes of the inner and outer coaxial conductors. Presumably, it is desired to make the coaxial line seem to be as high an impedance for the waveguide as possible. The shorter the distance the coaxial probe enters the waveguide, the less its presence will disturb the pattern there. How short the probe can be made in practice depends upon the sensitivity of the crystal and galvanometer or, more generally, upon the Q of the resonator. The impedance which the coaxial stub presents to the waveguide also depends upon the dimensions of the coaxial line. An adjustment of the ratio of the diameters of the outer to inner conductor of the coaxial line to the value 9.2 gives the least loss (highest shunt resistance as previously explained) because of absorption into the walls or center conductor of the coaxial line. Such absorption takes place because of the finite amount of resistance which the material has. It would be zero only if perfect conductors could be used.

Slug Tuning

After a cavity is designed and built to operate at a given frequency, it is often of interest to know how the resonant frequency can be changed over a small range without appreciably affecting the Q. Specifically, it can be modified by inserting a metallic slug into the volume, and depending upon the point of insertion, the resonant frequency can be raised or lowered.

Fig. 8-11 shows cross-sectional views of an E_o cylindrical cavity and a "Rhumbatron" cavity with appropriate slug positions marked to show which positions will raise the frequency and which will lower it. The general rule is that inserting the slug in a position which

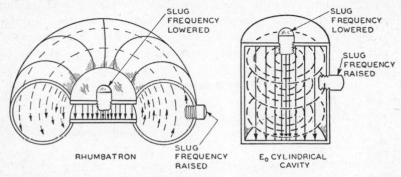

FIG. 8-11. The use of slugs to modify the resonant frequency of a cavity.

causes it to intercept more **H** lines than **E** lines will raise the frequency, while inserting it so that **E** lines are more efficiently interrupted will cause the resonant frequency to be lower. In the "Rhumbatron" cavity shown in Fig. 8-11, it is clear that the magnetic field is strongest in the doughnut portion of the volume and that a slug put in there will consequently raise the resonant frequency. The electric field is strongest in the web portion of the "Rhumbatron," so a slug in that part of the cavity will lower the resonant frequency. Similarly, in the E_o cylindrical cavity of Fig. 8-11, the magnetic field has some strength tangent to the side walls of the cylinder and will be affected the most by a slug there, while the electric field is most concentrated along the axis of the cylinder and consequently will be affected more by a slug extending along the axis.

A qualitative explanation of this situation is contained in a consideration of an analogous wired resonant circuit. Inserting a brass slug into a coil of wire and, therefore, into the magnetic field of the coil, will lower the inductance. Lines of magnetic induction are used up in generating eddy currents in the brass and are hence less effective in forming a counter emf. Lower inductance, of course, corresponds to raising the resonant frequency. Inserting a piece of metal between the plates of the condenser so as to interrupt the electric field, raises the capacitance value and, hence, lowers the resonant frequency.

Applications

In this chapter it has already been intimated that resonant cavities are useful in the measurement of frequency and that they are used as oscillator tank circuits. Not only have these uses been implied rather than definitely explained, but also many other uses have not even been mentioned. To describe them all in detail is a longer task than it is wished to undertake. Instead the following sections are designed to give an insight into a few cases in such a way that a general understanding will be reached. A list of cavity uses would at least include frequency and wavelength measurement, microwave-frequency filtering, cavity-frequency conversion, antenna termination, coaxial supports, amplifier tuned circuits, transmit-receive boxes, and frequency standards.

In Chapter 10 the use of microwave generators has been considered, so that no description of the complete oscillator operation will be given here. It will only be stated that cavities are used in conjunction with all three of the major kinds of generators. Klystrons and disk-seal tubes use the Rhumbatron type of cavity, while magnetrons generally use a modified form of cylindrical cavity with slot-coupling to the electron trajectories. Because the nature of a magnetron is such that no single electron beam is distinguished, this turns out to be the most logical procedure. In the case of the klystron and the disk-seal tube, however, all electrons follow essentially the same path and the resulting beam passes through the cavity. In Fig. 8-12 is shown a schematic representation of a klystron which indicates the way in which Rhumbatron type cavities may be made to surround the beam. The electrons pass through grids which are inserted in web-like center sections of the doughnut-shaped cavity.

With reference to Fig. 8-13, the method by which a Rhumbatron cavity operates with a klystron or disk-seal tube may be explained. In accord with principles to be discussed in Chapter 10, the electron

beam periodically adds energy to the electromagnetic fields of the
cavity by virtue of its motion along the path AA' of Fig. 8-13(A). The
arrangement of the fields may be seen in Fig. 8-13(B) which is a
cross-sectional view through BB' in Fig. 8-13(A). These fields give
rise to the Poynting vectors which are shown instantaneously as point-

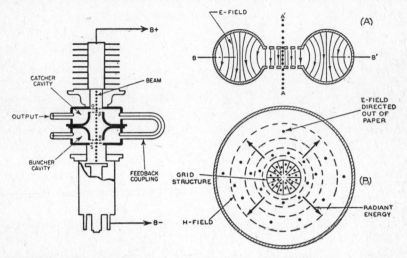

FIG. 8-12. The use of Rhumba-   FIG. 8-13. The Rhumbatron cavity.
tron cavities in a klystron.

ing outward in the figure. In accordance with periodic reversals of
the electric field these Poynting vectors reverse direction so as to
indicate an inward and outward flow of energy. The resonant frequency is determined by the transit time of radiant energy as it travels
from the beam to the periphery of the resonator and back again.

The reason that the rhumbatron type cavity is particularly valuable
in conjunction with tubes such as the klystron has to do with the
transit-time of the electrons through the cavity. The electrons must
pass through the electric field between the grids inserted in the webs
of the cavity in a time that is less than one-half cycle. A much shorter
transit time than this is desirable, in order to make possible a greater
variation of the beam current in the resonator. For example, it is clear
that in the extreme case in which the transit time is a whole cycle,
the coupling fails altogether because the average current in the cavity
remains constant. The reëntrant cavity makes it possible for the
beam to traverse a short distance through the cavity. How close to-

gether the grids can be brought is ordinarily limited only by voltage break-down and secondary emission troubles.

Cavity sections may be designed integrally into a waveguide transmission line so as to give selective transmission as a function of frequency. In schematic form, Fig. 8-14 shows three possible methods of such an arrangement. All should be classified as *narrow band-pass*

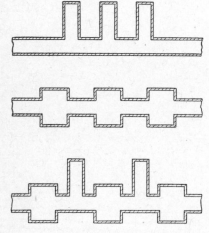

FIG. 8-14. The insertion of resonant cavities in a waveguide line so as to increase the frequency selectivity of the line.

filters. Waveguide transmission lines are in themselves broad bandpass filters, but by inserting cavity resonators in the line, the passband may be narrowed to such an extent that substantially only one chosen microwave frequency can be passed. The action may be best explained in terms of impedance. The cavities are coupled to the waveguide in such a fashion as to produce an impedance match at their resonant frequency and consequently a rather severe mismatch at any other frequency. This causes unwanted frequency components to be reflected back along the waveguide in the direction from which they came.

A superheterodyne receiver is usually used to receive microwave signals. An antenna and a microwave local oscillator, which are tuned to a frequency a few megacycles away from the carrier frequency, are connected in parallel with a rectifying crystal. The crystal is a non-linear impedance and, as is well known, conversion is obtained under such conditions. The voltage across the crystal has among others, a frequency component equal to the difference of the two microwave frequencies (usually 10 mc or so), and that component is modulated with whatever intelligence was initially present on the carrier. Since these rectifying crystals are normally of very small size, and since microwave frequencies are normally carried by a coaxial line or waveguide, the arrangement of the parallel microwave connection is not simply a matter of connecting wires to a terminal. Instead, the crystal is normally mounted in a metal enclosure into which both microwave signals are also fed. In a sense it may be argued that the metal enclosure is not a resonant cavity at all because

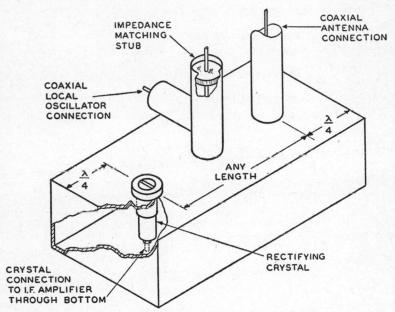

FIG. 8-15. How the connections are arranged in a frequency converter.

its object is not to store energy but to efficiently apply it to the crystal. One possible form of such an arrangement is shown in Fig. 8-15.

FOOTNOTES

1. In a resonant circuit containing $L, C,$ and R connected in series with an a-c source, which is tuned so as to produce oscillation at the resonant frequency f, the voltage across the elements are respectively given by:

$$V_R = Ri = voltage\ across\ the\ resistance$$
$$V_L = 2\pi f Li = voltage\ across\ the\ inductance$$
$$V_C = -(1/2\pi f C)\ i = voltage\ across\ the\ capacitance.$$

V_C and V_L are equal and opposite and all currents and voltages are given in terms of rms values. Now when peak current $(\sqrt{2}\,i)$ flows, all energy stored by the circuit is situated in the inductance since the condenser is at that instant completely uncharged. As explained in Chapter 4, the storage is then given by $1/2\ Li_p{}^2$ where i_p is the instantaneous current. Hence the total energy stored in the resonator may be written as

$$Energy\ stored = 1/2\ L\ (\sqrt{2}\ i)^2 = Li^2.$$

Similarly when the current is instantaneously zero, all the energy is stored in the condenser and is given by $1/2\ C\ V_p{}^2$, where $V_p\ (=\sqrt{2}\ V_c)$ is the peak voltage on the condenser. Hence the total energy stored by the resonant circuit may also be written as

$$Energy\ stored = 1/2\ C\ (\sqrt{2}\ V_c)^2 = C\ V_c{}^2.$$

For convenience these two expressions will be combined geometrically and written

$$Energy\ stored = \sqrt{L\ i^2\ C\ V_c{}^2} = i\ V_c\ \sqrt{LC}.$$

Replacing V_c by its equivalent makes this become

$$Energy\ stored = \frac{i^2}{2\pi f c}\ \sqrt{LC} = \frac{i^2}{2\pi f}\ \sqrt{\frac{L}{C}}$$

The power (energy per second) lost to the circuit is given by $i^2 R$ and the energy loss per radian of angular frequency is $\dfrac{i^2 R}{2\pi f}$. The ratio of energy stored to energy lost per cycle is therefore

$$Q = \frac{i^2}{2\pi f}\ \sqrt{\frac{L}{C}}\ \Big/\ \frac{i^2 R}{2\pi f} = \frac{\sqrt{L/C}}{R}$$

2. The relation between wave length, frequency, and velocity of a wave is $v = f\lambda$. If v changes with f then λ is not inversely proportional to f.

3. At $t = 0$, ϵ^{-kt} is unity since any number raised to the zero power has a value of one. Thus $S = A\epsilon^{-kt}$ must reduce to $50 = A$ at time $t = 0$. This determines A. At time $t = 100$ microseconds, and $S = 1$, we then have $1 = 50\epsilon^{-k(100)}$. A solution of this for k yields a value of 0.039.

Chapter 9

ANTENNAS

O NE OF THE MOST important novelties involved in the use of microwave radio lies in the construction of the radiation system. Because the wavelengths of the waves are only a few centimeters long (normally between 1/4 inch and 4 inches), it is easy to build radiating systems that are large in comparison with a wavelength. This is usually not possible at longer wavelengths. It is true that in rare cases extremely long antenna wires have been used with more conventional frequencies, and at wavelengths longer than those in the microwave portion of the spectrum, special configurations, such as loops and rhomboids, have successfully been utilized to create directional radio beams, but only at microwave frequencies is it practical to use specially constructed surfaces to focus the radio waves. Fig. 9-1 shows the comparable size of a simple parabolic reflector if it were used at three different frequencies. In all cases the designs are made so as to produce identical radio beams having a width of approximately two degrees.

FIG. 9-1. Relative sizes of parabolic dish-reflectors required to produce identical beams of approximately two degrees width at various frequencies.

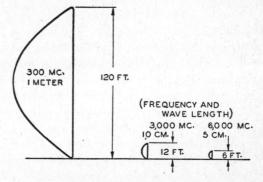

Most of the general types of microwave antennas are illustrated in Fig. 9-2. All of these structures are built so as to have dimensions as large as one or even many wavelengths. Except for the case of a single dipole or the stack of multiple dipoles, reflecting surfaces are involved which have dimensions equal to several wavelengths and the dipoles themselves are, of course, a half wavelength long.

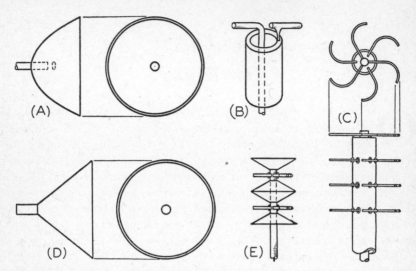

Fig. 9-2. Various types of microwave antennas. (A) parabolic dish with waveguide or coaxial feed to a dipole or other termination; (B) single dipole with coaxial connection; (C) a stacked array of single or multiple straight or deformed dipoles; (D) horn with waveguide feed; (E) stacked array of biconical horns with dipole excitation.

Parabolic Reflectors

The problem of constructing the most efficient reflecting surface behind a dipole radiator, so as to cause a large fraction of the energy to travel forward in a narrow beam, is similar to the one which is encountered in building a searchlight reflector or a reflecting telescope. Whenever light or radio waves of small length strike a reflecting surface (for example, when microwaves strike a good electrical conductor), they are reflected so that the angle of incidence is equal to the angle of reflection. As is shown in Fig. 9-3, if a line is drawn out from the surface so as to be perpendicular to the surface or to a tangent to the surface if curvature is involved, the angle of incidence is defined as the angle between that normal line and the incident radio wave. The angle of reflection is the angle between the normal and the reflected wave. Using this rule of equality between incident and reflected angles, paths may be drawn over which the radio energy will travel toward and away from the antenna.

Assuming a point source in a transmitting-antenna reflector or a point receiver for a receiving-antenna reflector, such drawings have

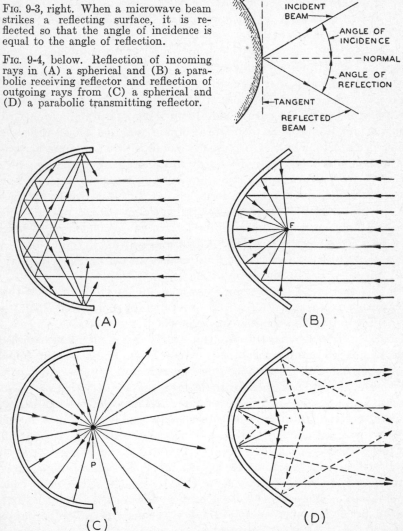

Fig. 9-3, right. When a microwave beam strikes a reflecting surface, it is reflected so that the angle of incidence is equal to the angle of reflection.

Fig. 9-4, below. Reflection of incoming rays in (A) a spherical and (B) a parabolic receiving reflector and reflection of outgoing rays from (C) a spherical and (D) a parabolic transmitting reflector.

been made in Fig. 9-4 for both spherical and parabolic surfaces. In Fig. 9-4(A), it is shown that if a spherical surface is used to intercept microwave radiation, the energy reaching various parts of the surface is not reflected to a single point at which a dipole or an open-ended waveguide might be situated to collect the energy and carry it back to the receiver proper. This is an extreme case; in practice it might be quite possible to use a more shallow spherical "dish" (reflector) and have the rays go to an approximate focus. Since in actual antennas the feed is always of some finite size, an exact focus is not imperative, and some deviation from an accurate paraboloid is possible and sometimes advantageous.

The lack of an exact focus (i.e., a point concentration of energy entering or leaving an antenna) will always be found with any shape of reflector except the paraboloid. In forming sharp and symmetrical microwave beams, it is therefore common practice to use dishes of that form. Although they are usually manufactured as quite accurate paraboloids, it is not really necessary to maintain very high precision. If they are of a form which approximates a paraboloid, they will have little enough aberration of the focus so that the feeds can be arranged effectively. Fig. 9-4(B) shows how all incident energy which strikes the parabolic surface is reflected back through a common point called the *focal point* of the parabola. A transmission line termination may be arranged at the focal point *F*, to collect all of the incident energy and to transport it to the receiver.

A spherical reflector is again shown in Fig. 9-4(C), but this time it is acting as a transmitter surface from a point source feed *P*, located at the center of the semi-circle from which the reflecting surface is generated. In this case, not only is a widely divergent beam obtained, but a special reinforcement or a cancellation effect is also found. Radiation from the point source to the reflecting surface must, after reflection, travel back through the source again. The reaction on the source will thus be such as to produce resonance if the radius is a quarter wavelength and an unloading effect if it is a half wavelength. This type of difficulty is at least partially overcome when a parabolic surface like the one in Fig. 9-4(D) is used. If the source is exactly at the focus, the exact reverse of the receiving case of Fig. 9-4(B) is obtained, and neither convergence or divergence of the radio beam is obtained because of the shape of the reflector. If, however, as is shown by broken lines in Fig. 9-4(D), the feed is located inside or outside the focal point, divergence or convergence are respectively obtained. Since a convergent beam of necessity has a cross-over point and then becomes divergent, either situation will in itself serve to lower the gain of the antenna.

The foregoing would seem to indicate that a properly formed antenna with an ideal feed arrangement should make it possible to transmit a microwave-radio beam which is exactly cylindrical in shape and has no spread at all except that which is occasioned by inaccuracies in the parabola and in the necessary divergence from an ideal feed system which supplies antenna excitation from a point exactly at the focus. Actually, it is impossible to get anything but a conical beam from a practical paraboloid which is fed at one point that is at or near the focus, both for the reasons already mentioned and for another which is far more important. Diffraction phenomena causes a spreading of the energy beyond the limits that would be predicted by geometrical optics. A similar phenomenon is observed with lights and reflectors, but because microwaves are very large in comparison to waves of visible light, it is somewhat more noticeable in the radio case.

It has been shown that parallel light passing through a circular hole (or being reflected from a circular mirror) produces a spot of light somewhat larger than the hole. For the same reason, light which is reflected from a perfect parabolic mirror will produce a small spot of light at the focal point rather than an ideal point of light as would be indicated by geometrical construction. This result is not due to any imperfection in the mirror but is a consequence of the nature of light itself. Although it is commonly said that light travels in straight lines, observation shows that it bends slightly at the edges of an obstruction. The spreading of a beam of light behind an obstacle, and more specifically the spreading of radio energy around the edges of a parabolic reflector, is called *diffraction*. Because of diffraction, microwave beams emitted from a paraboloid can never move out into space and keep a cross-section equal to that of the antenna from which they were sent, but instead must always diverge to some extent. Naturally, as the paraboloid is made larger and larger so that its edges are more wavelengths away from the feed, diffraction effects become less and less and the ideal case of Fig. 9-4(B), in which the radio beam does not spread, is approached. This fact is so important in determining the narrowness of the beam that for all practical purposes it is the only one which need be considered. If the placing of the feed and shaping of the dish are reasonably well done, then the narrowness of the radio beam will depend only on the size of the dish.

Fig. 9-5 shows a typical waveguide feed arrangement for a parabolic reflector. The waveguide enters the paraboloid from the back through an appropriate hole cut at the center. This waveguide is open-ended and a dipole is mounted in front of this open end. The dipole is energized by coupling to the electric and magnetic fields moving down the hollow-pipe waveguide. The dipole then radiates energy which travels to the main parabolic reflecting surface through the thin dielectric support shown or without that transition if the dipole is supported in some other fashion. A small reflecting plate is usually mounted near the dipole, as shown in Fig. 9-5, so that all of the energy must reflect

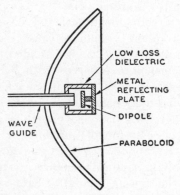

LOW LOSS
DIELECTRIC

METAL
REFLECTING
PLATE

DIPOLE

WAVE
GUIDE

PARABOLOID

FIG. 9-5. Cross-section view of a waveguide feed installed in a parabolic reflector.

from the parabolic mirror before becoming a part of the beam. This avoids any difficulty with interference which might otherwise arise from the fact that beam energy coming directly from the feed has a considerable path difference as compared to energy which travels from the dipole to the main reflecting system before moving on out into space. The small reflecting plate so shades the dipole that practically all energy from it must ultimately strike the parabolic surface.

In actual practice it is usually found desirable to locate the dipole of a feed like the one of Fig. 9-5 somewhat outside the focal point. It usually exceeds the focal distance by 10 to 20 percent. The convergence thus obtained will in part compensate for other divergence effects which are inherent in the structure.

If at a distance R, indicated in Fig. 9-6(A), from a parabolic transmitting antenna, readings of signal strength as a function of angle are made, while always staying the same distance R away from the antenna, a graph something like the one shown in Fig. 9-6(B) may be obtained. The general shape of the graph in Fig. 9-6(B) will remain the same (assuming transmission into free space) regardless of the value of R that is chosen. Also, the beam width, which is defined in accordance with the notation of Fig. 9-6(A) as $2\theta_1$, will be independent of R. As the field measuring equipment is carried in a circle around the antenna, maximum strength will be found directly in front of the reflector. This region is said to be the one which contains the *major* or *main lobe* of the antenna pattern. With increasing or decreasing angle from this position, the signal amplitude will decrease and ultimately become almost, if not exactly, zero. At still greater angles, small side or *minor* lobes will be encountered; these may often be neglected.

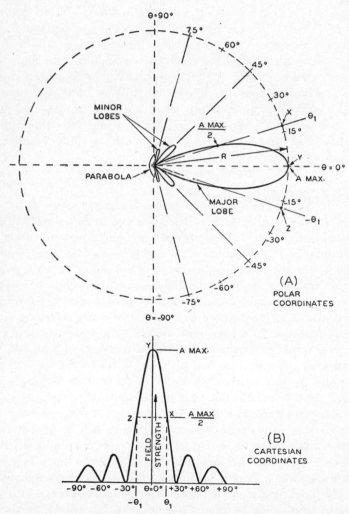

FIG. 9-6. An antenna pattern of a parabolic antenna plotted in polar coordinates (A) and in Cartesian coordinates in (B).

At some angle θ_1, points X and Z, in the main lobe, the signal amplitude will be just half that of the maximum value found immediately in front of the parabola. A point such as either X or Z in Fig. 9-6(B) is called a *half-power point* and marks one side of an angle which is commonly considered to measure the width of the beam.

The narrowness of a microwave radio beam which can be obtained with reasonably sized parabolas, depends mainly upon the opening or aperture of such a parabolic reflector. A handy rule to use is that the half-power width of a beam in degrees that is radiated from an aperture of D feet at a wavelength of λ centimeters is approximately $(2\lambda)/D$. Thus for a wavelength of 12 centimeters with an aperture of 12 feet, a beam with a half-power width of 2 degrees may be obtained. The rule contains a queer mixture of units, but purely by chance it comes out this simply when aperture is measured in feet and wavelength in centimeters. Experimenting with this rule will show that only true microwaves can be satisfactorily handled with parabolic reflectors.

Special Applications

A few special applications of the principle of using reflecting surfaces to obtain directional microwave antennas deserve mention. One of these involves the use of several dipole feeds in a single reflector. By such a combination it is possible to obtain antenna patterns which provide different coverages in azimuth (angle around the points of the compass) than are obtained in elevation (angle above horizon), and thus allows a transmission to be made to many receiving stations which are spread over a considerable area without appreciable loss of energy into directions where there are no receivers or where it is not desirable that the signal be detected.

In applications of microwave radio as in the use of longer wavelengths, it is by no means always desirable to have beams only a degree or so wide. In the case in which broad coverage over an azimuth sector of 30 degrees or so is desired, however, it may still be important that the edges of the beam be sharp, so that there is a definite differentiation between locations in which it is desired that the signal be received and others in which it is not wanted. This is best accomplished not by simply building a smaller parabola or by some other means which are equally applicable to longer wavelengths, but rather by the side-by-side overlapping of a number of very sharp beams. In this way it is possible to build up a wide coverage that still has beam edges which fall off as sharply as they do with a 2-degree beam. This is possible with microwaves even though only a single reflector is employed, by supplying that reflector with multiple feeds.

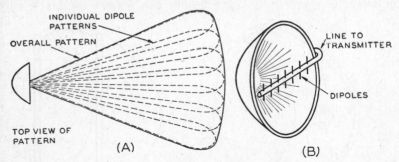

FIG. 9-7. By overlapping a number of narrow beams, a wide beam is obtained, as shown in (A); the multiple-feed antenna with a parabolic reflector to produce this type of beam is shown in (B).

The method of overlapping a number of narrow beams to give a wide beam with extremely sharp sides is illustrated in Fig. 9-7(A). An antenna feed system which uses this principle to create a beam of as much as 30 degrees coverage in azimuth but only 2 degrees or so in elevation, is shown in Fig. 9-7(B). This is an extremely advantageous arrangement inasmuch as the narrow elevation angle allows almost no power to be wasted in vertical transmission, while the sharp sides of the azimuth pattern indicates that a desired sector is covered with very little waste in other directions.

Another way of obtaining relatively broad coverage in one direction while sharply restricting beam coverage in another direction, consists in using only a partial section of a parabolic reflector. A full parabolic reflector that is designed to give the beam width wanted in the most narrow direction is in effect cut so as to reduce its width in the other direction down to a point corresponding to the desired wide beam coverage, as shown in Fig. 9-8(A). The dashed lines represent the full paraboloid, whereas the solid lines represent a cut section. Flat sides are then added, as is shown in Fig. 9-8(B). The resulting reflector, when properly fed, will be found to produce the proper radiation pattern in free space.

Although this type of antenna is not capable of as sharp pattern sides as the multiple-feed arrangement previously described, it is much simpler and smaller and is entirely adequate for some purposes.

For example, in a radio landing system for aircraft it is generally desirable to use sharp beams to mark the course in space over which the airplane is to fly, and yet it is also necessary to supply an off-course signal at angles some distance from the desired path so that a pilot may be successfully guided onto the correct approach path.

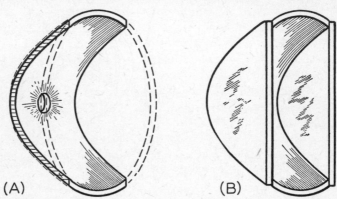

(A) (B)

FIG. 9-8. A section of a parabolic reflector cut so as to give wide azimuth coverage while restricting propagation into only a few degrees of elevation angle. The dashed lines in (A) represent the full paraboloid and the solid lines show the cut section, which is fitted with solid sides, as shown in (B).

Parabolas that are cut down in either width or height are ideally suited for giving such broad coverage in one direction, while still allowing reasonable gains to be obtained by virtue of restricted transmission in the other direction.

A class of dish-reflector type antennas generally known as *cosecant-squared* antennas are sometimes designed for a particular and quite

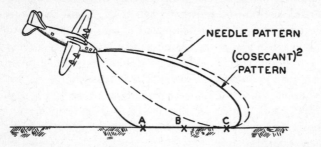

NEEDLE PATTERN

(COSECANT)² PATTERN

FIG. 9-9. The shape of the beam radiated from a cosecant-squared antenna reflector.

interesting application. One arrangement is shown in Fig. 9-9 where such a transmitting antenna is mounted on an aircraft. The problem is to give directional coverage which, without wasting power, will produce an adequately receivable signal from the airplane to ground stations located at points such as *A, B,* and *C.* In the case of radar, for which this antenna was originally developed, it is a matter of arranging suitable signal strengths at such points so as to produce satisfactory echo signals. It is immediately apparent that an ordinary sharp beam cannot do this very well; such a *needle-beam* pattern is indicated by broken lines in Fig. 9-9. It can be seen that although such a pattern may be so directed as to reach a point such as *C,* it will not then give adequate signals at nearer points along the ground. The type of pattern desired is more like the one marked (*cosecant*)². The name *csc²* is an allusion to a mathematical expression in polar coordinates which describes the sort of equal signal lines desired. The cosecant-squared technique can be equally well applied to a ground transmitter which is designed to contact aircraft which may be nearly over head or some distance away, but at reasonable altitudes.

Two general methods of constructing antennas which will produce cosecant-squared patterns have been tried with some success. One involves reshaping a parabolic dish so that the curvature of one side more nearly approaches the spherical while the curvature of the other side is almost reduced to flatness. If sufficient skill is used in supplying the feed and in arranging the mounting of such a dish, a rather satisfactory pattern may be obtained.

The other general scheme consists of using a parabolic reflector which produces the necessary bulge in the pattern by the use of additional feeds along one radius of the circle which forms the aperture of the dish. Recent work seems to indicate that this is the best way to produce the desired pattern, although it is more complicated.

Another type of directive antenna is the *corner-reflector,* which is constructed somewhat as shown in Fig. 9-10. Two frames of wood or other non-conductor are held apart and parallel with rigid dielectric braces. Wire or metal tubing is strung between the frames in the holes so as to form a group of parallel conductors in planes which form a 90-degree corner. For optimum performance a dipole feed is located 0.5 wavelength from the corner. The individual wires making up the reflecting planes should be at least as close as 0.1 wavelength.

A corner-antenna is easy to build for microwave use, and it then becomes quite feasible to use metal plates to form the surfaces. Generally speaking, however, the results obtained are inferior to those which are obtained with parabolas. One point of interest is that a corner-antenna produces a marked polarization. For horizontally polarized waves it is necessary to orient the corner-antenna so that the conductors comprising the planes are horizontal. To receive vertically polarized radiation, the antenna must be rotated 90 degrees. In principle this makes it possible, when used with radio links which are free from reflections or other causes of polarization change, to use

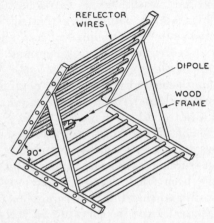

FIG. 9-10. A corner type antenna suitable for horizontally polarized ultrahigh-frequency radio waves.

pairs of identically oriented corners in order to discriminate among signals that are transmitted at the same frequency but from a corner-antenna that is oriented at right angles. This is the same sort of thing that is accomplished in the optical field by the use of Polaroid or a Nicol prism.

At true microwave frequencies, the corner-reflector has another use which is especially helpful in tests of radar systems. A corner-reflector, like the one shown in Fig. 9-11 is used without feeds of any sort as a simple and efficient source of echo signal. The addition of the third

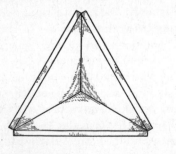

FIG. 9-11. A corner reflector, on the left, and an echo-box on the right, for producing strong reflection signals.

surface to the corner removes the possibility of polarization, and makes the target one which returns a signal to the radar set in a fashion that is reasonably independent of exact orientation. Also shown in Fig. 9-11 is what is often called an *echo-box*. It is simply a hollow metal cube with a small parabolic dish and feed fitted into one surface. The box acts as a resonant cavity and stores energy which strikes the antenna in bursts, and then retransmits it over a somewhat longer period of time although at reduced strength, as is discussed in Chapter 10 on resonant cavities. The echo-box is also useful in radar tests in which a pulse of energy is sent out and it is desired to receive echoes back at a later time so as to simulate distance measurement in terms of the time of flight of the radio energy.

Dipoles

An important unit in many microwave antenna feeds, as well as a useful radiating device in itself, is the half-wave dipole. Such an arrangement is shown connected to a coaxial line in Fig. 9-2(B) or as a parasitic source in conjunction with an open-ended wave-guide in Fig. 9-5. The parasitic source absorbs energy from the waveguide and reradiates it. Although workers in the field have christened them dipoles, or more accurately, half-wave dipoles, they are not dipoles in the sense in which the word is usually defined, but instead are center-fed half-wave antennas connected to balanced resonant lines. A dipole is, strictly speaking, a pair of oscillating or stationary charges or magnetic poles, which are separated by a distance that is very small in comparison to a wavelength and which have opposite polarity. Such an arrangement is described in most elementary books on electromagnetic theory and is capable of creating electromagnetic fields that have peculiar but well-known patterns. Here something somewhat different must be considered. Perhaps it is because of the relative smallness of everything connected with microwaves that what is commonly referred to as a dipole is a conductor which is nominally one-half wavelength long.

In Fig. 9-12 is shown a schematic representation of a half-wave dipole antenna, which is redrawn in Fig. 9-13(A) to give a three-dimensional view. The gap of the dipole is shown in Fig. 9-13(B) and the arrows indicate how Poynting's vector shows radial energy flow outward from this gap between the two halves of the dipole. The coupling to the transmitter is shown in both illustrations as an inductance and capacitance that are coupled to the oscillating tank circuit of the transmitter. In an actual microwave arrangement this would more likely be a resonant cavity. In other words, the tank circuit of the transmitter would consist of a resonant cavity, and coupling to it would either be made by a coaxial line fitted with a

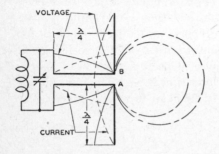

FIG. 9-12. Schematic diagram of a half-wave dipole antenna. The capacity-inductance representation would most likely be a resonant cavity in a microwave arrangement and the line connecting this circuit to the dipole would be either a coaxial line or a waveguide.

probe or loop, or else with a waveguide which opens directly into the cavity itself. Likewise, the transmission line, which is shown in Figs. 9-12 and 9-13(A) as a pair of parallel quarter-wave lines connecting the resonant circuit to the radiating conductors, would more likely

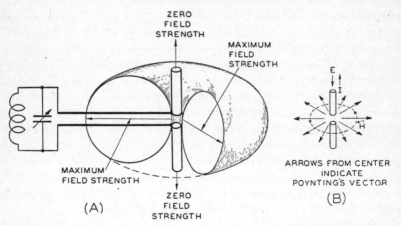

FIG. 9-13. A sectional radiation pattern of the dipole antenna shown schematically in Fig. 9-12, is shown in (A). The actual radiation from this dipole arises for the most part in the gap between the two parts of the antenna.

take the form of a coaxial line or a hollow-pipe waveguide. These factors do not affect the pattern or the operation of the radiators themselves, except that they provide a more efficient method of excitation. The sketch of Figs. 9-12 and 9-13 are used because it is easier to discuss current flow in wires than in waveguide.

As in any alternating-current connection, charge flows out of the source (here the tuned circuit) into the connecting wires. It moves in one direction until the polarity reverses, and then moves in the opposite direction until the next change. Changes occur in the time that the charge can move just a half-wavelength. Thus, charge leaving the source after one change of polarity has just had time to reach the end of one of the dipole radiators when it is time for it to start back. As has been explained before, a backward movement is equivalent to charge of the opposite sign coming up, or, in other words, that the current flow changes directions every half-cycle. Furthermore, since the polarity of the two source terminals is always opposite, charge is moving in toward the source on one of the radiator arms whenever it is moving out away from the source on the other. Thinking of two dipole arms alone, therefore, the effect is as if charge simply moved back and forth along the whole length. In the tuned transmission line the charge in each conductor is moving in opposite directions, so that any electromagnetic field set up by one current is just canceled by that in the other. Thus radiation is obtained only from the dipole itself and not from the associated feed circuit. The actual radiation arises chiefly in the gap between the two halves of the dipole, as shown in Fig. 9-13(B).

The current flow at the extreme ends of the dipole must be zero, since there is no further conductor for the charge to enter. At points A and B in Fig. 9-12 the current flow is a maximum and at the source another minimum is found. The dashed curves represent this condition and give some clue to the free-space radiation pattern which is to be expected and which is shown by the circular curves. Actually, in free space the radiation pattern is a surface instead of a curve, since it is symmetrical in all directions along the radiators. If the dashed circles shown in Fig. 9-12 are imagined to be rotated out of the paper so that they revolve around a point midway between A and B, they will generate surfaces one of which is shown in Fig. 9-13(A) and which are true antenna patterns inasmuch as every point on those surfaces will be a place at which an equal signal strength is encountered.

As has been pointed out, each half of a half-wave dipole is nominally a quarter wavelength long. Actually that length is only a nominal dimension, for in actual practice it is necessary to consider certain correction factors in order to arrive at the proper length, which usually turns out to be 10 to 20 percent shorter. The larger the diameter of the cylindrical stock from which the dipole is fabricated, the shorter it must be made. The electrical waves act as if the ends connected to the feed were not quite at the physical junction but rather some distance down the feed circuit. Interaction between the dipole and the surface of a reflecting dish when a dipole feed is used, produces a need for the same sort of correction. Normally, empirical rules are used for this part of the design. The antenna is set up in its final form but with the dipoles slightly too long, and the lengths are then trimmed until standing-wave-ratio measurements show that the antenna is accepting an optimum amount of power.

Deformed dipoles like those of Fig. 9-2(C) are sometimes used at more ordinary radio frequencies in order to construct a half-wave antenna which gives a more satisfactory impedance match to the transmission line which brings energy from the transmitter or delivers it to the receiver. The general idea of constructing dipole antennas so that the radiators do not consist of straight conductors has been carried much further in the case of microwave applications, although the motivation is somewhat different. In the microwave case, it is more a matter of building an antenna which does not have pattern nulls at the ends of the dipoles, as was the case of Figs. 9-12 and 9-13(A). Particularly in the case of aircraft antennas, it is important to obtain radiation patterns that extend in all horizontal directions,

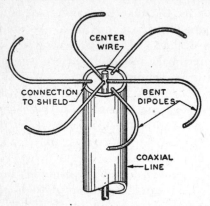

FIG. 9-14. A multiple deformed dipole of this type will provide an all-around radiation pattern, approximating a spherical surface.

and yet have an antenna that is small and light enough to mount on the exterior of an airplane. Such an antenna must, of course, be designed to have an absolute minimum of wind resistance.

To produce such an antenna it has been found possible to bend the dipoles and even to use them in multiple arrays, as is shown in Fig. 9-14. There a coaxial line has three dipoles terminating it and because there is this number and because each dipole is bent to spiral partially around the coaxial line, the resulting antenna pattern is one which approximates a spherical surface. As was shown in Fig. 9-13(A), the pattern from a single straight dipole has a maximum in a direction perpendicular to the length of the conductor. Adding more conductors, and bending them so that perpendicular lines drawn to them do not have a unique direction, causes the maximum to occur in nearly every direction. The important thing is that such an antenna can be designed so that it is efficient in applying a radiation load to a transmitter. Its usefulness is great because microwaves are so short; since all dimensions are small, the complete assembly of three half-wave antennas is only about the size of a silver dollar.

Antenna Arrays

It is frequently desirable to arrange a multiple dipole antenna so that even though it radiates energy equally in all horizontal directions, it nevertheless does not waste power in unnecessary vertical coverage. This is usually called *antenna gain*. It must be understood that there is never any actual power gain in an antenna: the principle of conservation of energy confirms that in antennas as well as anywhere else, no more energy can be radiated by the antenna than is received from the feed. So-called antenna gain comes about only because energy is selectively transmitted in a certain direction, since the antenna causes the electromagnetic field in one direction to be strengthened only by weakening the radiation in another direction. If the pattern of a given antenna is a perfect sphere, the antenna gain is said to be unity in all directions. If another antenna were constructed so that its pattern was a perfect hemisphere and was consequently so arranged that no energy was radiated in a backward direction, that antenna would be said to have a gain of 2 in all forward directions and a gain of zero in all backward directions. Generally speaking, the gain of an antenna should also specify the direction in which the measurement is made. Antenna gain is the ratio of the radiated field strength to the strength which would be observed if the same power were fed to an *isotropic radiator* in place of the given antenna. By the term isotropic radiator is meant an antenna which radiates equally in all directions.

Now again speaking in general, the usual problem for communication antennas is to choose a design which sends most or even all of the energy out so that it is equally spread toward the horizon and into a small angle above or below the horizon. It is not usually desired to waste much energy upward. An exception to this occurs in the case of aircraft communication where it is, of course, equally as important that contact be maintained with overhead airplanes as well as with those some distance away. Even there, however, the vertical distances involved are much less than the horizontal, so that some horizontal gain is still obtainable.

One effective method of getting antenna gain is realized by the use of arrays of radiating devices which would individually produce nearly unity gain. Direct interaction between the units may usually be neglected and the resulting pattern can be approximated by counting wavelengths and finding those parts of space in which energy from the separate radiators cancel or add. At a point where the path difference from two of the individual radiators is such that the fields are oppositely directed, no field from those two is found and the antenna gain is zero as far as that pair of elements is concerned. At points where the fields reinforce each other, additional power may be found and gain is realized.

At UHF, antenna arrays are utilized not only to produce radiation that is equal in all horizontal directions, but also to produce as sharp beams as are feasible at those wavelengths. With microwaves, para-

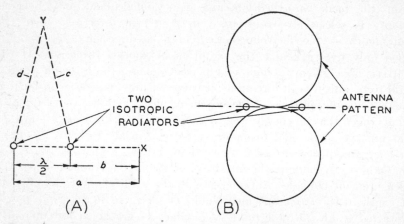

Fig. 9-15. Two isotropic radiators spaced a half wavelength apart and excited in the same phase. No energy is delivered in the X direction, but a maximum is radiated in the Y direction.

bolic reflectors are generally more effective, but simple arrays still have their place when light weight and compactness are important.

In Figs. 9-15 and 9-16 an approximation of the antenna patterns which may be obtained by combining dipole assemblies into arrays, are shown. The case of Fig. 9-15 is one in which two isotropic sources, such as the one shown in Fig. 9-14 are spaced one-half wavelength apart and excited together in the same phase. At points out in direction X, the half-wave difference in the path lengths, shown as a and b, in Fig. 9-15(A), mean that the waves from the two sources will be just out of phase and will deliver no energy. This will be true of any point in the direction X. In the direction Y, on the other hand, the path lengths, marked c and d in Fig. 9-15(A), are the same and reinforcement is found. At intermediate directions partial cancellation occurs, and it is necessary to come closer to the radiator in order to find the same field intensity as at Y, but a complete null is not encountered.

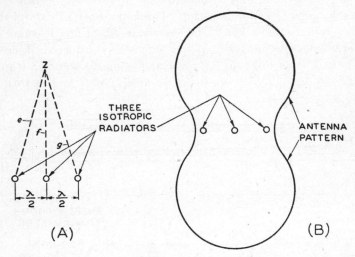

(A)   (B)

Fig. 9-16. Three isotropic radiators spaced at half-wave intervals and excited in phase.

Three isotropic radiators are shown in Fig. 9-16. Again they are excited in phase and spaced at half-wave intervals. This time, however, no exact null is found even in a direction along a line passing through the sources. Effectively, two of the three sources still cancel out in this direction but the third continues to supply energy so the gain there is only reduced to one third of what it is in the direction marked Z. It is assumed, and in practice it is true, that at a point such as Z, the distance to the antenna is great enough so that the slant differences between the lengths of the lines marked e, or g and the length of f is not important.

It is interesting to note that the horizontal gain of a vertical array of three isotropic radiators is greater than that of a pair, in spite of the fact that some vertical coverage is obtained with the triple set. The reason is that less energy is used in transmission into intermediate angles, so that more is available horizontally, even though some is needed for vertical transmission.

The triple-source arrangement shown in Fig. 9-16(B) is almost ideal for many aircraft installations, and is the one which was visualized in the drawing of Fig. 9-2(C). The weak overhead coverage allows an airplane to contact a station directly below, and yet the fact that rather high gain is available out toward the horizon, allows maximum range of communication. The importance of careful design in such a situation can hardly be over-emphasized and becomes quite apparent when the matter of power supply is considered. Increasing antenna gain from unity to ten for example, means that the transmitter needs to put out only one-tenth as much power and in turn, that

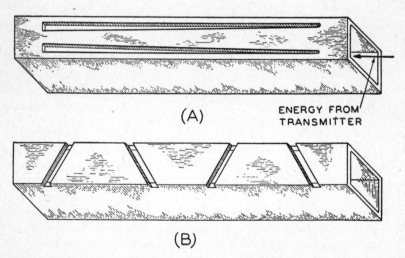

(A)

ENERGY FROM TRANSMITTER

(B)

FIG. 9-17. Two types of hollow-pipe waveguide antenna, the radiation being emitted from the slots in the waveguide.

means that it needs only a tenth as much power from the airplane's batteries. This often amounts to a very sizeable reduction in the weight of the aircraft equipment.

In certain specialized antenna arrangements, it has been found feasible to use slots in a hollow-pipe waveguide to take the place of actual physical dipoles. The antenna feed and the antenna itself in that case are really all one and the same thing. A piece of hollow-pipe waveguide carries the energy from the transmitter and, at the point where radiation is desired, holes or slots are cut and are so shaped and spaced that radiation from them is of the desired form. So far, this is a relatively difficult kind of antenna to design, but ultimately we may learn how to do it very efficiently. Two examples of ways in which such cuts are made to accomplish this purpose, are shown in Fig. 9-17.

Horns

Single-horn type antennas are best considered as transition pieces of hollow-pipe waveguide. Their use in every way is analogous to their acoustical operation in horn-type loudspeakers. If the antenna feed is a piece of cylindrical waveguide, for example, the horn may be looked upon as a flaring out of that waveguide until the aperture becomes large enough so that the transition into free space is gradual throughout. As is pointed out elsewhere in the discussion of waveguide bends and transition pieces, no energy will be reflected back in a transmission line if the changes in the line are sufficiently gradual.

Another way of speaking of the operation of a horn radiator is to say that it is a device for matching the impedance of the feed to that of free space, and since impedance match is a criterion for optimum energy transfer, this is again saying the same thing. Assuming there are only negligible dissipative losses, a failure to radiate efficiently energy which flows down the feed to the antenna, must mean that some energy is being reflected back along the feed toward the transmitter. Experimentally, this means that a standing-wave-ratio measurement in an antenna feed line is always sufficient to determine how well the impedance match has been arranged, and consequently how efficiently radiation is being produced. This is true of all transmitting antennas, whether they are of the horn type or not. It does not, of course, yield any information concerning antenna gain or whether a satisfactory pattern is being obtained.

In the acoustical field, many careful computations have been made with a view of ascertaining how a horn should best be flared. There is some reason to believe that an exponential shape is the best, or at least, very near the optimum shape. In actual experimental work, no significant difference in the patterns can normally be found no matter what exact law governs the rate at which the aperture of the horn increases with distance from the throat out toward the open end. The only factor that is important is that the area of cross-section change gradually enough so that wave reflections do not become severe. Five or six feet of length is not unreasonable for a horn designed to accept or radiate 10-centimeter radio energy, even when only a moderate directional effect is desired.

The directional effect of the antenna pattern which is realized with a single horn is not much different from that which is obtained from a parabolic reflector arrangement in which the reflector has the same dimensions as the open end of the horn. This means that to design an antenna so as to produce a beam of given width, the volume of the horn required is very much greater than that of an equivalent parabola. The increased bulk is such a great mechanical disadvantage that single horns are almost never used in modern microwave equipment. Virtually the only advantage of horn construction is the simplicity of the design requirements on the feed construction. When knowledge of how to build feeds for parabolic reflectors became known this ceased to be an advantage, because almost anything is easy to do if you know how to get it done.

A more practical use of horns is found in a biconical construction, used to produce an antenna with relatively high gain in all azimuthal directions. A pair of conical surfaces are mounted with their axes on a common vertical line and their apexes almost touching. A multiple dipole feed is installed at the point where the apexes touch. Such an arrangement produces an aperture which is the same in any azimuth direction, and yet prevents the propagation of appreciable amounts of energy into the vertical direction. The horns do not act like horns in the normal sense, inasmuch as the energy is not usually contained inside the horns, but rather finds the combined outside surfaces of the two cones to act like reflectors. It is even possible to shape the lengthwise dimensions of the cones so that they are parabolic and get some advantage in that way. It is also quite feasible to construct end-to-end arrays of such biconical horns so as to provide even greater horizontal gain than is convenient to obtain from a single unit. Such an arrangement was illustrated in Fig. 9-2(E). Stacks of as many as seven or eight such units are not at all impractical to build for microwave ground installations. Such an array would need to be only ten or twelve feet high and the largest diameter of the horns could be as little as 10 or 15 inches.

Special Antennas

In addition to the general purpose types of microwave antennas, which have already been discussed, a few other variations are of value for special purposes. For example, radar sets require not only that the microwave energy be radiated in a sharp beam so that when a reflection signal is received the target location will be well defined, but also such radar antennas generally must be arranged to scan the horizon and sky so as to facilitate a search for unknown targets. This problem of obtaining scanning is usually performed by arranging overall mechanical motion of a parabolic reflector. If frequencies corresponding to only about 2- or 3- centimeter wavelengths are used, this is quite feasible to do since the parabolic reflector will then only need to be 15 or 20 inches in diameter. Alternatively, the feed may be moved slightly in the paraboloid which is itself kept fixed. With careful design, only slightly inferior scanning over a limited sector can be obtained in that way.

For use on very high speed aircraft it may not always be possible to make an exterior mounting of antennas even as small as those mentioned. Two general procedures give promise of solving that problem. One involves mounting the antenna inside the airplane, as, for example, in the tail surface, and then providing a low-loss material as a covering of the aircraft at that point. The other solution consists in using slot-type antennas, which have been previously discussed and allowing those members to act simultaneously as antennas and support struts for the airplane wings.

Propagation

It is very important in working with radio waves to realize that the free-space antenna pattern is by no means the whole story. In any system where it is desired to transmit radio energy from one point on the earth's surface to another point which is on or near the surface of the earth, some energy from the transmitting antenna will surely hit the ground and be reflected. Even if the radio beam is only a degree or less wide and the desired receiver is so placed that the transmitted beam can be directed toward a point well above the horizon, still, because the definition of beam-width is not one which states that all of the energy is contained within its limits, a sensible amount of energy will still strike the ground. This energy, after reflection, will generally have a different phase than that which proceeded directly from the transmitting antenna. At some points partial interference will be observed, while at other points signal levels will occur which are greater than those to be expected from free-space patterns.

In the actual operation of a microwave antenna, the height at which it is mounted above the ground and the angle at which it is feasible to tilt it away from the ground, are important. The actual antenna pattern will depend upon these facts as well as upon the antenna design itself. This is also true of longer wavelengths, in fact the situation is worse at longer wavelengths, because wider beams result in more earth reflection. Only at microwave frequencies can radio beams so accurately mark out a line in space that even minor considerations become important, and earth reflection is certainly not a minor factor.

Chapter 10

MICROWAVE OSCILLATORS

Velocity Modulation Tubes

WHEN A SIGNAL is applied to the grid of an ordinary triode and it appears at the plate with the same or increased power or voltage, it is quite feasible to consider the beam of electrons which travels between the grid and plate as being an actual part of the transmission circuit. Considering a vacuum tube in this light makes it possible, at least in principle, to follow a signal completely through an electronic device without interruption. From this point of view it becomes unnecessary to talk of a vacuum tube as a slightly mysterious device, whose type must be carefully selected and which needs to be supplied with several rather accurately specified d-c voltages before a signal may be inserted and which appears at another electrode in a form which is modified in a desired way.

When the electron beam is thought of as being a part of the path over which a signal travels just as is a wire, an inductance, or a region of space through which radio waves travel, it becomes possible to examine qualitatively that type of tube which will best perform a given task. Also, it becomes easier to understand why certain d-c voltages are needed to cause the electron beam to transport the signal effectively. It will further be appreciated that stray signals on the beam-shaping electrodes can cause trouble by impressing themselves on the electron-beam leg of the transmission system.

A velocity-modulation vacuum tube is one in which a signal is transferred to the electron beam from the control grid connection in a way that is different from the method employed by ordinary triodes. Velocity modulation means that a control voltage speeds up or slows down the electrons of the beam rather than simply limiting or increasing their number.

As is illustrated by Fig. 10-1 an ordinary vacuum tube functions because of the ability of the control grid to modulate the strength of the electron beam which originates at the cathode. If, for example, the tube is being used to amplify a 1000-cycle note, the signal voltage on the grid will reduce 1000 times each second the number of electrons between the grid and plate; it will also increase the number present an equal number of times. These increases and decreases, as shown by the various cases of Fig. 10-1, are indicated as having become effective throughout the grid-to-plate space.

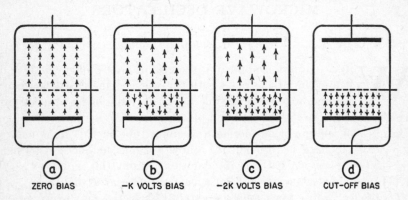

FIG. 10-1. Amplitude modulation of an electron beam as used in ordinary vacuum tubes. At various grid voltages, more or fewer electrons arrive at the plate, thus creating a plate voltage that depends on the grid voltage.

Actually, of course, this is not instantaneously true. A perfectly finite transit time exists for the electrons of the beam, and this time must pass before a changed voltage on a grid is correctly felt by the plate. Ordinarily the signal frequency is so low that the electron transit time between cathode and plate is a small fraction of a cycle. Certainly this is true of all conventional tubes used in devices such as home radios. If such amplitude-modulated tubes are used at very high frequencies, however, the transit time may not be small compared to the period of the modulation frequency. In that case undesirable effects are noted. The circuits used with the tube are subject to what is known as *beam loading*, and the efficiency of the whole circuit is impaired. The term beam loading as here used has reference to the loading of the resonant circuit or cavity by the beam.

In contrast, tubes using velocity modulation need have small transit times over only a very small distance, namely that which exists between a pair of closely spaced grids. Moreover, the average number of electrons remains the same throughout the length of the beam and the electrons need only be speeded up or slowed down to represent a signal. Both of these facts make velocity modulation very advantageous for tubes that are being designed to operate at ultra-high or microwave frequencies. In fact, it is only at such very high frequencies that velocity modulation is useful, and then its use seems imperative.

Fig. 10-2 illustrates how an electron beam may be velocity modulated. Instead of connecting the input signal between the control grid and the cathode, as is usual with amplitude-modulation tubes, a pair of grids called *buncher grids* are used where the control grid might

FIG. 10-2. The use of the double buncher grids to introduce velocity modulation on the electron beam and the use of double catcher grids to remove the amplified signal.

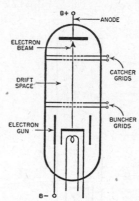

normally be installed, and the input voltage is connected between this closely-spaced pair. Moreover, the usual cathode is replaced by a complete electron gun something like the assembly which produces an electron beam in a cathode-ray tube. This assembly, which consists of a heater, a cathode, and a focusing electrode, functions so that the electron beam is already well formed, and on the average the electrons that it contains, are all moving with approximately the same velocity. When they reach the first buncher grid they enter the bunching space without hesitation because the buncher voltages are completely disconnected from the cathode. In the buncher space, however, they are speeded up or slowed down in accordance with the voltage condition there. If the second buncher grid happens to be positive with respect to the first buncher grid, the electrons are urged to increase their velocity; whereas, if the polarity of the buncher grids is such that the second grid is negative with respect to the first, the electron beam will be reduced in velocity.

Now if an alternating voltage is placed on the buncher grids, as it normally will be if the velocity-modulation tube is used as an oscillator, the electrons of the beam will alternately be speeded up and slowed down as they pass through this part of the tube. Furthermore, if this buncher signal is of extremely high frequency, it may well be possible to arrange the geometry of the tube so that even though the transit time between the buncher grids is small in comparison to a cycle, the transit time along the drift space, which lies just beyond the buncher, is not. Under such conditions the electrons, which were speeded up at the buncher, will have time, as they pass along the drift space, to catch up with the slower electrons which were at the buncher at an earlier time, and which were in consequence slowed down. This gives rise to bunches, or pulses, of electrons as is illustrated in Fig. 10-3.

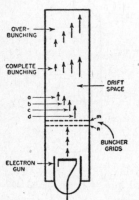

FIG. 10-3. The arrows of this vector representation of the electrons in a beam, not only show the relative positions of the various electrons which have undergone periodic bunching, but also indicate by their length, the relative velocity of each electron.

There the electrons are shown as arrows which depict their velocity as well as position. The three electrons shown between the electron gun and the buncher are indicated by arrows which are of equal length, since all three have the same velocity. On the other hand, electrons, such as the one labeled a, are shown with a very short vector because they are moving with a relatively slow speed. Their velocity is low because they happened to pass through the buncher grids at times when grid n was positive with respect to grid m, and consequently they had to move against an electric field that urged them to go the other way. Electrons, such as those labeled b, c, and d, are respectively shown with longer and longer velocity vectors because they received less hindrance, or even help, from the buncher field at the time they passed through. In the case of electron d, grid m was at a maximum positive voltage with respect to n, and a maximum added acceleration was received in passing through the buncher space.

With all this in mind, it is easy to see that velocity modulation of an electron beam will result, after the transit of a drift space of proper length, in an amplitude-modulated beam. Directly beyond the buncher, the faster electrons will not yet have had time to overtake the slower ones and the beam will still be more or less homogenous, as is indicated in Fig. 10-3. At a point further along the drift space, an area of *complete bunching* may be encountered where electrons are found only in pulses or bunches. It is interesting to note that if the drift space is too long, the fast electrons may not only overtake but also pass the slower ones. This is known as *overbunching*.

Since a drift space of a proper length to obtain complete bunching can, in conjunction with a pair of buncher grids, turn velocity modulation into amplitude modulation, it is clear that in principle, an ordinary plate might be installed at the end of the drift tube and used to collect the signal from the electron beam. The voltage of the plate would rise and fall as it was struck by bunches of electrons, and as these electrons leaked away between times by virtue of a plate resistor. Unfortunately, this sort of energy collection is seldom if ever feasible. Velocity modulation tubes are only practical at such high frequencies that it is conveniently possible to make drift tubes long enough so as to have a transit time of the order of one cycle. At such high frequencies, however, it is not only impossible to use ordinary vacuum tubes because of beam loading, but it is also impossible to use ordinary "wired" circuits, because of stray capacity which cannot be avoided and which by itself gives time constants that are too long to allow response to such high frequencies.

Fortunately, it is not at all necessary to use a plate to collect energy from the beam. As shown in Fig. 10-2, a pair of grids that are similar to the buncher grids, and which are usually referred to as *catcher grids*, can be installed at the point of maximum bunching, and will serve effectively as a means of obtaining an output signal from the tube. Whenever a bunch of electrons passes between these catcher grids, a voltage will appear across them; between bunches this voltage will drop to zero. The net effect is that an alternating voltage is obtained at the catcher grids in response to the one applied to the buncher grids.

Only one really successful method of applying or taking off the necessary ultra-high frequency alternating voltages that are needed in conjunction with bunchers and catchers has been devised. It consists of surrounding the grid pairs with a resonant cavity. Such a cavity is not limited by the stray capacity of ordinary tank circuits, and can be made to supply or receive a voltage at just about any frequency that is desired. Such a velocity-modulation tube is generally known as a *klystron*, a cut-away view of which is shown in Fig. 10-4. The particular type shown is designed for operation in the 10-cm wavelength region and is tunable by means of flexible diaphragms which allow adjustment of grid spacing without disturbing the vacuum seal. A tuner consisting of a mechanical arrangement fitting the rings labeled *tuning rings* may be obtained. With a klystron tuner properly adjusted, frequency change may be effected simply by rotating

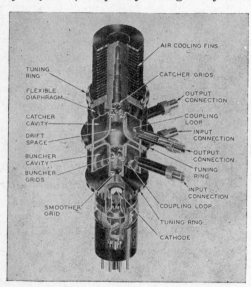

AIR COOLING FINS

TUNING RING

CATCHER GRIDS

FLEXIBLE DIAPHRAGM

OUTPUT CONNECTION

CATCHER CAVITY

COUPLING LOOP

DRIFT SPACE

INPUT CONNECTION

BUNCHER CAVITY

OUTPUT CONNECTION

BUNCHER GRIDS

TUNING RING

INPUT CONNECTION

SMOOTHER GRID

COUPLING LOOP

TUNING RING

CATHODE

Fig. 10-4. A cut-away view of a klystron, a velocity-modulated tube. *Courtesy of Sperry Gyroscope Co.*

a single knob. Electrons leave the cathode and are accelerated toward the body of the klystron and in particular toward the so-called *smoother grid*, as shown in Fig. 10-4. This grid, as well as the whole body of the tube which is entirely made of metal, act as the anode. Normally the body is mounted directly on a chassis and maintained at ground potential while the cathode is at a negative B voltage. After the electrons have passed through the smoother grid, they are subject to no further d-c voltage, and from there on, they are influenced only by the r-f voltages on the cavity grids as has already been described.

Klystron Operation

All the elements necessary to the operation of a klystron, i.e. a velocity-modulation tube using cavities and suitable for microwave use, have now been given. Cavities of various sorts have been discussed; velocity modulation of the electron beam has been described;

even a discussion of what an electron can do to give up (i.e. radiate) energy into the cavities was given in Chapter 6. Only a small point remains in that connection. Usually charge acceleration and hence radiation is obtained by causing charge to oscillate back and forth as in a dipole.

In the klystron the radiation of a continuous wave is obtained in a different manner. Instead of trying to keep a single charge constantly oscillating, which is manifestly difficult to do at the very high frequencies of the microwave region, a technique is used which requires acceleration in only one direction and secures the rapid repetition of the radiated pulses necessary to form wave-trains by using a "bunched" electron beam. This is illustrated in Fig. 10-5, which shows

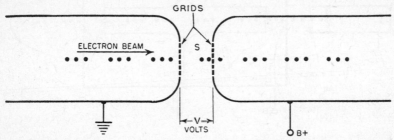

FIG. 10-5. The generation of a radio wave by the successive acceleration of bunches of charge. This is an alternative to the charge oscillating to and fro on an antenna.

a pair of grids capable of playing the role analogous to the control grid or plate of an ordinary vacuum tube. An electron beam consisting of groups of charges, separated by space containing relatively little charge, moves down inside a hollow electrode, through grids and the intervening space, into a second hollow electrode. Only in the space S do these charges receive acceleration and hence radiate out into space. Pulses of radiant energy are thus successively emitted for each bunch of electrons so that a radio wave is formed, the frequency of which is dictated by the constant velocity of the beam before acceleration and by the closeness of the bunches.

Recognizing this possibility of generating radio waves, the problem of the klystron then becomes clear. It is to devise a vacuum tube which will supply such a bunched beam across the catcher grids, and arrange an efficient method of collecting the radiated wave and transmitting it to the antenna where it can be sent out into space in accordance with a desired pattern. The way this is done in a standard two-chamber tube is shown in Fig. 10-6. The electron beam emerges from the *electron gun* traveling from left to right with a certain initial velocity. In some accidental way connected with the starting of the tube some bunching of the beam occurs so that, in the space between the *catcher grids*, successive bunches are accelerated and radiation

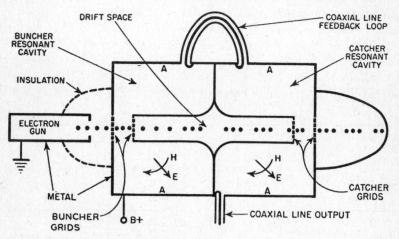

Fɪɢ. 10-6. Schematic diagram of a typical double-cavity klystron, showing the bunching effect of the electron stream.

pulses are sent out. The *catcher cavity* is of just the right dimensions so that these E and H waves travel out to the metal wall at *A* and are reflected back to the electron beam just in time to be strengthened and sent out again by the radiation from the next bunch. When this happens it is said that the cavity is at resonance, and the energy density in the catcher cavity then builds up to a maximum. Energy can then be taken off in the *coaxial line output*.

Aside from being concerned about how the first bunch is formed, it can also now easily be understood how the bunching is maintained. In addition to the output coaxial line, a second coaxial fitting is connected to the catcher resonator to serve as a *feedback loop*. Through this some energy flows back to the *buncher resonant cavity*, which is geometrically just like the catcher cavity. Here, also, electromagnetic waves start traveling back and forth between the electron beam and the wall *A*. At the times when the field is at the electron beam in the buncher, it generates a voltage between the *buncher grids*. This causes the electrons to be accelerated periodically as they move in this region. Thus, as the electron beam enters the field-free space, called the *drift space,* some of the electrons have been accelerated and are traveling faster than others. These faster electrons then catch up with their slower contemporaries while crossing the drift space, and reach the catcher grids in the form of bunches.

Amplifiers and Frequency Multipliers and Tuning

Klystrons can be used in other ways than as oscillators. For instance, if the feedback loop shown in Fig. 10-6 be broken and an externally derived signal be inserted into the buncher cavity, the same microwave frequency may be extracted from the catcher cavity that is 1000 times stronger than the input signal. In other words, modern klystrons have power amplifying capabilities up to 1000 and they are capable of output power in excess of 100 watts.

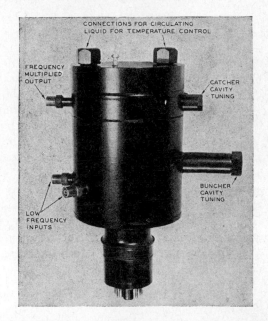

FIG. 10-7. A fixed-grid type of frequency multiplier klystron using paddle tuning. *Courtesy Sperry Gyroscope Co.*

Klystrons also can easily be made to function as frequency multipliers. This is done by tuning the catcher cavity to a frequency which is a multiple of that supplied to the buncher cavity. Fig. 10-7 shows a modern version of a klystron frequency-multiplier and Fig. 10-8 is a diagrammatic representation of an earlier diaphragm type of the same tube. Because of the nature of velocity modulation, klystron multiplier stages function very well as the beam is so rich in harmonic content that multiplication factors as high as 20 are easily obtained.

It may be noticed that in Fig. 10-7 bolt heads protrude from the side of the tube and are labeled as tuning adjustments. This is a

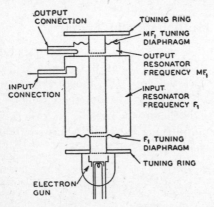

OUTPUT CONNECTION

TUNING RING

MF₁ TUNING DIAPHRAGM

OUTPUT RESONATOR FREQUENCY MF₁

INPUT CONNECTION

INPUT RESONATOR FREQUENCY F₁

F₁ TUNING DIAPHRAGM

TUNING RING

ELECTRON GUN

FIG. 10-8. Sectional view of a frequency-multiplier klystron using diaphragm tuning.

different system than the one spoken of in conjunction with Fig. 10-4, where flexible diaphragms are flexed to adjust grid spacings and consequently the resonant frequency of the associated cavity. In the system shown in Fig. 10-7 the grids are rigidly held in place and the effective volume of the cavity is changed by rotating the tuning head.

In one system, the rotation turns a paddle-like arrangement inside the cavity by flexing a thin vacuum retaining cylindrical wall. In another scheme, a corrugated cylinder is compressed or stretched so as to move a tuning slug in or out of the cavity in question. In general, tuning by means of grid motion is best when economy of design and large ranges of tuning are desired. The other systems give greater promise for high precision tuning and when used with liquid temperature control, they can be adjusted and kept in tune at a given microwave frequency with extreme accuracy.

Applegate Diagram

In order to discuss the operation of velocity modulation tubes in a more quantitative manner, it is perhaps best next to discuss some fairly disconnected ideas, of which some are more a matter of definition than of discovery. The first of these might very well be the Applegate diagram, of which a sample is shown in Fig. 10-9.

This space time sort of diagram is useful in describing electron bunching phenomenon. Time is measured along the horizontal axis, and the position of the electrons along the drift space is plotted as the vertical coordinate. Thus each line tells the space time history of a particular electron in the beam. Before reaching the buncher, the electrons all have approximately the same velocity and, as can be seen by the equal spacing of the electron lines ahead of the buncher, the electrons chosen for representation by the lines are those which are equally spaced upon entering the buncher. An electron such as the one whose history is represented by the line marked A in Fig.

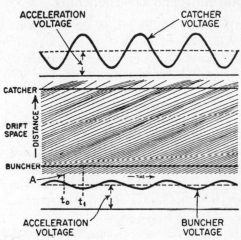

FIG. 10-9. Time-space diagram showing the bunching action of velocity modulation. This is called an Applegate diagram.

10-9 is, for example, one which proceeds from the electron gun to the buncher in the time which elapses between time t_o and time t_1. This is the same length of time as that which elapses for any other electron. As electron A passes the buncher it is slowed down because at time t_1 the buncher voltage is negative, as shown by the plot of buncher voltage against time. This is indicated in the diagram by the fact that line A bends so as to have a smaller slope beyond the buncher; this means that as line A is followed along in time, the electron is moving less rapidly along the space coordinate which is, of course, the desired representative of a lowered velocity. In other words, the electron velocity is represented by the slope of the lines which describe the history of the electron.

Having understood the workings of the buncher and its representation upon the Applegate diagram, it is fairly easy to see the value of such a plot. Suppose in actually building a tube, a certain length drift tube is chosen. This then determines the position of the catcher, and a line such as the horizontal catcher line of Fig. 10-9 may be drawn. Then by following along this line with time, the density of the inter-sected electron lines show that at any given time a certain number of electrons will be present between the catcher grids. Actually, since general interest is in obtaining the greatest possible catcher voltage, this means that the catcher will be located where the greatest density changes occur, as indicated in Fig. 10-9.

Debunching and Overbunching

A practical limitation on the design of voltage-amplifier tubes of the velocity-modulation type is encountered because of a difficulty closely akin to some of the space-charge troubles that sometimes arise with amplitude-modulation tubes. This difficulty is known as *debunch-ing*, and is encountered because of the electrostatic forces that exist between neighboring electrons of the beam. Its effect is to make the electron bunch less dense at a given point and time than would other-wise be expected.

If, for example, the neighborhood around a given electron starts to become more and more thickly populated because of a prearranged bunching action which hurried the electrons behind and delayed those ahead, then, as that population increases, so also does the repulsive force of the neighborhood. The result is that the maximum density is obtained somewhat sooner than would be calculated. The last electrons, which under only the rules shown by the Applegate diagram would have added still more to the density of the surroundings, are unable even to reach the vicinity of the given electron. Debunching thus makes it necessary to build drift spaces somewhat shorter than would be expected.

Overbunching is the condition which exists in a velocity-modulation tube when the drift space is too long or, what amounts to the same thing, if the acceleration and buncher voltages are too high. What happens is that the point of maximum bunching occurs somewhere along the drift space so that by the time the catcher grids are reached the faster electrons have not only caught up with the slower ones which were originally ahead of them, but also have actually passed the slower moving charge and gotten some distance ahead of them. It is clear that if this sort of action continues long enough, a second bunching may take place when the slow electrons are overtaken by the fast ones of the preceding cycle. Tubes that are operated with a drift space that is longer than that needed to reach the first condition of optimum bunching are said to use overbunching.

Bunching Parameter

A convenient quantity to use in discussing the operation of a velocity-modulation tube is one which is generally known as the *bunching parameter*. It is frequently represented as x and may, for example, be defined as

$$x = \pi N \frac{V_1}{V_o}$$

where N is the number of cycles of the frequency being generated which elapse during the time of transit through the drift space of an electron of average velocity. N may have any value in an amplifier tube but it is restricted to certain values which satisfy the proper phase relations if the velocity-modulation tube is to be used as an oscillator by virtue of diverting some of the catcher grid voltage back to the buncher grids. V_1 and V_o are respectively the peak-buncher voltage and the d-c beam voltage between cathode and anode. To the extent that certain approximations may be made and certain difficulties such as debunching neglected, it will be shown that a given velocity-modulation tube will be operating with optimum bunching when it is adjusted so that the bunching parameter is equal to 1.84.

The usefulness of the bunching parameter depends upon the fact that its value is the factor which, according to simple bunching theory, determines the output of the tube. With an ordinary triode, for example, plate current is often plotted as a function of grid voltage. With a velocity-modulation tube, a graph showing output current as a function of buncher drive voltage does not have the same usefulness, because the shape of such a curve is intimately tied in with factors which are concerned with the drift space, and because increased drive on a given tube does not simply increase the output but instead gives an output which varies as a Bessel function. The Bessel function dependence cannot be avoided, but if output is plotted against the bunching parameter, all the factors of simple bunching theory which can influence the output of the tube are specifically considered.

Fig. 10-10 shows the Bessel function $J_1(x)$ which serves to establish a relation between the bunching parameter and the output of a velocity-modulation tube. The optimum adjustment is indicated as

1.84, and it is clear that such a value can generally be reached in any one of several ways. For example the bunching parameter can be decreased by reducing N or V_1; it may also be decreased by making V_0 larger. The decision as to how the adjustment is to be made in a given case depends upon many factors such as efficiency, stability, and convenience. Voltages higher than a few hundred, or at the most a

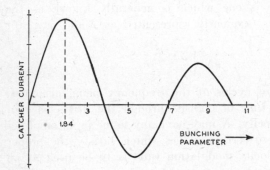

FIG. 10-10. The Bessel function $J_1(x)$ which expresses the relation between the tube output and the value of the bunching parameter.

few thousand, volts are at best inconvenient. Unusually long drift spaces make the electron optics problem difficult and usually cause the efficiency to be less. Stability criteria may, in certain applications, even be so important as to cause a tube to be operated not at the first maximum, but rather on some lesser maximum of the Bessel curve.

Saw-Tooth Bunching

From a purely theoretical point of view the sinusoidal bunching conditions illustrated in Fig. 10-9 may not produce optimum results. Except for certain practical considerations which are dictated by the cavity system commonly used to supply the buncher voltage, it does not at all follow that some sort of waveform other than the sine wave may not serve better as a voltage for exciting the buncher grids. This was recognized as long ago as 1937 [1] when some German workers wrote about the application of a saw-tooth voltage to the buncher grids in order to produce more dense bunching.

Fig. 10-11 shows an Applegate diagram for such a bunching condition. Here it is assumed for simplicity that the buncher voltage can only speed up the electrons of the beam and never slow them down. Electrons from the gun which reach the buncher at times like those labeled t_o in Fig. 10-11 pass on with only very small change in their velocity. Electrons which arrive later than that, up to and including time t_1, are speeded up; in fact, they are speeded up by an amount which is exactly proportional to their lateness. Thus all the electrons which arrive at the buncher between times t_o and t_1 are able to catch up with the t_o electron at the same time. With such a bunching condition, the Applegate diagram forecasts that bunches of extremely

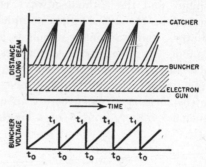

FIG. 10-11. When a saw-tooth voltage is applied to the buncher, an Applegate diagram predicts that electron bunches of high density are formed between the grids of a correctly placed catcher cavity.

high density can be made to form between the grids of a correctly placed catcher cavity. Actually, of course, debunching effects come into play and it will probably always be impossible to approximate more than very roughly the saw-tooth voltage needed for the buncher. At present saw-tooth bunching is therefore only a scientific curiosity, as far as its actual use is concerned.

A saw-tooth-bunched tube can serve well as a model for approximate calculations. Such a model demonstrates one way in which the velocities of a beam of electrons might be arranged so that at some point along the beam a catcher can be installed, which in theory will have no charge at all passing through it most of the time and then at certain times will be traversed with a very large current as the perfect bunches reach it. If such a velocity-modulation tube could be built, it would be 100% efficient as far as bunching goes. Any practical tube will have an Applegate diagram more like that of Fig. 10-9 where the beam through the catcher only changes in magnitude and never becomes zero or even extremely large. The design problem of velocity modulation is therefore one of trying to construct tubes in which the beam will act as much as possible as if it were modulated with a saw-tooth voltage. The merit of the results of a design is often spoken of in terms of percentage efficiency of perfect bunching. By this is meant the power output of the actual tube divided by the power that would be available from the same tube if it could be operated with a saw-tooth drive.

Magnetron Oscillators

All magnetron vacuum tubes have some general features of construction in common. The anodes are always essentially cylindrical in shape, and the cathode always consists of a wire-like structure placed along the axis of that cylinder. Such tubes are used only as oscillators, and a resonant circuit is always used in conjunction with the anode. As with many other types of electronic oscillators, at low frequencies this resonant circuit may consist of a combination of lumped inductance and capacitance. At higher frequencies it may take the form of an open-wire transmission line, while at microwave frequencies it may consist of a single or multiple array of resonant cavities.

Electron Trajectories

The first thing that is necessary in analyzing the operation of a magnetron is to understand the action that a magnetic field has on a current. If a wire that is carrying current is placed between the poles of a powerful magnet as shown in Fig. 10-12(A), it will not be attracted to either the north or the south pole, but instead will be forced to move away from the poles in the direction F. A magnetic field always has this effect on a current, for it does not cause the current to move parallel with the field, but rather urges it to move sideways.

The direction of motion is sometimes described by what is called the right-hand rule of motors. The thumb and first two fingers of the right hand are used and are so held as to be mutually perpendicular. This may be accomplished, for example, by causing the right thumb to point to the left, by directing the first finger straight out forward from the body, and by bending the second finger so as to make it point downward. With the thumb and first two fingers of the right hand held in this position and the thumb oriented to show the direction of positive current flow, while the first finger shows the direction of the magnetic field, the second finger will point in the direction in which the current-carrying wire is urged to move. This is illustrated in Fig. 10-12(B).

A simpler scheme is one which involves the ordinary right-hand rule plus a rule which states that a current-carrying wire in a magnetic field will be urged to move away from the side in which the magnetic lines are most dense and toward the side where the density is less. In

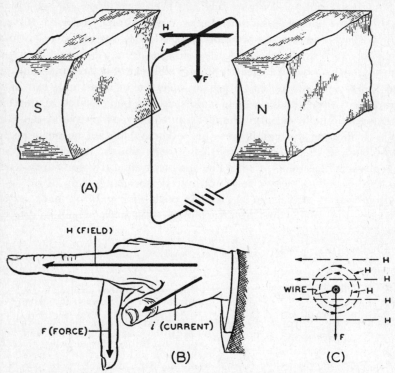

FIG. 10-12. The force on a wire carrying current transversely through a magnetic field is illustrated by the right-hand rule as indicated in (B). In (C) the magnetic forces of the constant field and that due to the current in the wire, shows how the force on the wire is downward in this case.

Fig. 10-12(A) for example, the magnetic field arising from the permanent magnet is uniform throughout the space occupied by the conductor on which attention is focused, but near the wire it is modified by the magnetic field generated by the current. Thus, as is shown in Fig. 10-12(C), magnetic lines of force around the wire are in the same direction as the external-magnetic field when points above the wire are considered, but at points below the wire the directions are reversed. The actual field above the wire is therefore represented by adding the strengths indicated by the two sets of lines while that below is found by subtraction. The fact that there is a larger net density of lines above the wire than below may be taken to mean that the wire will be forced downward in this particular case.

A moving electron is a current, just as is moving charge in a wire. Although the motion of a wire has just been mentioned, the wire plays no role in the phenomenon and electric charges forced to move through empty space can just as well be spoken of as feeling an additional force as can a wire, which as a special case, may be carrying them. Consequently, when the electric field which exists between the cathode and anode of a magnetron urges an electron to move outward along a radius of the cylinder which makes up the body of the magnetron, the magnetic field will urge the electron to move sideways at the same time. Under certain conditions this sideways motion becomes cumulative and if the magnetic field is strong enough, the electron may never reach the anode at all. The magnetic field, by constantly forcing the charge sideways, may ultimately so change this direction of motion that it travels in a circular path and ends up back at the cathode. Fig. 10-13 illustrates various possible paths which an electron

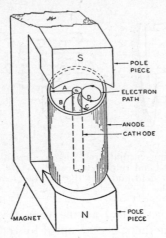

Fig. 10-13. Various electron paths possible in a magnetron under static conditions. With zero magnetic field, electrons follow path A; with a small magnetic field, path B will be followed; when the field is increased further, the curve of the path will be more pronounced, as C, until the field is so strong that the electron will not reach the anode, path D.

may follow in a magnetron under static conditions. When the magnetic field is zero, the electrons travel in a straight line from the cathode to the anode, as indicated by path A. With a small magnetic field the path of the electrons shows some bending due to the magnetic action, as shown by path B. With a still stronger magnetic field, the bending becomes still more pronounced, as illustrated by path C. Finally, if the magnetic field is increased still more, a point is reached at which the electrons fail entirely to reach the anode and travel in a circular path which barely grazes the anode, as shown by the *critical* path *D*. This value of a magnetic field is approximately the one used in one practical type of tube. If the magnetic field continues to be increased beyond this point, the electrons move in circles of smaller and smaller diameter and in the static case do not ever get far from the cathode. Such field-strength arrangements are also used in producing r-f energy but are not advantageous at microwave frequencies.

Even assuming a perfectly cylindrical anode and cathode of known size, a theoretical analysis of the electron paths is still a difficult computation. The computation has been made for the case in which the cathode is relatively small in comparison to the internal diameter of the anode and the critical value of the magnetic field is found to be

$$B = \frac{6.7\sqrt{V_a}}{D}$$

where *B* is the magnetic-flux density in gauss, V_a is the anode voltage in volts, and *D* is the internal diameter of the anode in centimeters. The assumption of a small cathode is true of all practical tubes, for otherwise the efficiency becomes too low. This *critical value* of the magnetic field to which the above expression applies, is the value at which electrons just fail to reach the anode. If, under the static conditions being discussed, anode current is plotted against magnetic field, a point will be found at which the anode current drops suddenly to nearly zero. This is the critical value of the magnetic field.

An important effect has been neglected thus far, namely, the collision of electrons which are returning to the cathode with electrons and positive ions which are attracted into the neighborhood of the cathode. These give rise to a cloud of stationary or randomly moving electrons which closely surround the cathode. This region acts like a part of the cathode, and is therefore called a *virtual cathode*. The physical significance is that in an actual tube the cathode acts as if it had a diameter larger than its actual physical diameter. More important, it acts as if it had a diameter of rather indefinite dimensions. Because of this, the anode current does not decrease entirely to zero even for fields which are considerably larger than the critical value. Under practical conditions some current always flows to the anode, and if the history of any individual electron is traced over enough revolutions, it may be assumed to reach the anode ultimately.

Another effect of the return of electrons to the cathode, which is more serious in practical tube construction, has to do with the heat generated by electron bombardment. This often results in an objectionable rise in cathode temperature and places a severe limitation on the smallness of cathodes which may be used. The rise in filament temperature, moreover, may be a cascading phenomenon. At higher cathode temperatures, the number of electrons in the inter-electrode space may be increased, and thus increase the plate current as well as cause a further bombardment of the cathode thereby producing a still higher cathode temperature. For this reason it is often necessary to make use of special control circuits in the filament supply. These may consist of arrangements which reduce the filament voltage whenever the anode current tends to increase or, in extreme cases, may even automatically disconnect the filament voltage as soon as oscillations begin. In the later case, cathode heating depends entirely upon reverse electron bombardment.

Classes of Magnetrons

It has been shown that every magnetron has a resonant circuit which is used in conjunction with its anode. The very earliest magnetrons were designed to produce oscillations at low frequencies and a solid cylindrical anode was used. At radio frequencies, and particularly at microwave frequencies, this method is of no interest because oscillation then depends on varying the magnetic field, which is certainly out of the question at very high frequencies. Consequently designs of the so-called split-anode type only shall be considered. The anode is not a continuous metal cylinder but is instead made up of two half-cylinders which are insulated from each other, as shown in Figs. 10-14 and 10-15; at least they are half-cylinders, if a two-section anode is used. Most modern designs use a much larger number of anode sections, so that the anode actually consists of a cylinder which is cut lengthwise into several sections, and the sections are then put together with insulating material between them. The case which is considered in Fig. 10-17 indicates this and shows an eight-section anode.

Two main types of magnetrons using split-anode construction may be distinguished. Only the type which is commonly referred to as a *transit-time magnetron* is really of interest at true microwave frequencies. Consequently most of the following discussion will be cen-

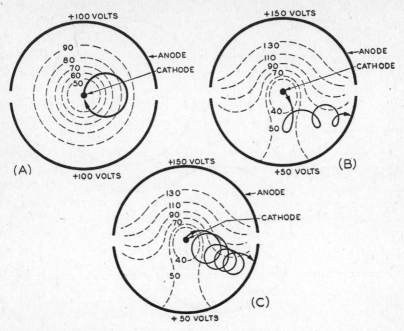

Fig. 10-14. Electron paths in a split-anode negative-resistance magnetron under static conditions.

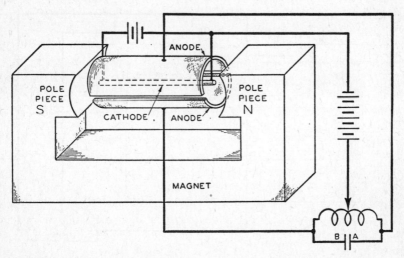

Fig. 10-15. Circuit arrangement for a split-anode negative-resistance magnetron.

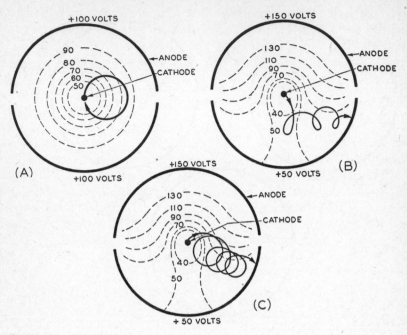

FIG. 10-14. Electron paths in a split-anode negative-resistance magnetron under static conditions.

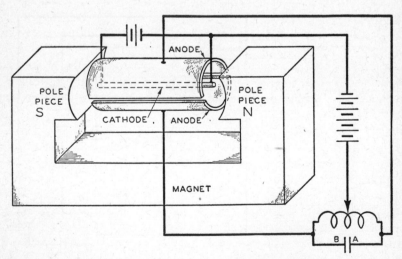

FIG. 10-15. Circuit arrangement for a split-anode negative-resistance magnetron.

tered around tubes of this type, but because it is relatively easy to confuse the two kinds of operation and because much more has been written about the other type, it will be well to review first the principles of the older type so that no confusion will be encountered later.

Negative-Resistance Magnetron (Dynatron)

This older and less useful type of magnetron is called a *negative-resistance* or *dynatron* type. It operates efficiently only at frequencies which are low in comparison to the transit time, and hence has many of the limitations for microwave work that are inherent in ordinary triodes. Negative-resistance magnetrons are suitable for the generation of wavelengths that are longer than about 50 centimeters. They can deliver several hundred watts of power at a fairly good efficiency, which can be 60 percent or better at these relatively long wavelengths. To obtain very small transit times in such magnetrons so as to allow one to go to real microwave frequencies, it would be necessary to use unreasonably strong magnetic fields. For example, an efficiency of 30 percent at a wavelength of 10 centimeters would require a flux density of approximately 8000 gauss. Moreover, in order to operate such a tube properly at such high magnetic fields it would be necessary to use a small anode diameter. Cooling problems then appear to be insurmountable. Most of these difficulties are not encountered in transit-time magnetrons.

Negative-resistance magnetrons are called by that name because the relation between the anode voltage and current not only does not obey Ohm's law, but actually goes in the wrong direction. Of course, there is no reason to expect any vacuum tube to act like a resistance and obey the simple relation $E = IR$. Most non-linear devices such as vacuum tubes do, however, operate in a fashion similar to what might be expected by Ohm's law, in that an increased voltage causes an increased current. Negative-resistance magnetrons do not even do this. If the two sections of the anode are at different voltages with respect to the cathode, more current flows to the anode section having the lower voltage. If the currents are measured to each half of the anode and their difference plotted against the potential difference between the two segments, it is found that increased voltage difference is accompanied by a decreased amount of current. Such a curve is said to have a negative-resistance slope, even though it is not one which is obtained by substituting negative numbers for resistance in Ohm's law.

The main feature which insures that a given magnetron will operate as a negative-resistance oscillator is that the magnetic field strength is adjusted to a point well above its critical value; values of 1.5 to 2 times the critical value are commonly used. Under such conditions the electron trajectories are closed curves which are small compared to the distance between the cathode and anode. In Fig. 10-14 electron paths are drawn for certain static conditions of anode voltage. A discussion of this figure should show the negative-resistance properties of the tube and make possible an explanation of its operation as an oscillator.

In Fig. 10-14(A) the two halves of the anode are at an equal voltage above the cathode. Under this condition the anode acts as if it were not split, and any electron emitted from the cathode travels in a small circle, shown as a solid line, and returns to the cathode without even coming close to the anode, in accordance with principles which have been previously discussed. Fig. 10-14(A) also shows concentric (dashed) circles drawn in the anode cylinder; these are equipotential lines. If an electron at the anode surface is 100 volts higher in potential than one at the cathode, then an electron located anywhere on any of these equipotential lines will be at a potential higher than the cathode by the amount shown.

Perhaps the description will be clearer, if it is described in terms of energy per unit charge, which is the same thing as voltage. With 100 volts potential between the cathode and the anode, a charge traveling over that distance is speeded up so that it carries one hundred units of kinetic energy when it strikes the anode. As shown in Fig. 10-14(A), it is the nature of the electric fields in a concentric arrangement that most of this energy is imparted to the charge soon after it leaves the cathode. When it has reached the equipotential line marked 50, it has already been speeded up so as to have half the energy it will have in going the whole distance. In other words, as far as the radial component of the electron's motion is concerned, the equipotential lines may be considered as telling how fast the electron is moving. When the electron is moving outward toward the anode, it is being speeded up; when it is moving inward and away from the anode, it is being slowed down.

In Figs. 10-14(B) and (C) are shown sample electron paths when the two anode sections are at different voltages. The upper anode section is indicated to be 150 volt units above the cathode, while the lower half is at only 50 volts. As a result, the equal potential lines are no longer concentric circles, but assume quite a different form. Moreover, electrons emitted from the cathode do not return to the cathode, but instead continue to move in a series of loops. What is most important is that on the average the electrons are more apt to end up at the 50-volt electrode than at the one of higher voltage. In Fig. 10-14(B) the case is shown for an electron which is initially headed toward the lower half of the anode, while in Fig. 10-14(C), an electron is initially headed in the opposite direction.

As has been pointed out, maximum increases in the radial velocity are obtained when the electron can most rapidly cross equipotential lines while heading toward the anode. This happens when an electron is moving toward the 150-volt anode section, but since the magnetic field causes the electron to turn, and since this radial velocity component is lost as the electron comes back toward the center of the tube again, the high voltage of the upper anode section is not the controlling factor in determining current flow. Experimental evidence as well as theoretical calculations show that the electrons are more apt to reach the lower voltage section of the anode. It is difficult to give simple and convincing reasons for this. Perhaps it is helpful simply to say that outward radial velocities directly generated by anode voltage are nullified by the magnetic field, and that in the low-voltage region the electrons travel slower and spend more time, so that there is a better chance of them finally reaching the anode there.

The connections of a circuit which will make use of a negative-resistance magnetron, are shown in Fig. 10-15. The glass envelope, which is necessary to allow evacuation of the tube, is not shown but must be assumed to be present. As with most oscillators, nothing is mentioned about how the oscillation starts, except that some small irregularity is the cause; therefore, begin by assuming that oscillation has started in the resonant circuit and that it may be looked upon as being caused by a flow of electrons from plate A of the condenser around through the inductance to plate B and then back again with a regular period. The battery connected between the anode and the cathode in the absence of oscillation will cause both sections of the anode to be at a given potential above the cathode. The motion of the oscillating charge in the resonant circuit superimposes itself on this constant battery voltage, so that first anode section A and then anode section B is at a lower potential. Whenever the oscillating charge is at A, the voltage of A is lessened but, due to the negative-resistance properties of the tube, this does not mean that that section receives less anode current; in fact it receives more. Thus, the supply of negative charge at A which next flows through the inductance to B is enhanced by the action of the magnetron. When the charge gets to B, it is anode section B which is at the lower voltage, and hence receives a major portion of the electrons flowing through the tube. This means that the flow in the resonant circuit is constantly increased until losses just balance the additions of energy. Some of these losses will consist of a useful load which extracts energy in one way or another.

Transit-Time Magnetrons

Magnetrons which operate as transit-time oscillators are distinguished by the fact that the magnetic field is adjusted into the neighborhood of its critical value, instead of this field being considerably stronger as it is for negative-resistance operation. The frequency of oscillation is controlled not only by the resonant circuits or cavities, but also by the strengths of the electric and magnetic fields. This is because the actual transit time of the electrons as they move through approximately circular orbits, is itself a factor in determining the frequency. It is now no longer necessary that this transit time be made small in terms of a cycle as it was for the negative-resistance case. In fact, adjustment is made which causes the transit time to bear a definite relation to the generated frequency. The electron paths do not normally include a single rotation and return to the cathode, any more than they did with the negative-resistance type. Instead, they just graze the anode soon after leaving the cathode, and then continue on around the cathode in a fashion more or less like that illustrated in Fig. 10-16. Because of this utilization instead of neglect of transit time, it is possible to make tubes which are useful at wavelengths as small as 6 millimeters.

The way in which energy is transferred from the electrons to the resonant circuits or cavities may be described as being similar to the mechanism of the Barkhausen-Kurz positive-grid tubes: the transfer of radio-frequency energy to the anodes, and hence to the resonators, does not depend upon the actual transfer of electrons from the cathode to the anode. Instead, the motion of the electrons in the space between the cathode and anode causes induced currents to flow in the resonators. It is these induced currents which cause electromagnetic fields to be built up in cavity resonators and allow rather large energy densities to be maintained there. As electrons move outward from the cathode toward the anode, they accumulate energy from the d-c voltages applied to the tube. At certain points in their rotation around the cathode their presence and motion cause energy to be transferred to the adjacent sector of the magnetron anode, and the electrons in consequence drop back to smaller radii and continue their rotation with smaller linear velocities. The design of a transit-time magnetron to operate at a given frequency thus depends on getting the rotational velocity right, so that the electrons will have accumulated energy from the d-c fields at the proper time and then be ready to give it to the r-f fields of the resonators which are connected between adjacent anode

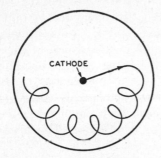

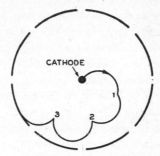

Fig. 10-16. A possible electron path in a transit-time magnetron.

Fig. 10-17. Electron path in an oscillating multiple-cavity magnetron.

sectors. These resonators are constructed so that the oscillation which they support is ready to accept a "push" of energy from the electrons as they drop back to a smaller radii.

Fig. 10-17 indicates how the changing radius of the path of an electron is indicative of the conversion of d-c power into energy at microwave frequency. When the electrons first leave the cathode they have very little energy because they are moving slowly and with only just enough speed to break away from the emitting surface. This is thermal energy which they received because of the filament temperature. Immediately, however, they are urged to move outward toward the anode because of the anode potential and are speeded up by the electric pull. As they speed up, they gather energy in their outward flight. If a particular electron approaches an anode sector just as that part of the anode is being urged to become positively charged by virtue of the resonant devices connected between it and the adjacent sectors, the electron's approach will help the action along and in doing so the electron will itself be reduced to a smaller orbit. It must be reduced to a smaller radius of rotation around the cathode in order to give up energy. In Fig. 10-17 this sort of thing is happening at points *1, 2,* and *3* of the trajectory. During these falls to points closer to the cathode, the oscillation in the associated resonators is given a boost; after each of these falls the electron begins again to spiral outward toward an anode and pick up more energy.

It is by no means necessary to restrict the situation to a case of two anode sections. It may equally well apply to any larger number as shown in Fig. 10-17. It is feasible to use as many as eight, or even more, anode sections. With a larger number of anode sections, it is not necessary to cause the electrons to travel around the cathode nearly so fast in order to develop a given frequency. They only need to travel from a position opposite one sector to another position opposite a second sector that is separated in time equal to one cycle, rather than having to travel around the entire anode circumference.

It is quite possible for a magnetron of many sections to develop microwave energy at several frequencies; however, if the resonators are of reasonably high Q, other frequencies than the main one may be of much lower power and exist only as a nuisance. The magnetron is then said to oscillate in different modes.

An eight-section magnetron may oscillate at one particular frequency because an electron delivers energy to alternate sectors, whereas in another magnetron it will be a different frequency because the electron makes its delivery of energy to every third section. The shortest possible wave which can be generated has a wavelength equal to twice the distance between the centers of adjacent anode sectors. Thus if the anode is divided into N sections, there can be only $N/2$ waves around the circumference at most. There may be any number less than this, so $N/2$ is the total number of possible modes. As in the case of resonant cavities, one must be cautioned that wavelength here is not free-space wavelength, and it does not follow that the frequencies of the various modes follow in simple harmonic progression.

The whole idea of modes brings up one of the two most serious difficulties which limit the usefulness of this type of microwave generator. The other is the matter of cathode life to which reference has already been made. The difficulty to be discussed now has to do with frequency control. The fact that modes of various frequencies exist and the fact their strength depends upon the electric and magnetic field strength indicates that one of the chief design problems is to arrange a tube so that undesired frequency modes are as far away from the desired one as possible. This can be done at some frequencies under auspicious conditions; however, the very fact that unwanted modes make their appearance is indicative of the fact that the Q of the resonators associated with magnetrons cannot usually be made high enough. The very fact that the resonant devices have to be heavily loaded by the electrons in the space between the cathode and anode, makes this true. Furthermore, the mechanical difficulty of tuning a number of resonators to exactly the same frequency makes it easy to see that it is indeed difficult to obtain a magnetron oscillator which transmits a narrow band signal. Signals several megacycles wide are usually produced at microwave frequencies. Since the magnetron is fundamentally an oscillator and not an amplifier which might be tied back to a crystal controlled source, it is difficult to get good clean spectrum allocations with existing magnetron oscillators.

To get a better general physical picture of how a transit-time magnetron operates, it is necessary to discuss a matter which is usually referred to as the phasing problem of the electrons. The initial question has to do with the approach of an outwardly bound electron to a positively charged anode section. It was previously mentioned how energy was transferred to the resonators, but at that time it was assumed that the electrons would move outward at the right time. Since electrons are continually emitted from the cathode, the question might be asked why it is that some of them do not go the wrong way at the wrong time, so as to remove as much energy from the r-f circuits as the properly moving ones add? The answer to this question is not easy to give in terms of physical ideas. For the purposes here, it is necessary merely to state that the improperly moving electrons initially have so little energy that their wrong phase is not very harmful, and that before they get far enough out in their orbit to be important from an energy standpoint, at least a majority of them have been pulled over in phase so as to be an aid instead of a hinderance. In another way, however, the effect of out-of-phase electrons is more serious, namely, when as a result of giving up r-f energy the electron gets out of step while traveling in a high-energy outer orbit. When this happens, it is necessary to elminate the electron before it can drain appreciable energy from the resonators.

In each cycle of oscillation of an electron that gives up energy, the distance through which the electron moves decreases because of the sharper curvature of its path. The oscillation of the electron therefore advances in phase relative to the alternating plate voltage. This is indicated in Fig. 10-17 where it may be noticed that dip 3 is shown to come at a later point of its corresponding anode section than did dip 2. If this phase advancement continues over enough cycles, a given electron will ultimately move in such a phase as to extract rather than insert energy into the resonators. Before this happens the electron must be removed from the inter-electrode space. One method of removing the electrons is by tilting the magnetic field with respect to the cathode so that there is a component of motion along the length of the tube in order that the electrons are carried off the end before their phase becomes too greatly advanced. Another possibility includes the use of a longitudinal electric field which slowly pulls the electrons out of the inter-electrode space before they can do harm. In any event the magnetron must be equipped with end plates to absorb these undesired electrons.

Magnetron Cavities

An eight-section-anode magnetron requires eight resonant devices to be connected between the adjacent sectors. Except for radiation difficulties with the circuits themselves, each resonant device could, in principle, be made up of a lumped value of inductance connected across the capacitance existing between adjacent anode sections. In actual practice, resonant cavities are used instead, for they not only get away from the radiation difficulty but they allow a simple and rigid method of construction.

Fig. 10-18 shows the general external appearance of a microwave magnetron as it is mounted between the pole pieces of a magnet and **ready** for operation. The body of the tube is the anode and consists

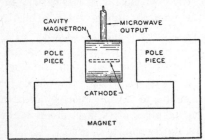

FIG. 10-18. The pole pieces of a magnet are so arranged that the magnetic field passes through the cavity magnetron parallel to its cathode.

of a copper cylinder with heavy walls in which the resonant cavities are cut. The cathode is placed axially in this cylinder, and the tube as a whole is mounted between the magnet pole pieces so that the cathode lies approximately parallel to the magnetic lines of force which exist between the pole pieces. The magnet itself may either be an electromagnet energized by a separate d-c source or it may be a permanent magnet. Permanent magnets have been so much improved in recent years that they are generally the most convenient to use.

To extract a useful load from a microwave magnetron, a coupling loop is generally inserted into one of the resonant cavities, and the energy which it collects is brought out through a coaxial line, as shown in Fig. 10-18. It is sufficient to make the connection to only one of the eight or more resonant cavities because, in a practical tube, all the resonant cavities are so closely coupled together that extracting energy from one is the same as taking it from them all. Results have been published concerning tubes of this type which produce 300 watts of continuous power at 9-cm wavelengths. A plate potential of 4400 volts and a magnetic field of 1950 gauss was used.

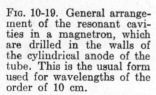

FIG. 10-19. General arrangement of the resonant cavities in a magnetron, which are drilled in the walls of the cylindrical anode of the tube. This is the usual form used for wavelengths of the order of 10 cm.

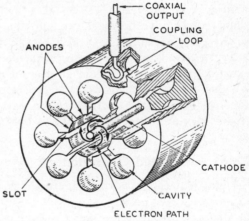

Fig. 10-19 illustrates the nature of the resonant cavities that are cut into the walls of the cylindrical anode of the tube. They have been cut out by drilling holes lengthwise through the flat ends of the hollow cylinder walls. They connect electrically to the central core of the cylinder by means of suitable slots. By very precise mechanical dimensioning, their resonant frequency can be made to lie very close (within a few mc) to the microwave frequency that is desired. When they are operated close to their resonant frequency, the cavities present as high an impedance path between adjacent anode sections as would any other kind of split anode section. A tube built like the one shown in Fig. 10-19 is as truly a split-anode type as was the tube of Fig. 10-15. The fact that the various anode parts that are exposed to the circulating electrons are mechanically made of a single piece of solid copper does not change the fact that they are electrically a half-wave apart, so that r-f voltages across the slots leading into the cavities cannot be short-circuited by any path back through the walls of the tube.

It is by no means necessary that the magnetron cavities be of exactly the shape shown in Fig. 10-19, although that is a usual and convenient form for wavelengths around 10 cm. At still shorter wavelengths it may be more convenient to use only slots for the resonant cavities, while at longer wavelengths, the connecting slots shown in Fig. 10-19 may be circular holes that overlap the circular cuts shown, as well as the central core opening of the tube.

Disk-Seal Tubes

In spite of the intrinsic difficulties with electron transit times and shunt capacitance between vacuum tube elements, as was explained in the section dealing with klystrons, a kind of triode vacuum tube known generally as the *disk-seal* type has proven useful at frequencies extending up into the region of true microwave frequencies, i.e. 3000 mc and higher. Because of the general appearance of this kind of tube, as shown in Fig. 10-20, disk-seal tubes for use at very high frequencies are often referred to as *lighthouse tubes*.

Construction and Operation

Details of the construction are shown in Fig. 10-21 which shows a view of a low-power model that is suitable for local-oscillator use in a superheterodyne receiver. A comparison of the illustration helps explain the novel method of assembly which is so important in extending the frequency range in which triode operation is possible in spite of transit time and shunt capacitance difficulties. The time it takes for an electron to travel from the cathode to the plate is greatly reduced in a tube like the one shown in Fig. 10-21 by the simple expedient of mounting the cathode, grid, and plate very close together. The unwanted inductance and capacitance values associated with the electrode connections, are reduced to an absolute minimum by constructing the grid, plate, and cathode assemblies as entirely separate entities which are brought together only for final assembly and are then attached together only through the glass which forms the vacuum seal. The arrangement for assembly of such tubes normally utilizes special jigs which position the three parts with great accuracy and

Fig. 10-20, left. A typical disk-seal tube without the cavities in place. *Courtesy General Electric Co.*

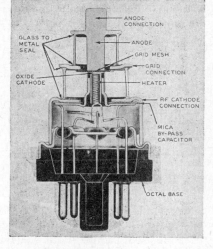

Fig. 10-21, right. Cross-section view of the G.E. type 2C40 disk-seal tube, showing general arrangement. *Courtesy General Electric Co.*

hold that position until after the glass seals have been made. A glass which can be sealed directly to silver-plated low-carbon steel is used. A typical disk-seal tube has a cathode-grid spacing of .004 inch and a grid-plate spacing of .012 inch. It is holding these dimensions to good accuracy that makes the tube so successful.

When a typical disk-seal oscillator tube is operated in circuits arranged for successively higher and higher frequencies, the power available from those circuits (or cavity arrangements) drops off with increasing frequency something like the way that is shown in the curve of Fig. 10-22. That curve was actually taken for tubes of the type shown in Fig. 10-21, but it is also of the correct general shape for any high-frequency disk-seal tube. In other words, although the disk-seal tube extends the frequency range of triode vacuum tubes, it does not alter their general mode of operation. As a result a frequency limitation somewhere in the lower microwave range is encountered.

A description of the operation of a disk-seal tube is much the same as that of any other triode. A small signal voltage applied between

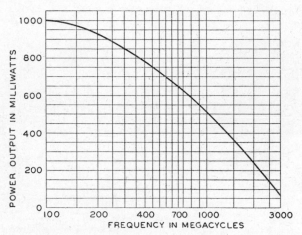

FIG. 10-22. The power output of the disk-seal tube drops off with an increase in frequency; this is typical of the tube type shown in Fig. 10-21 with $E_{bb} = 250$ volts and $R_g = 10,000$ ohms.

the grid and the cathode reduces or increases the number of electrons traveling from cathode to plate. Because the grid is much closer to the cathode than is the plate (.004 inch compared to .016 inch), a small grid voltage is able to cause a much larger change of plate voltage. This is simply a matter concerned with the way in which charges affect each other as a function of their separation. Consequently, the well-known triode characteristic in which a small grid voltage produces a large change in plate voltage, is obtained. The only distinctive features of the high-frequency disk-seal tubes are that the grid determines the strength of the electrons flowing from the cathode to the plate, and they actually arrive at the plate an exceedingly short length of time later. Also because of the low inter-electrode capacitance, very little charge has to go into that capacitance in order to get charge to appear on the actual mesh of the grid where it is desired.

Operation as an Amplifier

Just as with other types of vacuum tubes operating above about 300 mc, wired circuits have too much radiation loss to be useful for high-frequency applications of the disk-seal tube. Resonant cavities must be employed, just as they are with klystrons or magnetrons. Fig. 10-23 shows a pair of such cavities mounted on a tube of the type shown in Fig. 10-21. Actually the part placed external to the vacuum tubes makes up only a part of the cavity enclosure but that

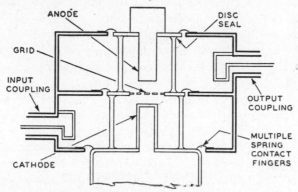

FIG. 10-23. Cavities mounted on a disk-seal tube.

part, in conjunction with the disks and anode (or cathode) support, together with one side of the grid mesh, complete the cavity and cause it to be effectively of the sort shown in Fig. 10-24, which is recognized

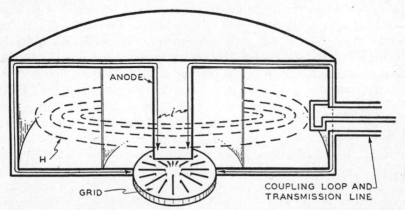

FIG. 10-24. A rhumbatron type cavity as it is formed by a disk-seal tube and an external shell. This cross-section of the cavity is used to show the current path over which charge oscillates.

as being similar to the rhumbatron cavity tube, which has already been discussed. The weak spot in such an arrangement is almost always the spring clips that are used to connect the external cavity to the tube. These connectors are designed to allow the vacuum tube to be plugged into the cavity and are really the heart of the system of using cavities that are separable from the vacuum tube. Unfortunately they must come at points of maximum current flow, and it is exceedingly difficult to design them so that they will not introduce appreciable losses after considerable use under service conditions.

The way in which the anode-grid cavity of a disk-seal tube is fed by the electron beam is also similar to the klystron case, although here it may be stated even more simply because there need no longer be any reticence about speaking of the voltage difference between grid and plate. Unless it is so desired, there is no need to bring in the concept of electric field between vacuum tube electrodes. The operation can be directly described by saying that very high-frequency alternating voltages appearing between grid and plate, cause charge to oscillate back and forth over the current path shown in Fig. 10-24. The resonant frequency of the cavity is the one in which the time for flow around the path is correct so that the voltage reverses at the proper time to cause the return flow. Such a current forms a changing magnetic field as indicated in Fig. 10-24, and this passes through a coupling loop so as to deliver energy to a transmission line.

The operation of the cathode-grid cavity may be described in a manner very similar to that employed in the anode-grid case although cause and effect are now interchanged. As can be seen in Fig. 10-23, the geometry of the two cases is very nearly the same, so that Fig. 10-24 could equally well serve as a picture of a cathode-grid cavity. The only difference is that the cavity needs to be turned over and that part designated anode, be marked cathode instead. Energy from the transmission line now forms a changing magnetic field in the cathode-grid cavity, which induces a current into the walls of the cavity so as to form a high-frequency voltage between cathode and grid.

Other Uses

A disk-seal tube may be made to serve as an oscillator in much the same way as a two-resonator klystron. It is only necessary to divert some of the high-frequency energy in the transmission line from the anode-grid cavity and insert it into the cathode-grid cavity connection. The amount which must be diverted in this manner is small and does not greatly reduce the useful energy available.

The disk-seal tube may also be used as a frequency multiplier by the simple expedient of using a smaller anode-grid cavity than is used for the cathode-grid cavity. If the anode-grid cavity is tuned to double or triple the frequency of the cathode-grid resonator, the output frequency is twice or three times respectively that of the input. Such an arrangement is shown in Fig. 10-25. Aside from maintaining the idea of using fields in a cavity to cause voltages to be applied to the grid and plate, the method of operation is the same as it is for low-frequency multipliers.

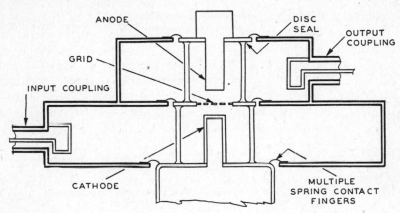

FIG. 10-25. A disk-seal tube used as a frequency multiplier.

Only at the high end of the frequency spectrum over which disk-seal tubes are useful is it necessary to use re-entrant cavities. At lower frequencies (slightly below true microwave levels), re-entrant cavities become too bulky for convenience and it is usual to resort to double concentric-line cavities of the sort shown in Fig. 10-26. In general, re-entrant type cavities are recommended at frequencies above 2000 mc; double concentric-line types are best between 300 and 2000 mc; below 300 mc open wire lines and lumped impedances may be used.

The operation of coaxial-line cavities of Fig. 10-26 is the same as that of resonant-coaxial cavities, which have been described before. The length of the coaxial line to the short circuit at its far end is made an odd number of quarter wavelengths long and energy is picked up or delivered by the transmission lines through coupling loops as has been described earlier. The only difference between the arrange-

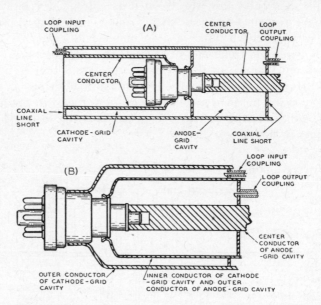

FIG. 10-26. Coupling loops are used to pick up energy or deliver it to the cavities. The only difference between the cavities of (A) and (B) is that the cathode-grid cavity of the latter is folded back over the anode-grid cavity, making for a more compact arrangement.

ment of Fig. 10-26(A) and Fig. 10-26(B) is that purely for mechanical convenience, the cathode-grid cavity of Fig. 10-26(B) is folded back over the anode-grid cavity. This makes a more compact arrangement in which the tube is more accessible.

FOOTNOTE

1. Bruche, E. and A. Recknagel—Zeit fur Phys.—Vol. 108, p. 459-482.

Chapter 11

RADAR AND COMMUNICATION

THE APPLICATION of microwaves to radar and communication involves somewhat different techniques. For radar, the task is one of transmitting a very powerful but extremely brief pulse of energy in a precisely known direction, so that the angle from which the reflected energy returns can be accurately known and so that the time of flight of the radio energy can be accurately timed, thus determining the range and direction of the target. For communication, it is generally desired that the transmitter send out energy continuously, and that intelligence be supplied by modulation in more or less the same way as in ordinary radio communication. It is also generally desired that the antennas have somewhat lower gain than for radar, so that contact can be established with stations not directly along a given line.

As a consequence of the need for pulse transmission of radar signals, it follows that radar systems generally utilize a very broad band of frequencies. If, for example, a microwave oscillator having a frequency of F megacycles per second is turned on for one-half of a microsecond and then turned off, the frequency of the energy generated is not just F megacycles per second, but instead comprises a whole band of frequencies which centers about the frequency F and extends over at least a 4-megacycle range. The reason is no harder to understand than the generation of sidebands when an ordinary transmitter is modulated with a sine-wave audio signal. Turning the oscillator on may be viewed as a very severe type of amplitude modulation, and turning it off after it has been operating so briefly makes it correspond to an extreme case indeed. Fortunately the bandspread is easily computed and is shown in Fig. 11-1, although the definition of bandwidth is not quite the same as that which is generally used. In any event, radar transmission links use extremely broad-band transmission, and make up for the resulting poor signal-to-noise ratio by the extreme strength of the transmitted signal. Precise frequency control is not generally necessary for that very reason. Reasonable drifts of the oscillator frequency are not enough to carry the signal outside of the acceptance range of the receiver.

In a microwave-transmission set used for communication, much narrower frequency bands are more advantageous. Multiple-channel operation is usually needed, and those channels must be fitted into a frequency range which can be accommodated by the bandpass characteristics of the associated waveguide and the tuning range of resonant cavities. Also, because peak microwave transmission strengths are generally lower in communication systems, not only because of continuous operation but also because of lower antenna gains, it is generally necessary to take advantage of the superior signal-to-noise

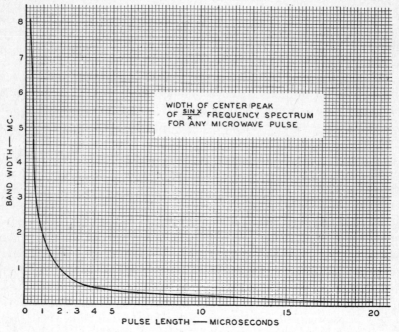

FIG. 11-1. Approximate minimum band-pass characteristic needed for reception of microwave pulses.

ratios that are realized when intelligence can be restricted to a relatively narrow band of frequencies. This requires that the microwave transmitters and receivers that are used for communication must have some means of frequency control that operates with a high degree of accuracy. Quartz crystal control is about the only satisfactory method that has been found so far.

It is the general purpose of this chapter to discuss the overall arrangements of radar and microwave communication systems. To do so, there is a need to consider first the limits of receiver sensitivity that are encountered, and to know a little more about wave propagation.

The Perfect Receiver

There is a definite theoretical limit to how sensitive a radio receiver can be made. If less than a certain threshold signal strength is inserted into the antenna connection of the receiver, satisfactory reception cannot be accomplished no matter how much gain the receiver has, nor how well the mechanical construction details are carried out. This is a severe limitation on the radio art in general, because it imposes a definite limitation on the maximum distance at which a given radio station can be heard. It does, however, serve as a reference level, because it allows the calculation of the performance of an ideal receiver, and it then can be determined how much worse any actual receiver which may be built is in reference to the ideal case. At microwave frequencies in particular, this type of analysis is especially valuable, because receivers can be built which do approach the performance of the ideal. At longer wavelengths, static and other external disturbances often place a limitation on reception which has nothing to do with calculable theoretical performance. A microwave receiver, on the other hand, is quite free from all limitations of this sort. Static and other external interferences simply do not have appreciable components which affect microwave reception as has been demonstrated many times. Under conditions in which long-wave communication was impossible due to interference, the microwave equipment worked normally over the same transmission path.

A perfect receiver is limited in its sensitivity by the thermal noise in the resistive component of the input impedance of the receiver. This may mean the input impedance of the receiving antenna, the first converter, or what is most likely, the input impedance of the first i-f stage. Since, as will be shown presently, the exact value of the input resistance does not need to be known in order to calculate the performance of a perfect receiver, it is not necessary for this discussion that its position be located. Its existence need only be recognized.

To build an extremely good microwave receiver is a different matter. The problems that are faced then are, for the most part, the same as those encountered in any receiver design and are beyond the scope of this book. This fact will be particularly appreciated after examination of the block diagrams of systems that are given in a later part of this chapter, and there may be seen to what extent a microwave receiver is identical to one which is designed for use at lower frequencies.

The crux of the situation, as far as the thermal noise limitation of a perfect receiver, is that any resistor contains electrons which in the presence, or even in the absence of a current, have random motions, in addition to any systematic drift occasioned by the desired signal. These random motions cause the resistor to act like a source of power and to furnish noise signals to the receiver in addition to the desired signal. Such noise is well known to anyone who has operated a sensitive receiver. Even with the antenna disconnected, noise can be heard in the earphones or loudspeaker if the volume-control is advanced sufficiently. A very weak signal can be made to yield intelligence only if it bears a definite relation in strength as compared to the strength of the unavoidable noise. The minimum criterion normally accepted for satisfactory operation is that the signals have as much amplitude as the noise. The difference between a body which is hot and one which is cold is the amount of molecular, atomic, and sub-atomic motion which is going on inside the body. This sheet of paper, which is seemingly quite stationary, is nevertheless made up of many atomic particles which are in constant vibration or rotation. If the paper is made colder the motion is reduced, and only if the paper could be made very cold indeed (—273 degrees centigrade) would the motion cease entirely. At higher temperatures the motion increases in amplitude and, in the case of tungsten, the electrons even get to moving so fast at sufficiently high temperatures that they leave the metal entirely, as they do in tungsten-filament vacuum tubes. Even at room temperature the charge in a resistor moves about in a perfectly random way and with sufficient amplitude so that a voltage of completely arbitrary waveform appears across the ends of the resistor. This voltage is very small in terms of volts, but it is nevertheless finite, and is large enough so that it does place an end limitation on the performance of a radio receiver.

Fortunately, by virtue of many careful measurements, an accurate expression has been obtained for this noise voltage of a resistor. The equation giving the value is

$$e^2 = 4\,k\,T\,R\,\Delta f \tag{1}$$

where e is the noise voltage in volts; k is a constant called Boltzmann's constant, after the man who made early measurements of the phenomenon, and which is equal to 1.37×10^{-23} joules per degree Kelvin; T is the temperature in degrees Kelvin; R is the resistance in ohms; and Δf is the bandwidth over which the noise component is to be evaluated. T is the approximate temperature of the resistor measured according to a temperature scale which uses degrees of the same size as those of the centigrade scale but the zero of which is coincident with an absolute zero temperature at which all atomic motion ceases. The temperature of a body in degrees Kelvin can always be easily computed by adding 273 to its temperature as measured on the centigrade scale. The symbol Δf is, in practice, the bandwidth of the i-f amplifier in cycles.

Since the waveform of the noise voltage generated in a resistor is perfectly random, it contains all frequencies in equal amounts. If an actual plot of the voltage across a resistor could be made against time, and then the irregular curve which results, duplicated by adding up very small sine waves of many frequencies, it would be found that sine waves of all frequencies would be needed. This is no more than an explanation of random motion. Since the resistor charge moves about in a way which is not systemized, a voltage peak may appear at any point in time and consequently a voltage wave of any frequency may be needed to simulate that peak. Saying it all more simply, noise contains components of all frequencies, and to find the amount which lies in a given bandwidth as specified by the band-pass width of the receiver, it is necessary to multiply by the width of that pass-band, which is symbolized as Δf.

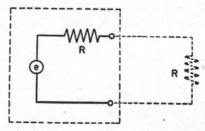

Fig. 11-2. Equivalent circuit for noise generation in the resistive component of the input impedance of a radio receiver.

In Fig. 11-2 the equivalent circuit of the resistive component of the input impedance to a receiver is indicated as an impedance-less generator of noise voltage connected in series with a resistor. If such a device is short circuited the power used inside the device is e^2/R.

The maximum power obtainable from such a device, however, is obtained when a matched load is used. Matching is, of course, not done in order to obtain maximum noise purposely, but this must be closely approached in order to get optimum transfer of the desired signal, which must also pass through the receiver input impedance. The result is that the noise power P in watts available into the matched external resistor of Fig. 11-2, is given by

$$P = \frac{e^2}{4R} \ watts \quad or \quad e^2 = 4RP$$

Substituting this value of e^2 in equation (1), there is obtained

$$Noise \ power = k \ T \ \Delta f \ watts.$$

Thus, if the signal is to have a strength equal to noise, it must, even in a perfect receiver, be able to supply this number of watts to the receiver.

Putting numerical values into the formula, and assuming the resistor to be at normal room temperature (18 degrees C. = 291 degrees Kelvin), the minimum number of watts which must be available to the receiver is

$$E_o = 1.37 \times 10^{-23} \times 291 \times \Delta f = 3.99 \times 10^{-21} \ \Delta f \ watts$$

A plot of the noise power produced for various bandwidths is shown in Fig. 11-3.

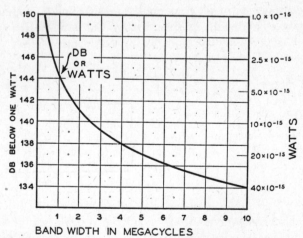

FIG. 11-3. Power in watts and in db below one watt needed at an ideal receiver to produce unity signal-to-noise ratio.

Noise Figures and Practical Receivers

It is generally most convenient to use db in calculating the various factors which enter into signal-strength problems. At the receiver and at the transmitter computations are made with respect to a power of one watt. Elsewhere db gain or loss is calculated in comparison to a standard or ideal arrangement. Thus, in Fig. 11-3, the ideal receiver sensitivity is shown in terms of db below one watt as well as in actual watts. The advantage of using db in this way is that the factors of satisfactory radar or communication transmission can be broken down into separate items. Such a list of factors will be found below. When db values are assigned to each factor (positive numbers for gains and negative numbers for losses), it is only necessary to add them all up to see by what margin the transmission may be accomplished or by what amount it is unsuccessful.

Practical receivers may be assigned a db loss which denotes the amount by which they lack the performance of an ideal receiver. Such a number is usually called the *receiver noise factor*, and for the best practical receivers, it ranges between 6 and 10 db. The method of measuring the noise factor is not easy, although, as in most electrical measurments, the difficulties are primarily those of setting up suitable equipment. What is wanted is to find the ratio of the signal-to-noise at the input as compared to that at the output. If, as is usually done, the noise introduced in the antenna itself is neglected, the problem is simply one of connecting a signal of known noise content, and comparing its signal-to-noise ratio to that which is observed at the input to the detector.

The Propagation Problem

The most uncertain factor in any microwave radar or communication problem is the one which accounts for the signal attenuation resulting from actual transmission through space. The problem is difficult because several things enter in a way that is hard to analyze, and because some of them are difficult to measure. These factors include inverse-square loss due to distance, refraction effects which bend the radio waves so that they do not travel in straight lines, interference phenomena arising from the recombination of energy going directly to the receiving antenna and that which follows a path including a reflection from the earth, and in the case of radar, the matter of how efficient the target is as a reflector. To these might be added factors concerned with antenna gains but this is not usually done. In fact, best practice calls for the inclusion of separate items to give definite isolation to the problem of propagation as distinguished from those which have to do with apparatus.

From the viewpoint of the transmitter and receiver engineer, propagation loss is a factor which relates the power supplied to the transmitting antenna to that which is available from the receiving antenna. On the other hand, the engineer concerned with propagation, wishes to consider the field strength near the receiving antenna as a function of that at a given distance from the transmitting antenna. To bridge this gap it is good practice to introduce decibel factors, which may be respectively called *isotropic transmitting antenna factor* and *isotropic receiver cross-section factor*. The first factor gives a relation between the maximum energy passing through a square meter located a meter from an isotropic transmitting antenna and the power flowing into that antenna. The second factor compares the maximum power passing through an area of one square meter near an isotropic receiving antenna with that which is available from such an antenna. Together with the number of decibels that represent the antenna gains, these give a complete transition from the apparatus itself into the realm of space propagation.

The Isotropic Transmitting Antenna Factor

To compare the energy in a square meter which is one meter away from an isotropic antenna to the total energy which is going into such an antenna is a simple geometric problem. By the definition of an isotropic antenna, the energy moves out into space as concentric spheres and at a distance of one meter it is spread over the surface of a sphere of one meter radius. In other words it is spread over an area of 4π square meters. If W watts go into the antenna, $W/4\pi$ watts are present in each square meter. The decibel loss is therefore given by

$$db \ loss = 10 \ log \ 4\pi$$

This has a numerical value of about 11 so it may be said that the isotropic transmitting antenna factor is 11 db. It is interesting to note that it is entirely independent of frequency and everything else.

The Isotropic Receiver Cross-Section Factor

An isotropic receiving antenna is effectively able to deliver to a receiver all the energy which passes by at a distance that is closer than that fraction of a wavelength λ which is represented by one radian, namely $\lambda/2\pi$. That is, if a small non-directional antenna is mounted at a point in space and radio waves from a remote transmitter are present in the neighborhood of the antenna, some of this energy is absorbed by the antenna. That which passes close to the antenna is absorbed most efficiently, while that which is further away is less well absorbed. The total absorption of a point-isotropic receiving antenna is such that an amount of energy equivalent to that which passes within $\lambda/2\pi$ (one radian) of the antenna is available for the receiver. To calculate the energy absorption, it may be assumed that the antenna acts as if it had an absorbing cross-section of area equivalent to that of a circle $\lambda/2\pi$ centimeters in radius and was able to deliver to the receiver all the energy passing through that area. The cross-section area σ of an isotropic receiving antenna is therefore

$$\sigma = \frac{\lambda^2}{4\pi}.$$

If W watts pass through a square meter of area near the receiving antenna, the energy passing through the antenna cross-section is σW

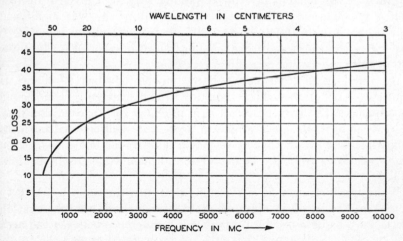

Fig. 11-4. Isotropic receiving antenna cross-section factor.

and, as has been pointed out, this is also the amount of energy made available to the receiver. The isotropic receiver cross-section factor in decibels is therefore

$$db \ loss = 10 \ log \ \frac{4\pi}{\lambda^2}$$

where λ is measured in meters. This factor is shown in graphical form in Fig. 11-4.

As a matter of caution, it is well to point out that Fig. 11-4 taken alone seems to show microwaves to poorer advantage than the truth warrants. Although it is true that absorbing cross-sections are much greater for longer wavelengths, the antenna gain is much smaller and these effects tend to cancel.

Propagation Difficulties

With the assistance of the two decibel relationships just discussed, the problem of measuring and describing the efficiency with which radio energy is carried through space, can now be formulated. The problem is "given a field strength at a distance of one meter from an isotropic transmitter, what is the field strength at some remote point where it is desired to place a receiver?" More specifically the problem is "what db difference is in the field strengths at the two points?" A theory which solves this problem, while taking in account all of the factors, will make it possible to predict whether a given transmission is possible and with what margin of safety. As was mentioned before, this is unfortunately very difficult to do. Only in the case of free-space transmission through a uniform atmosphere can a simple and definite calculation be made.

By a free-space transmission is meant one in which no energy is allowed to strike the surface of the earth and undergo reflection as a consequence. The only practical case in which such a condition may be realized is when one airplane in flight uses a directional beam to communicate with another or to locate it by radar reflections. Even then, reflections from the bodies of the airplanes may result in difficulties.

When free-space conditions obtain, and when the radio beams may be assumed to travel in approximately straight lines, the propagation factor may be obtained by taking the db difference between the area of a one-meter sphere and that of a sphere centered around the transmitting antenna but containing the receiving antenna on its surface. The picture is again one of transmission by expanding spherical waves. Whatever energy exists per square meter in the one-meter sphere will be distributed over a corresponding large number of square meters in

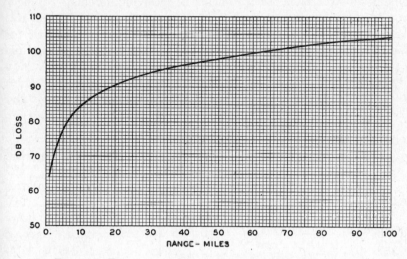

FIG. 11-5. Free-space values of the propagation loss factor.

the sphere which includes the receiving antenna. Fig. 11-5 shows the free-space propagation loss as a function of distance. It is based on

$$db \ loss = 10 \ log \ \frac{4\pi d^2}{4\pi} = 20 \ log \ d$$

where d is the distance between the transmitter and the receiver measured in meters.

When ground reflections are allowed to enter into the picture, the values in Fig. 11-5 may be changed so that the resulting loss is anywhere from 6 db less than that shown to almost an infinite amount greater. Suppose, for example, that a situation like that shown in Fig. 11-6(A) is encountered so that earth reflection is 100% efficient. Then the two waves reaching the receiving antenna will be of the same strength. The one reflected from the earth has traveled a greater distance. It has traveled one-half wavelength further and would therefore seem to be behind the other. It would seem that its peaks might fill in valleys of the other wave, so that no wave at all would result. As was pointed out in Chapter 6, however, reflection from a more dense medium causes a 180-degree phase shift. The peaks and valleys are once interchanged in the reflected wave at the point of reflection. The electrical tardiness of the reflected wave is therefore not effective in reducing the signal strength but instead the two waves combine to strengthen the field near the receiving antenna. Strangely enough, they do not just double the strength there, but instead they increase it by a factor of 4. The strengths of both the electric and magnetic fields are doubled and, as has been previously pointed out,

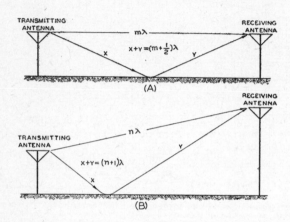

Fig. 11-6. Interference effects in radio-wave propagation.

energy is related by Poynting's vector, which is the product of electric and magnetic field strengths. Multiplying together two quantities that have been doubled yields a factor of 4 in the field strength. This corresponds to a reduction of the space attenuation by 6 db.

On the other hand, in Fig. 11-6(B) the two path lengths are different by a whole wavelength, so that the reflection phase change causes the two waves to be just out of phase, and they therefore interfere with each other. If the reflected wave is indeed of the same strength as the direct wave, no energy at all will be found in the neighborhood of the receiving antenna and the propagation loss becomes infinite.

Since reception at points where maximum reflection interference occurs is possible only if the reflection wave is of less strength than its directly transmitted counterpart, it is important to know about the reflection properties of the terrain over which a transmission is to take place. To date, average figures are relatively untrustworthy and particular values can only be known when the exact nature of the surface is known. Only values for quiet sea water are easily calculable.

Here only a few elements of this problem will be considered. First, the phase-shift is dependent upon the polarization of the wave, and for one polarization at least it is also dependent upon the angle of incidence. Second, the efficiency of reflection is not 100%, except possibly with grazing angles of incidence. Third, there is almost always an effect due to the roughness of the surface, which at microwave frequencies can be as great as those factors already mentioned. Fourth, because of the shortness of microwaves, interference maxima and minima may under certain conditions appear very close together, and even shift due to mobility of the receiver or some other effect, so that the interference effects may partially cancel out.

Feasibility of Communication

That which follows is a list of the factors which enter into determining whether transmission is possible over a given communication or radar range. In any actual system, it is presumed that a number of db (positive for gains, negative for losses) can be assigned to each item. Then if positive, the algebraic sum gives the margin for satisfactory operation, and if negative, tells the margin by which such operation is lacking. Each item is named and discussed at sufficient length to show how it is determined, or else is referred to a previous discussion of its determination, and the difficulties that are incurred. It will be noticed throughout that frequent reference is made to *power available*. By this is meant the amount of power which can be extracted when perfect impedance matching is accomplished. If the impedances are not matched, additional losses must be accounted for.

1. *Oscillator Power.* The output of the transmitter itself, before connection to the transmission line which carries energy to the transmitting antenna, may usually be measured with a wattmeter and a matched load. If the transmission is a pulse type, such a wattmeter reading may well give only an average value so that the transmitter duty cycle needs to be introduced in order to convert to peak power values. If a modulated continuous-wave transmission is used the wattmeter reading can be used directly. Wattmeters used at microwave frequencies almost always depend upon calorimeter methods for their calibration, in which the ability of the r-f power to heat a flowing liquid is measured. In any event, the source of r-f power is

subject to accurate measurement, and may be expressed as a number of db above one watt by the expression

$$db = 10 \ log \ \frac{(power \ in \ watts)}{1 \ Watt}$$

The oscillator power is a gain and is therefore a positive number, except when the output is less than 1 watt.

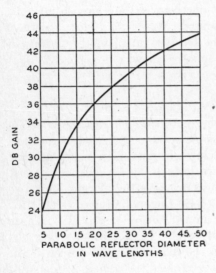

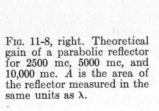

Fig. 11-7, left. Theoretical gain of a parabolic reflector antenna based on gain equal to $w^2 n^2$ where n equals radius of reflector measured in wavelengths.

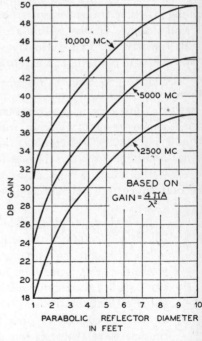

Fig. 11-8, right. Theoretical gain of a parabolic reflector for 2500 mc, 5000 mc, and 10,000 mc. A is the area of the reflector measured in the same units as λ.

2. *Transmitter Cable Loss.* This is the db relation between the power obtainable from the cable at the antenna and that inserted at the transmitter end. In certain cases it may well also be used to account for losses in a send-receive switch and

the like. It is definitely a loss and therefore comes out as a negative number of db.

$$db\ loss = 10\ log \frac{Power\ out\ of\ cable\ to\ matched\ load}{Power\ into\ cable}$$

3. *Isotropic Transmitting Antenna Factor.* As has been already explained, this is a constant loss factor of about 11 db. It bridges the gap between the apparatus and space.

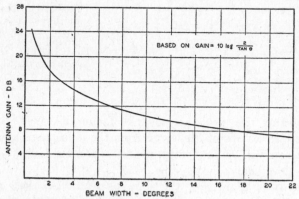

Fig. 11-9. Antenna gain when only vertical directivity is used.

4. *Transmitting Antenna Gain.* This quantity is definitely positive. This was previously defined, and will not be done here again. Figs. 11-7, 11-8, and 11-9, are normally sufficiently accurate for judging the gain of most microwave antennas.

5. *Propagation Loss.* If free-space transmission is assured, values for this may be taken from Fig. 11-5. Normally this cannot be done, and difficult measurements or calculations must be performed in order to correct the values of Fig. 11-5. In particular transmissions, the values shown in Fig. 11-5 may be far too small or even up to 6 db too large. Good practice demands an allowance of 20 to 30 db to account for the fact

Fig. 11-10. Line-of-sight limitation occasioned by earth's curvature.

that the values of Fig. 11-5 may be too small. It also should be pointed out that line-of-sight limitations enter into the measurement of propagation loss. Fig. 11-10 shows how the earth's curvature may limit microwave transmission in this way. Fig. 11-11 is a chart showing line-of-sight limitation when one antenna is at ground level and the other is elevated by the amount shown on the ordinate scale. When, with due allowance for refraction, the curvature of the earth makes it impossible to draw a radio beam path between the transmitting and receiving

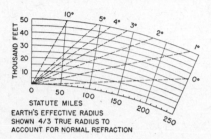

FIG. 11-11. Chart showing the line-of-sight limitation when one antenna is at ground level and the other elevated by the amount shown on the ordinate scale.

antennas, the propagation loss factor becomes very large. Microwaves are not reflected from the ionosphere as are longer wavelengths, consequently, no sky wave, such as is used in the broadcast band, is possible.

In the radar case, the data of Fig. 11-5 does not apply directly. Not only is there reflection efficiency to consider, but also the distance is effective in proportion to its 4th power, because the decrease in the intensity of spherical waves must be thought of not only during the trip from transmitter to target, but also on the return trip from target to receiver.

6. *Isotropic Receiver Cross-Section Factor.* At all true microwave frequencies, the absorption cross-section of an isotropic antenna is smaller than one square meter. This quantity is therefore one which represents a loss and the values taken from Fig. 11-4 should be written with a negative sign.

7. *Receiving Antenna Gain.* This is calculated in the same way as transmitting antenna gain and may be estimated from the same graphs.

8. *Receiver Cable Loss.* The discussion concerning transmitter cable loss may be interpreted to fit this item also.

9. *Perfect Receiver Sensitivity.* The positive number of db to represent the sensitivity of a perfect receiver has been discussed and may be obtained from Fig. 11-3.

10. *Receiver Noise Factor.* This item tells how much worse an actual receiver is than the ideal. It is a loss, and is there-

fore a negative number of db. A 10 db receiver is about as good as can be built for actual use.

11. *Receiver Threshold.* This is chiefly a psychological or human factor. In the discussion of a perfect receiver unity signal-to-noise at the input of the detector as a measure of satisfactory communication was adopted. This is not always true. The number of db by which the signal must surpass noise in order to suit the operator may also be called the *receiver threshold.* In the sense in which db requirements have been entered, this factor is usually a loss and is entered as a negative number. In usual voice communication sets the operators can be satisfied with a receiver threshold figure of about 3 db.

A Radar System

In Fig. 11-12 is shown a sample block diagram arrangement of a microwave radar set. A circuit such as a blocking oscillator or a multi-

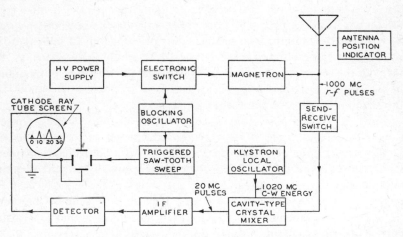

Fig. 11-12. Sample block diagram of a microwave radar set.

vibrator is arranged to produce a waveform that consists of a series of 1/4-microsecond pulses occurring at the rate of say 200 per second, that is, one pulse every .005 second or 5000 microseconds. These need not be the actual values used and, in fact, they are not the best values to use for all applications. These values have been chosen as well as the frequencies shown in Fig. 11-12, in order to make the explanation as definite as possible. This series of pulses is employed to perform at least two things: (1) they trigger a saw-tooth sweep voltage connected to the horizontal plates of a cathode-ray tube; (2) during the very short intervals of time that they are present, they close a switch so as to apply voltage to a magnetron oscillator. Thus 200 times a second, the magnetron oscillates at 1000 mc for a very short period of time (¼ microsecond), and this microwave energy is transmitted from an antenna. Some microseconds later this energy returns as an echo signal. Since transmission is no longer taking place, the receiver is ready for reception. The 1000-mc received pulse goes into a resonant-cavity mixer where it is mixed with a C-W signal of 1020 mc, which is supplied by a klystron local oscillator. As in any mixer, the difference frequency is obtained and 20-mc pulses result. These pulses are amplified, detected, and applied to the vertical plates of the cathode-ray tube. Since the linear sweep of the cathode-ray tube is synchronized to start just as the pulses leave the transmitting antenna, the position on the sweep at which the detected echo pulses occur depends upon the time elapsing during their travel to and from the target. Consequently the horizontal trace on the oscilloscope may be calibrated in miles. The pattern shown in Fig. 11-12 indicates the presence of three objects respectively 10, 20, and 29 miles away. By viewing the scope and reading the exact angle of elevation and azimuth in which the antenna beam is directed, it is possible to know the direction and range of the target.

Suppose, for example, that an airplane is 30 miles from a ground radar station the beam from which is so directed as to spot the airplane. Then, using the numerical values to which reference has been made, pulses of microwave energy will be sent out toward the airplane every 5000 microseconds (1/200 of a second). These pulses last for only a quarter of a microsecond, and each one is followed by more than 4999 microseconds in which the transmitter is not operating. Now since radio energy travels through space at the rate of 186,000 miles per second, the time of travel over 60 miles (30 miles each way) is 60/186,000 second or about 322 microseconds. If the saw-tooth sweep on the indicator cathode-ray tube is designed to travel across the screen in just 322 microseconds, then the particular reflection to which reference has been made will occur at just the end of the sweep and give a peak more or less like the one shown at the far right end of the oscilloscope of Fig. 11-12. Since new pulses are sent out and received 200 times a second and for each sweep of the cathode-ray tube, the peak representing a target appears as a steady mark on the trace which moves only as the range changes.

Several of the blocks shown in Fig. 11-12 need some further explanation. Almost all of them are rather special in the details of their construction, at least as viewed in terms of ordinary radio components. Since there is no desire here to give radar construction data, the comment will not be exhaustive nor will circuit diagrams be given.

The blocking oscillator itself, although a well-known arrangement, is difficult to design so as to create such short pulses of voltage (one four-millionth of a second in duration). The trick is essentially contained in the design of the iron-cored transformer which provides feedback between the plate and grid circuits. Only with the use of very special core materials is it possible to get as strong interaction as is necessary for giving the very steep and square edges to such a brief pulse, without introducing inductive lags that would destroy the desired waveform. Voltage pulses of roughly 100 volts amplitude are normally created.

The magnetron switching circuit is another device which has unusual and severe requirements. The blocking oscillator pulses must be able to connect a voltage of many thousands of volts momentarily to the magnetron. This can be done by using a high-voltage triode or screen-grid tube. The positive-going blocking-oscillator pulse is applied to the grid and momentarily causes the tube to become conducting, although the tube is normally biased beyond cutoff. Special high-voltage thyratrons and spark-gap devices have also been used.

In general, it may be desirable that the transmitted pulse make some mark on the oscilloscope to serve as a zero time-of-flight reference. It is not desirable, however, that the full transmitter power shall be fed into the cavity mixer during the time of transmission. To do so would burn out the crystal rectifier in the microwave mixer cavity, and would overload all of the receiver circuits assuming that such a burn-out could be avoided. This problem is normally solved by using a transmit-receive switch in the receiver antenna line. It may take the form of a spark-gap in a waveguide which is fired during the intervals when the transmission is taking place. The resulting ions serve effectively as a barrier in the waveguide, and prevent the transmitted energy from directly entering the receiver. In any event, the function is to disconnect the receiver partially during transmission so that the initial transmitted pulse will have a very small effect on the receiver. This must be done in such a way that the receiver regains its sensitivity almost immediately after the transmission so as to be ready to receive echo pulses.

Other types of cathode-ray tube scanning may also be used. In one popular kind, known as the plan-position-indicator (PPI), the receiver output is allowed to change the intensity of the cathode-ray tube beam rather than to deflect it. A sweep of the beam is then arranged so that the beam is continually swept from the center of the screen out to a point on the periphery. If the direction of this radial motion is made to correspond to the point of the compass toward which the radio beam is directed, and if this direction is constantly changing as the beam scans the horizon, the results will look very much like a map, with targets appearing as bright spots on the screen and so located that those distant appear near the edge and closer ones near the center.

It has already been pointed out that the angular resolving power of a radar set depends upon the narrowness of the beam from the antenna. If a one-half degree conical beam is used, that beam will cover about 1400 feet at a 30-mile range and will consequently be unable to distinguish between 2 targets which are closer together than that and which are at a 30-mile range. The range resolving power depends chiefly upon the speed of the oscilloscope sweep which is used and somewhat on the shortness of the pulse. A quarter-microsecond pulse, for example, has a duration which corresponds to a round trip travel of radio energy over a distance of about 125 feet. Such pulses cannot differentiate between targets which do not have a separation that is in excess of 125 feet.

The Radar Transmission Problem

During the brief periods of transmission, suppose that the energy passing through one square meter of area which is located one meter in front of a radar antenna, be represented as W watts. Then, in the free-space case, Fig. 11-5 shows the energy per square meter in the neighborhood of the target. Suppose that an airplane target is 10 miles from the radar set, then the power per square-meter at the airplane will be 84 db below W watts. Now an average aircraft target has a cross-section for reflection (target cross-section) that is just about equal to one square meter. This means that an average aircraft will act as if it intercepted all the energy incident on a square meter of area and retransmitted that energy equally in all directions. If the target cross-section were 2 square meters, it would retransmit twice that amount and the db level of retransmission would be increased by 3 db. This may seem like a roundabout way to define the reflecting ability of a radar target for targets do not take out all of the energy from a given area because they absorb some energy and reflect the rest. Also, they do not radiate isotropically. It is an established convention, however, to rate radar targets in terms of target cross-section. A radar target is rated as a given area measured in square meters and has a reflection ability that is equal to that of an isotropic radiator fed with the power passing through that area.

After finding the strength of the apparent isotropic radiator which simulates the radar target (84 db below the field strength in front of the transmitter for the numerical example), an 11-db loss is introduced (as in the isotropic transmitting antenna factor) to get the reflected field strength one meter in front of the target. After doing this, the db loss from Fig. 11-5 is re-introduced in order to obtain the reflected signal strength near the radar set. Thus the complete radar propagation loss for the numerical example being considered, is,

$$db\ loss = 84 + 11 + 84 = 179$$

and in general, it is given by

$$db\ loss = 2A + B + 11$$

where A is the db quantity taken from Fig. 11-5 and B is a number given by

$$B = 10\ log\ \frac{target\ cross\text{-}section\ in\ square\ meters.}{one\ square\ meter}$$

All this is true only when free-space conditions hold.

It is now possible to work out an example that shows how the various components of a radar system must perform in order to find a target successfully. Values in db shall be tabulated for each item and arranged in two columns, with the loss quantities (negative values) in one and the gain values (positive quantities) in the other. What is shown is not the only condition under which a target can be detected when it is 10 miles away; the values may be changed so that the gain column continues to be greater than the loss column.

Example. The detection of an airplane of one square-meter target cross-section at a distance of 10 miles.

Gains			*Losses*	
Oscillator Power			Transmitter Cable Loss	−1 db
4,000 watts	46 db		Isotropic Transmitting	
Transmitting **Antenna**			Antenna Factor	−11 db
Gain (30-in. diameter) ..	28 db		Propagation Loss	**−179 db**
Receiving Antenna Gain	28 db		Isotropic Receiver Cross-	
Perfect Receiver Sensi-			Section (10-cm wave-	
tivity (8-mc bandwidth)	135 db		length)	−31 db
			Receiver Cable Loss....	−1 lb
			Receiver Noise Factor..	−10 db
			Receiver Threshold....	−2 db
Total Gain	237 db		Total Loss	−235 db

Since the gains exceed the losses by 2 db, the target will be successfully found.

Microwave Communication

There are as many ways to arrange a one-way microwave transmission as there are ways to communicate with long-wave radio. Amplitude and frequency modulation are both feasible. Teletype, facsimile, and even television can without doubt be made feasible on microwaves. Because of this variety of possible applications, they cannot all be described, and as a matter of fact there is little need to do so because on paper the methods look very much like their low-frequency counterparts. Most microwave communication systems are really modifications of existing methods used at low frequencies, and only the way in which the microwave frequency level is utilized, is new. The microwave transmitter may consist of what would normally be a complete low-frequency unit plus a system of frequency multiplication to raise the frequency to the desired level. Power amplification is added at the final frequency, rather than at the lower frequency, so that the unit which might be designated as a low-frequency transmitter, becomes a small low-power and compact unit but is otherwise essentially unchanged. Likewise the receiver, which is almost always of the heterodyne type, consists of a unit which almost exactly corresponds to an ordinary receiver, but which is preceded by another converted and a microwave local oscillator that transforms the received signal down to frequency levels to which the receiver proper can tune.

Fig. 11-13 illustrates the application of microwaves to frequency-modulation voice communication. A 5-mc crystal in the transmitter controls the frequency of the microwave energy used. The output of the crystal oscillator is frequency modulated in any one of several

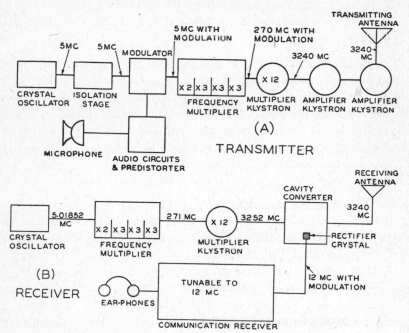

FIG. 11-13. Block diagram of microwave transmitter (A) and receiver (B) for communication.

more-or-less standard ways. For example, one system splits the crystal oscillator signal into two parts. One part is then shifted 90 degrees in phase, and then subjected to amplitude modulation in a balanced modulator. The two halves are then recombined and the unchanged half finds itself shifted in phase in accord with the modulation. Fig. 11-14 helps in understanding how this occurs. Vector A

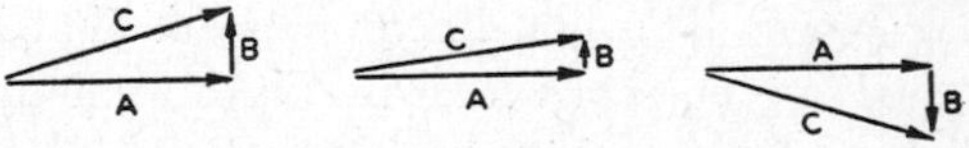

FIG. 11-14. Phase modulation of a crystal-controlled oscillator.

represents the crystal oscillator voltage with a phase corresponding to no modulation; this condition of the phase is represented by the fact that the arrows are directed toward the right-hand margin of the page. Vector B signifies the phase-shifted signal derived from the crystal oscillator and in accord with the audio signal it has magnitude and polarity somewhere in the range shown. In accord with the value of B, the resulting 5-mc signal from the modulator, represented by C, has a phase somewhere in the range shown and an amplitude that is almost constant.

The resulting modulation is really phase modulation rather than true frequency modulation, but the two are indistinguishable when proper predistortion of the audio-frequency signal is used. This can be seen by thinking about the act of changing the phase of a sine wave. While the phase is being changed, the wavelengths are shortened or lengthened and that corresponds to a change of frequency. Such phase modulation will emphasize the high audio-frequency signals unless they are weakened in the predistortion circuit.

The output of the modulator of Fig. 11-13(A) is arranged to have a rather small frequency deviation, even when the highest audio frequency is being transmitted. This is desirable because the frequency deviations are multiplied at the same time that the carrier frequency level is increased. The first four multiplications may well be accomplished by ordinary vacuum tubes, but at frequency levels of 270 mc or more, velocity modulation must be used. Fortunately, multiplier klystrons may be used to raise frequencies in rather large steps. Also, since resonant cavities are used, the last multiplier stage consists of a klystron and nothing else.

The receiver of Fig. 11-13(B) uses a frequency-multiplier chain similar to the one in the transmitter, but a slightly higher frequency crystal is used so that the microwave frequency which results is 12 mc higher than the undeviated transmitter frequency. The microwave signal developed in the receiver serves as a local oscillator for the cavity mixer, which mixes the local-oscillator signal with the received signal to produce a 12-mc frequency beat which carries the intelligence. The non-linear element that is required in the mixer is a rectifying crystal which is suitably mounted in the cavity and from which the i-f signal is obtained. Once the microwave intelligence exists on the 12-mc carrier, it may be amplified and detected just as it would be in any conventional 12-mc transmission.

Other Methods

If crystal control of frequency is elminated, a considerable simplification of the FM system shown in Fig. 11-13 may be accomplished. It is then possible to insert the modulation directly into the microwave generator, and this can be done in at least two ways. It can be accomplished by allowing the audio signal to vary the reflector voltage of a reflex klystron, or else the audio voltage may be used to modify the cathode potential of a multiple-chamber tube. In the latter case especially, a considerable amount of audio power is needed, but except for the undesirable bulk of the audio amplifier, this presents no particular difficulty. The receiver, which is operated without crystal control, is approximately the same as the one described before except that a free-running (self-oscillating) reflex oscillator takes the place of the frequency-multiplication equipment.

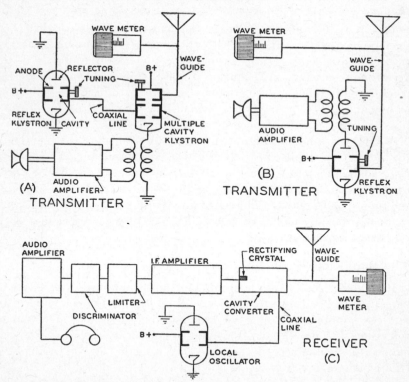

FIG. 11-15. Possible arrangements for microwave F-M transmission and reception without using crystal control.

In Fig. 11-15 are shown block diagrams of two transmitters and a receiver. The transmitter of Fig. 11-15(A) may be expected to deliver 10 to 100 watts, while the simpler one shown in Fig. 11-15(B) will probably be limited to less than 4 watts. Its power output is limited because of the properties of the tubes which have thus far been built. There seems to be no definite reason to say that higher power tubes capable of operation in accord with scheme of Fig. 11-15(B) cannot be built.

Frequency drift in schemes like those shown in Fig. 11-15 cannot be avoided when components that have thus far been manufactured are used. It is therefore necessary to use wavemeters to indicate the frequency roughly, and, in the case of the receiver, final tuning must be dictated by the quality of the reception desired.

When it is desired to use amplitude modulation of microwaves, the technique of modulating at low frequencies, and then raising the frequency level by multiplication, is not very satisfactory. The reason is that it is too difficult to design the multiplier stages so that their gains and losses are constant with changing level of input. It is also rather unsatisfactory to try to influence the signal amplitude in the klystrons themselves. AM operation may be obtained by causing the modulation to influence the grid or plate voltage of the last multiplier, or by causing it to change the characteristics of the microwave transmission lines which carry energy to the transmitting antenna.

A different kind of microwave communication must be mentioned for the sake of completeness. It uses what has become known as *pulse-time modulation*. Magnetron oscillators in pulse service may be used in the transmitter, and the audio intelligence is inserted by changing the time spacing between pulses. It may be thought of as square-wave frequency modulation. The series of magnetron pulses change their repetition rate in response to the audio modulation.

The Bandwidth Problem

Reasonably good audio transmission can be obtained over telephone wires with a bandwidth of 3000 cycles or less. Other communication services require more or less bandwidth but, with the exception of television, the intelligence conveying requirement requires often less bandwidth than is necessitated for other reasons. This is particularly true of microwave frequencies where bandwidths of 250 kc (as compared with 10 kc in the broadcast band) are considered to be narrow, particularly in comparison with the bandwidths used in radar.

Two factors are influential in limiting the narrowness of the bandwidth of a microwave communication system: (1) the frequency stability which can reasonably be maintained even with crystal stabilization, and (2) the necessity for using frequency deviations that are sufficiently large to mask small random fluctuations. It must also be remembered that the frequency deviation of the intelligence is increased by frequency multiplication of the carrier. This means that the masking of random frequency fluctuations at the 5-mc level will yield a much larger final deviation, and consequently demands a greater bandwidth than would be required by conventional FM broadcast systems.

Quartz crystals can reasonably be required to maintain frequency with an accuracy of about 10 parts in a million. If frequency multiplication by a factor of 500 or 1000 is used, this means that the microwave energy will have stability of the same order of magnitude, namely, that the microwave energy will maintain its frequency accurately to about 2.5 to 5 kc. Allowing for both the transmitter and receiver, about 10 kc of bandwidth is necessary to take care of frequency drift. Adding this to the bandwidth required for frequency deviation when FM is employed, means that a microwave communication receiver needs to be sensitive to frequencies in a 200-to-300-kc band.

Communication Propagation Loss

Because lower-gain antennas are used, it is very seldom that free-space values of propagation loss are of much value in checking the feasibility of communication over a given link. Neither experimentally or theoretically are the range of values likely to be encountered under service conditions that are well known. Theory requires the assumption of numerical values which describe the refraction properties of the atmosphere and the reflection efficiency of the earth. How much these values change under different day-to-day conditions and in different parts of the world, is not well known. About the best that can be done here is to show a reasonable balance sheet of gains and losses which are written in accord with experience but with the propagation loss indicated by the letter X. The end result of such a tabulation is a solution for a maximum value of the propagation loss. It may be presumed that measurements and calculations of this sort will ultimately show more about the values of propagation loss which are likely to be encountered in a given transmission.

Example. Transmission between two antennas located well above the surrounding terrain and separated by 100 miles.

Gains		Losses	
Oscillator Power 10 watts	10 db	Transmitter Cable Loss.	–1 db
Transmitting Antenna Gain (16 degree beam)..	8 db	Isotropic Transmitting Antenna Factor	–11 db
		Propagation Loss	–X db
Receiving Antenna Gain (16 degree beam)..	8 db	Isotropic Receiver Cross-Section (10 cm wave-	
Perfect Receiver Sensitivity (250 kc bandwidth)	150 db	length)	–31 db
		Receiver Cable Loss....	–1 db
		Receiver Noise Factor...	–10 db
		Receiver Threshold	–2 db
Total Gain 176 db		Total Loss $-(56 + X)$ db	

From this it is apparent that the propagation loss must be less than 120 db for satisfactory communication.

SECTION II

MICROWAVE TERMS, IDEAS, AND THEOREMS

THE FOLLOWING LIST of terms, ideas, and theorems is primarily intended to give discussions and introductions to concepts rather than rigorous definitions. The sentences in italics, however, are meant to summarize the idea in each paragraph and will serve as definitions that are accurate enough for most purposes. This section as well as the earlier part of the book, is intended to be read for general information as well as used for reference.

Admittance — Y

If an a-c voltage is impressed across a load, a certain alternating current will flow. In the same way that Ohm's law for d.c. allows us to define the resistance or conductance of a load by $R = V_{dc}/I_{dc}$ or $G = I_{dc}/V_{dc}$, so impedance Z or admittance Y may be defined for a.c. by $Z = V_{ac}/I_{ac}$, or $Y = I_{ac}/V_{ac}$, where the V's and I's are peak values. Moreover, it is often desirable that Y also show the phase relation between the current and voltage. To accomplish this, it is more usual to write $Y = G + jB$. The conductance G then represents the value of the in-phase component of the current divided by the voltage and the susceptance B gives the ratio of the out-of-phase current to the same voltage. The operator $j = \sqrt{-1}$ distinguishes between the two.

This is possible because a sine-wave plot of the actual current as a function of time may be replaced by the sum of two sine waves, one in-phase and the other out-of-phase with the voltage. In other words, it is possible to consider the current as made up of two currents, one of which is in-phase with the voltage and gives a ratio G to the voltage, while the other is out-of-phase and is B times as large as the voltage. *The admittance of an electrical load is a vector quantity the magnitude of which is the ratio of the a-c current to the a-c voltage and the direction of which in reference to a vector representing the voltage is at an angle equal to the phase angle between the current and voltage; Y is commonly written in the form $Y = G + jB$, where G and B respectively represent ratios to the voltage of the in-phase and out-of-phase currents.*

289

When Z is said to be equal to $1/Y = 1/(G + jB) = [G/(G^2 + B^2)]$ $- j [B/(G^2 + B^2)] = R + jX$, more is implied than just a relation between the vector magnitudes of Y and Z. If, as is shown in Fig. 1, Y represents a vector θ degrees counterclockwise from the voltage reference vector lying along the positive x-axis of a Cartesian coordinate system on which imaginary quantities are plotted along the ordinate and real quantities along the abscissa, then Z automatically

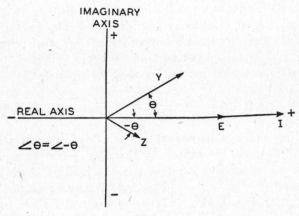

FIG. 1

becomes a vector θ degrees clockwise from a reference current vector which also lies along the abscissa. Thus even in terms of complex notation, Y and Z are rigorously reciprocals of each other. It is necessary, however, to remember that while the conductance G and the susceptance B, which comprise admittance, are ratios of current components to the total voltage, resistance R and reactance X are ratios of voltage components to the total current. Hence, except in the case of a pure reactance or pure resistance, G is not the reciprocal of R nor is B the reciprocal of X.

Ampere

An ampere of current is a flow of electric charge in strength just sufficient to transfer one coulomb of charge per second.

Ampere's Circuital Law

The Biot-Savart law for determining the value of a magnetic field

H requires a knowledge of conditions in all space or, at least, in all that portion of space which can appreciably affect the computation. It does not easily lend itself to the examination of a region in a space which elsewhere contains unknown currents. Ampere's circuital law, on the other hand, specifies a relation that depends upon only a single current or current distribution and, while it alone does not directly yield a value of *H* nor in general apply to other than steady currents, nevertheless it is useful and does add to our knowledge of the nature of *H*.

If any closed path is traversed in a direction so as to keep the enclosed area on the left and, if for every small length of that path, the tangential component of *H* in the direction of travel is represented by H_s and multiplied by the incremental length ds, then the sum of these products taken around the entire path is called the magneto-motive force (mmf) of that circuit. In calculus notation this is written as a line integral, namely,

$$mmf = \oint H_s \cdot ds$$

More simply, *mmf* is of the nature of a magnetic field multiplied by a distance; the definition just given requires the field considered to be in the direction of the path, allows for the field to have varying values along the path, and indicates our interest in closed magnetic circuits. In terms of *mmf* the circuital law may be simply stated. *The magnetomotive force around any closed path is 4π times the current crossing any surface of which the path is the boundary and is independent of all other currents.* Symbolically this may be stated as

$$\oint H_s \, ds = 4\pi I$$

In MKS units, **H** is in amperes per meter, *I* in amperes, and ds in meters; in emu, **H** is in oersteds, *I* in emu amperes, and ds in cm. In the latter case a proportionality factor of $1/c$ must be used and the law written as $\oint H_s \, ds = \dfrac{4\pi}{c} I$. If a wire carries a current which is distributed uniformly throughout the cross-section, we may easily find the **H**-field within the wire. By symmetry, the magnetic lines of force within the wire must be circles concentric with the wire and the field must be of equal intensity around any one of these circular paths. Thus if *r* is the distance of a path from the axis of the wire, the *mmf* must be $2\pi r$H. The current within the circle of radius r is just the fraction of the total current given by the ratio of the area of the circle to the cross-section area of the wire. Hence, by the circuital law, $2\pi r$H $=4\pi i \ (\pi r^2)/(\pi R^2)$, where R is the radius of the wire. Solving for H we have H $= 2Ir/R^2$ for the field inside the wire as compared to the well-known relation, H $= \dfrac{2I}{r}$ for the field outside.

Ampere's Rule

Whenever an electric charge passes through a magnetic field it is in general subject to a force which tends to move it in a direction perpendicular to both the magnetic field and its own motion. Only in the special case in which the charge is moving parallel to the magnetic field does this force become zero, although it is a maximum when the motion is at right angles to the magnetic field. Ampere's rule gives a method of calculating this force. *It is* $F = BQV \ sin \ \phi$ *where* F *is the force in newtons on a charge of strength Q coulombs, which is moving V meters per second in a field of strength* B *webers per square meter in a direction ϕ degrees away from the direction of motion.* These are the units which apply when the MKS system is used. In the gaussian system of units F is in dynes, B in gauss, Q in emu coulombs (a unit 10 times as large as a practical coulomb), and V in cm. per sec.

Ampere's rule is also often stated for a wire carrying current through a magnetic field. It is then $F = BIL \ sin \ \phi$ where, in the MKS system, I is in amperes, and L is in meters, representing the length of the wire. F may then be considered as the force on the wire.

Antenna Cross-Section

It is often convenient to describe the ability of a receiving antenna in terms of an area which is called antenna cross-section. *The merit of a receiving antenna is described by an area, called antenna cross-section, which when placed perpendicular to the incident radiation is just able to intercept an amount of energy equal to that which the actual antenna delivers to a receiver, the antenna being assumed to be perfectly matched to the receiver.* The antenna cross-section of an isotropic receiving antenna is the area of a circle whose radius is one radian of wavelength. In other words, it is the area of a circle of

$\lambda/2\pi$ radius, where λ is the wavelength of the signal in free space. The antenna cross-section of any other antenna (in the direction of maximum sensitivity) may be found by multiplying the isotropic cross-section area by the antenna gain.

Antenna Gain

In a sense, no antenna can have the effect of giving a gain in power. The energy radiated can never exceed that fed to the antenna, and practically it is somewhat less. Antenna gain is therefore not like a gain which describes the operation of a vacuum tube amplifier stage, but rather represents an increase in transmission efficiency in a certain direction at the expense of the efficiency in another direction. An antenna having a high gain is therefore always one which is highly directional. Microwaves particularly lend themselves to the use of highly directional antennas and therefore allow a high gain to be practically realizable. *Antenna gain may be defined as the ratio of the intensity of radiation in the direction of maximum intensity to the intensity that would be available if the antenna emitted the same total power, but in a manner so as to spread it out uniformly in all directions.*

Suppose, for example, an antenna pattern is obtained which radiates a signal the strength of which is completely independent of the azimuth angle and which depends upon the elevation angle in a manner that may be approximated by $P = P_o \epsilon^{-180\theta^2}$, where P is the power emitted per unit, solid angle at an angle θ radians above or below the horizontal. Such a pattern is of pancake shape. It has a maximum radiative power of P_o at zero degrees elevation where $\epsilon^{-180\theta^2}$ is equal to one and falls off to about one-half that amount at $+11$ degrees of elevation. The total solid angle contained between the elevation angles θ and $\theta + d\theta$ is $2 \cos \theta d\theta$, so the total radiation through that element of elevation angle is $2P_o \cos \theta \epsilon^{-180\theta^2} d\theta$.

To find the average power per solid radian, it is only necessary to perform an integration and divide by the 4π radians contained in a complete sphere. Actually, the integration is difficult. It may be approximated however from tables of the normal error function by taking $\cos \theta$ equal to unity under the assumption that the exponential term is small for all other values. The average power P_{av} comes out in this case to be $(1/24)P_o$.

Antenna Reciprocity Theorem

When applied to a pair of antennas or to any other four-terminal network containing only linear impedance elements, the essential idea of the reciprocity theorem is that an impedanceless voltage source and an impedanceless ammeter may be interchanged in position without affecting the reading of the ammeter. This theorem was first discovered by Rayleigh and was extended to include radio communication by John R. Carson. For antennas, it states that *if an alternating voltage from a zero-impedance source is connected to one antenna and a zero-impedance ammeter is connected into another antenna remote from the first, the alternating current in the ammeter will be unchanged in both magnitude and phase if its position is exchanged with that of the voltage source in the other antenna.*

The only exceptions occur to the extent that radio waves are appreciably affected by the earth's magnetic field in conjunction with an ionized atmosphere. If one antenna is moved about another antenna and an impedanceless ammeter imagined to be read in series with the portable antenna, then from readings of that ammeter the radiation pattern of the fixed antenna can at least be plotted for distances which are large compared to the antenna dimensions. By the reciprocity theorem this plot will also represent the receiving pattern of the fixed antenna. Thus, the reciprocity theorem has an important corollary that *the receiving and transmitting patterns of any antenna array must be identical.*

Applegate Diagram

An Applegate diagram is a geometrical construction which determines the location of the electron bunches in a klystron as a function of time. As is shown in Fig. 2 the abscissa represents time and the ordinate shows distances along the electron beam away from the buncher. The plotted lines show how velocity modulation is possible, namely, how a varying voltage somewhere along the beam can cause a periodic appearance of a high charge density further along the beam.

The voltage across the buncher grids varies approximately as is shown in the lower part of the diagram. This voltage accelerates or decelerates the electrons, and hence determines the velocity with which they travel through the drift space. In the diagram the velocity is represented by the slope of a line; thus each line represents the path followed in space time by an electron leaving the buncher at a

given time. If the buncher-grid voltages are known, then the electron
path lines may be assigned slopes in accord with that voltage, and the
optimum position for the catcher can then be located. In the case

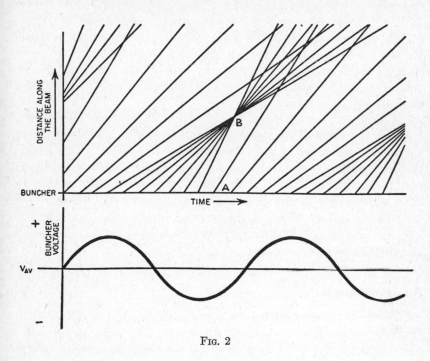

Fɪɢ. 2

shown, maximum bunching occurs at a point B along the beam. The
distance AB represents the field-free drift space between the buncher
and catcher. The diagram does not take into account the debunching
caused by space charge.

Attenuation Constant—α

This constant describes the way in which a signal is attenuated as
it travels along a uniform line. It is possible and convenient to make
such a description with a single factor containing only one disposable
constant because of the special properties of the number ϵ (base of
natural Logarithms = 2.7183) and because the loss of signal in any
very small length of a uniform line is always the same fraction of the
signal entering that element of line.

Suppose, for example, a signal of strength P enters a line 20 inches long and is attenuated at the rate of 1/20 of its strength per inch. If we loosely interpret this to mean that in each 2 inches the signal strength is reduced by 1/10, then after the first 2 inches the strength is $0.90P$, after the next 2 inches only $0.81P$, at the end of 6 inches $0.729P$, and so on until after 20 inches the signal strength is $0.349P$. On the other hand, if we work in one-inch steps assuming that a 5% loss occurs in each inch, then at the ends of the 1st, 2nd, 3rd, and 20th inches, the signal strength is $0.95P$, $0.9025P$, $0.857P$, and $0.358P$, respectively.

To obtain a correct result, the loss in an infinitesimal length must be used and calculations made on that basis. When that is done, the signal present at the end of the 20 inches is $0.3679P$. This number 0.3679 is just ϵ^{-1}. Furthermore, $P\epsilon^{-0.5}$ gives the signal strength half way along the line, $P\epsilon^{-0.25}$ at the quarterway point, etc., so that $P\epsilon^{-x}$ gives the strength at any point x inches along the line where α is the attenuation rate in terms of the fraction of the signal lost per inch. *The attenuation constant α expresses a rate of signal loss in terms of the fraction of the signal lost per unit length.*

Azimuth Angle

In order to specify the direction of a radio beam it is convenient to state the orientation in terms of two angles. One gives the inclination above or below the horizon and is called the *elevation angle*. The other is an angle which designates a particular point of the compass. *The azimuth angle of a radio beam means the angle between the beam and some reference line drawn at the same elevation angle.*

Beam-Loading

Resonant cavities, such as those found in a magnetron or klystron, lose energy because of the presence of the electron beam. It is also true that they may gain their energy from the beam, but usually that occurs over only a part of a cycle. During the rest of the cycle the beam acts as a load on the resonator and, particularly because of secondary emission, it may be an important factor in determining the shunt resistance of the cavity. *Energy loss from a cavity due to the coupling of the cavity to an electron beam is known as beam-loading.*

Bessel Functions—J and Y

Although somewhat less familiar than ordinary trigonometric functions, Bessel functions serve much the same kind of purpose. Sines and cosines lend themselves to particularly simple definitions in terms of right triangles. Although no similar description can be given for Bessel functions, that is a relatively minor point. The important thing is that in certain physical problems, such as a pendulum swinging through a small angle, a descriptive differential equation based on physical laws may be written in the form

$$\frac{d^2x}{dt^2} = Ax$$

When solved in conjunction with proper boundary conditions, such an equation involves only trigonometric functions in specifying the action of the physical apparatus. In another large class of physical problems the differential equation is

$$\frac{d^2x}{dt^2} + \frac{1}{t}\frac{dx}{dt} + \left(1 - \frac{k^2}{t^2}\right)x = 0$$

This time it turns out that trigonometric functions will not suffice. Instead a new kind of function called a Bessel function is needed. The differential equation just given is called Bessel's equation. *Solutions of Bessel's equation are known as Bessel functions.* Every value of the parameter k is associated with a pair of solutions called **Bessel functions** of order k. One of them, which is finite at $t = 0$, is called a Bessel function of the first kind and often represented by J_k; the other is called a Bessel function of the second kind and is sometimes represented by Y_k. Just as with sines and cosines, tables of values of J_0, Y_0; J_1, $J_{\frac{3}{2}}$, etc., are available which give numerical values of the functions for various values of their argument.

Many other functions, which are well known to mathematicians, also represent solutions of differential equations that are occasionally encountered in physical problems. Among these are hyperbolic and elliptic functions, Legendre polynomials, Henkle functions, Tesseral harmonics, and others.

The propagation of energy in a circular waveguide having attenuation and the calculation of antenna patterns, especially from horn radiators, are examples of microwave problems which involve Bessel functions.

Biot-Savart Law

Generally the magnetic field **H** at any point in the neighborhood of a wire carrying a current can be found by computing a vector sum of the field components arising from each incremental length of the wire. The components are individually given by $d\mathbf{H} = (I\,dl\sin\theta)/r^2$, *where I is a current, dl is the incremental length, r is the distance from dl to the point in question, and θ is the angle between r and a tangent to the wire at dl; each of the components is perpendicular to r and dl and is directed in accord with the way in which the right-hand rule causes the fingers to point when the thumb shows the direction of the current through dl. If* **H** *is to come out in oersteds, I must be in emu amperes and l and r in centimeters.*

The law is most clearly justified by differentiating the rigorously obtainable expression for the magnetic field produced by a single closed circuit (see Ampere's Circuital Law.) It must always give a correct result if the summation of incremental currents is carried around one or more closed paths. The principle of summing over multiple closed circuits may even be extended to the case of current distributions, which are considered to be made up of an infinite number of closed current filaments. When only portions of a current-carrying wire are considered, however, it is not certain that there may not be false contributions to the field which would cancel out for a closed path integration.

Of great practical importance is the fact that while the Biot-Savart law is strictly true only for closed circuits or an infinite straight filament, it is approximately true for wire bent into any shape, provided the point at which it is desired to calculate **H** is close to the wire in comparison to the linear dimensions of the whole circuit.

Black-Body Radiation

J. C. Slater has pointed out that an independent proof of the equivalence of the receiving and transmitting patterns of an antenna can be obtained from the well-known properties of black-body radiation. *A black-body is defined in the study of optics and thermodynamics as one which absorbs all radiation incident upon it and reflects none.* Thus a small hole in a hollow box approximates a perfect black-body. All energy reaching the hole passes on into the box and is indefinitely subject to multiple internal reflections. When thermal equilibrium is reached, however, the interior of the box, like any ordinary body, must emit energy at the same rate that it is received. *The energy emitted from a black-body is characterized by a perfectly random direction of travel and depends only upon temperature.*

It is possible to imagine the space around a given antenna to be so filled with this sort of radiation that there is equilibrium between the transmission and reception properties of the antenna. In that case it is relatively easy to show that the transmitting and receiving efficiencies of the antenna must be equal. It remains only to particularize about emission and absorption in definite directions to confirm the pattern equivalence established by the reciprocity theorem.

The theory of black-body radiation is also useful in the calculation of the noise that is due to the finite temperature of resistances used in electronic circuits.

Boundary Conditions

An algebraic equation has a single and perfectly definite solution if it contains only one unknown and if that unknown appears only in the first power. The solution is a number which can be used to replace the symbol representing the unknown, and which will thereupon cause the equation to reduce to an identity. A quadratic equation, or an algebraic equation of still higher degree, has similar properties except that more than one number may fulfill the mathematical requirements for a solution. When such cases arise in connection with physical phenomena, it is usual to choose among the solutions on the basis of experimental knowledge.[1] In the case of differential equations the same sort of situation exists, except that the number of possible solutions is often infinite. *Boundary conditions are those known relations in a given physical problem which allow us to select the proper solution of one or more differential equations.* When the variables of the problem are distances, the boundary conditions may well take the form of numbers which represent the value of the variable at some outer boundary of the space under consideration; when a variable of the problem is time, part of the boundary conditions may be the initial and final values of the unknowns.

It is because of the role of boundary conditions that it is possible to write down a set of equations as general as Maxwell's equations and say that they cover all of the phenomena of macroscopic electricity and magnetism. What is meant is that whenever proper boundary conditions can be formulated and the required mathematics carried through which enable a proper solution of the equations, then that solution will indeed describe the results of the physical experiment. This is believed to be the case because Maxwell's equations contain the general conditions of magnetic induction, field orthogonality, continuity, etc., and because no macroscopic case has ever been found in which proper methods have yielded a wrong answer.

The job of the theorist working with Maxwell's equations is to formulate boundary values of the variables in accordance with the nature of the apparatus at hand, and to seek a solution of the equations which satisfies proper boundary values of the variables. This is possible in many cases, but it is also impracticably laborious in others.

Centimeter-dyne

Both torque and work or energy are measured in units which have the dimension of a force multiplied by a distance. The two units are consequently indistinguishable as far as dimensions are concerned. In the case of work or energy, the units are customarily written as an erg (dyne-centimeter) or as a foot-pound. When a torque unit is intended, the order is often inverted. *The centimeter-dyne is a metric unit of torque.* Similarly the pound-foot is a torque unit in the English system of units.

Characteristic Impedance—Z_o

The characteristic impedance Z_o of a transmission line or of a series of recurring networks is by definition the impedance of an infinitely long line or of a network made up of an infinite number of sections. Practically, of course, a truly infinite line is never realized, but if the line is sufficiently long so that a voltage-versus-current measurement can be made before energy is reflected from the far end, the effect of an infinite line is obtained. Impedance of this sort is also often referred to as *surge impedance.*

If an infinite line is cut at some point and terminated by some impedance Z, then the amount of energy flowing in the line which will be reflected back along the line at that point is uniquely determined by the complex value of Z. In particular, if $Z = Z_o$, no reflection occurs and all the energy is absorbed in the termination. This is generally the desired condition for filters, electrically-long wired circuits, and waveguides.

With constant-voltage lines (i.e., electrically-short lines in which a wavelength is long compared to the line's physical length) the characteristic impedance does not usually play an important role. The input impedance to the line, which must match the impedance of the source in order to obtain a maximum transfer of energy into the line, is primarily dependent upon the load impedance. With electrically-long lines, however, this is not true. The input impedance to the line depends upon both the load impedance and upon the characteristic line impedance and, when the load end of the line is perfectly matched, the input impedance becomes just equal to the characteristic impedance.

Constant-Voltage Line

In contradistinction to an electrically-long line, *a constant-voltage transmission line is one the length of which is short compared to the wavelength of the electrical energy traveling in it.* Most ordinary power lines and other common electrical connections are of this type. Electrical energy travels so rapidly that at ordinary frequencies an electric current has ample time to travel completely around most circuits before the source voltage can appreciably change. A line has to be extremely long at audio frequencies if there is to be time for the source voltage to change while the current previously generated is still enroute to the load. That is what happens when an electrically-long line is encountered and an appreciable fraction of a wavelength or even several wavelengths are contained within the extent of the transmission system.

The velocity of electromagnetic waves in a transmission line of negligible resistance is given by $\dfrac{1}{\sqrt{L'C'}}$ where $L'\,C'$ are respectively inductance and capacitance per unit length. For any pair of parallel straight conductors of uniform cross-section, the product of L' and C' is just $1/c^2$; hence the velocity of a wave moving along such a pair of conductors is just that of light. In ordinary circuits carrying audio frequencies as high as 10,000 cycles per second, a wavelength would be 18.6 miles long, so any connection less than several miles in length qualifies as a constant-voltage line.

Coulomb

The electrostatic unit of charge (statcoulomb) is defined as that amount of charge which placed one centimeter away from an identical charge will be repelled by a force of one dyne. The statcoulomb, however, is such a small quantity of electricity that for practical purposes a larger unit called the coulomb is used. *A coulomb is a quantity of electricity equal to 3×10^9 statcoulombs.* The *ampere* is a current which transfers one coulomb of charge per second. The *volt* is the potential drop found when one coulomb of charge is transferred through one ohm of resistance in a second or, alternatively, the *volt* is the potential difference between two points when one joule of energy is involved in transferring one coulomb of charge between the two points.

Coulomb's Law

In 1875, Coulomb made a series of measurements designed to find how the force of attraction or repulsion between point stationary electric charges varies with the distance between them. He found the force to fall off as the inverse square of the distance. The force also depends upon the medium in which the charge is located. *Analytically, the law may be stated as $F = Q_1 Q_2 / K r^2$ where F is measured in dynes, Q_1 and Q_2 are in esu coulombs, r is the distance between the charges in cm, and K is the dielectric constant in the electrostatic system of units.*

In this system of units, K is unity for a vacuum and Coulomb's law serves as a convenient definition of an esu coulomb. In media other than a vacuum K is more than one, and the force **F** is decreased. This is because the polarized charges of the medium, which are more or less symmetrically distributed around the free charges, screen part of the force from the charges.

Coulomb's law is also approximately true for the electrostatic force between two charged metallic balls. It is true to the extent that the charge remains spread smoothly over the surface of each ball instead of being bunched up as a result of interaction with the other ball. This approximation is usually considered valid if r is large compared to the diameters of the balls.

Curl

The curl is an operator and generally has no properties assigned to it except as it works on a vector. In this respect it is like the operator (d/dx) or *sine*, which have no meaning except as they are prefixed before a symbol. Thereupon dy/dx symbolizes the slope of a curve which is a plot of y against x, and *sine* θ represents a number somewhere between -1 and $+1$, depending on the value of θ. In the same way that the *sine* works on an angle and results in a number which we represent by *sine* θ, so when the curl operates on a vector such as **A** it may specify a new vector which we call curl **A**.

The sort of vector which curl **A** symbolizes does not depend upon the magnitude or direction of **A**, but only upon the way in which that magnitude and direction are changing. For example, if **A** is a vector representing the velocity of a point on the rim of a wheel rotating with an angular velocity ω, then curl **A** is a vector of magnitude 2ω, which points along the axis of the wheel in the direction of the progression of a right-hand screw which turns with the wheel. *The curl of a vector is a new vector which describes a rotary motion that may be associated with the first vector. It may be calculated by*

$$Curl \; \mathbf{A} = \mathbf{i}\left(\frac{\delta Az}{\delta y} - \frac{\delta Ay}{\delta z}\right) + \mathbf{j}\left(\frac{\delta Ax}{\delta z} - \frac{\delta Az}{\delta x}\right) + \mathbf{k}\left(\frac{\delta Ay}{\delta x} - \frac{\delta Ax}{\delta y}\right)$$

in rectangular coordinates, or by other well known formulas in other coordinate systems. The resulting vector is, of course, independent of the coordinate systems in which **A** is specified and in which the calculation is made.

In Maxwell's equation, curl **H** is set equal to $\mathbf{I} + \dfrac{\delta \mathbf{D}}{\delta t}$. If **D** is a constant then this becomes just curl $\mathbf{H} = \mathbf{I}$ and corresponds, for example, to a circular magnetic field **H** around a wire arising from a current $\mathbf{I} = $ curl **H**, flowing in the wire.

D'Alembert's Equation

Differential equations which have a particular form, are often given names, usually the name of a man who made early use of the equation. Thus, equations are named after Bessel, Poisson, Lagrange, and D'Alembert. Contemporary writers do not always agree on these names. Such equations are found repeatedly in the study of physical phenomena, and their properties become well known to students of theory so that whenever they appear, certain facts about the problem at hand are at once known.

For example, the well-known wave equation,

$$\nabla^2 A = \frac{1}{c^2} \frac{d^2 A}{dt^2}$$

is one which appears in the study of acoustics, optics, hydrodynamics, quantum mechanics, and electricity. The meaning of the letter **A** will be different in each case, but always the equation will represent a wave of **A** moving through a medium with the velocity c.

To be able to read satisfactorily mathematical discussions, it is very helpful to become acquainted with at least some of the properties of as many such equations as possible. *D'Alembert's equation* is

$$\nabla^2 A - \frac{1}{c^2} \frac{d^2 A}{dt^2} = f(x, y, z, t)$$

It is of particular interest because it may be interpreted as a basic relation derived and defined from Maxwell's equations to dictate all antenna patterns when the current and charge in the antenna are known. In order, however, for D'Alembert's equation to do this, it is necessary that **A** shall not directly represent the electric and magnetic fields but rather shall indicate potential functions, which, when once found, make possible the calculation of **E**, and **H**. For the electric field, the potential function is ordinary electric potential and $f(x, y, z, t)$ is a term representing charge and the distribution in space and time. For the magnetic field, **A** represents a vector potential defined in a rather special way and the right-hand member of the equation is an expression for current density.

An interesting property of D'Alembert's equation is that in the absence of charge and current it reduces to the wave equation referred to before. When the charge and current are constant with time, the

equation becomes Poisson's equation namely, $\nabla^2 A = -\frac{4\pi}{k} \rho$ where

ρ represents charge per unit volume and we find ourselves dealing only with electrostatic and magnetostatic phenomena. It is also noteworthy that certain solutions of D'Alembert's equation involve retarded potentials. This corresponds to the fact that the field at a point in space depends upon charge and current at other points of space as they existed at previous times in order to account for the finite time of travel of electromagnetic energy.

Decibel-db

Most quantities which enter into the transmission of a radio signal are geometric in their measure. That is, if a signal of magnitude A is inserted into some device, it is normally received out of that device at a level which may be represented as some percentage of A. If the device is an amplifier with a gain of 8, the output is 800% A. If the device is an attenuator, it may be 90% A, or 10% A, or any other percentage less than 100. When several devices are connected in series the product of all the gain or loss factors must be taken together. This is sometimes inconvenient because of the labor of making the calculations. When db are used to measure the gain or loss of various elements in the transmission path, the characteristic numbers involve only addition or subtraction.

A db value must always compare one signal to another. Normally it compares the output of a certain device to the input. *If the input and output are measured in watts*

$$db = 10 \ log_{10} \frac{output\ power}{input\ power} \ .$$

If the input and output are measured in volts or amperes, and the input and output resistances are equal, the definition is given as

$$db = 20 \ log_{10} \frac{output}{input} \ .$$

In the unique case of an oscillator which has no input, db may still be used as a measure of the output power by making a comparison to some artificial reference level such as one watt.

The *neper* is another unit which is sometimes used to fulfill the same purpose as the decibel. It is defined by

$$N = \frac{1}{2} log_e \frac{P_1}{P_2}$$

To convert nepers to db, the relation 1 neper = 8.69 decibels may be employed.

The decibel was originally used in the acoustical measurement of sound levels. The British have recently introduced the *phon* as a specific unit of loudness. It is supposed to measure loudness as perceived by the ear quite independently of frequency. The loudness of sound in phons is numerically equal to the sound intensity in decibels of an equally loud 1000-cycle pure note as compared to the intensity of sound at the average lower limit of audibility, which has been standardized upon as 10^{-16} watts per square cm.

Deformed Dipoles

A deformed-dipole radiator is a center-fed half-wave antenna in which the radiating conductors are not straight. At long wavelengths the quarter-wave sections are often folded back on themselves for the purpose of conserving space. Such a half-wave antenna is often called a *folded-dipole radiator*. At true microwave frequencies there is seldom a need to use deformed dipoles solely to save space, but bent conductors are nevertheless used to obtain particular types of radiation patterns.

Del

The symbol ∇, which is the Greek letter delta printed upside down, is commonly used to represent a certain operator. *In Cartesian coordinates it is*

$$\nabla = i\frac{\delta}{\delta x} + j\frac{\delta}{\delta y} + k\frac{\delta}{\delta z}$$

where i, j, k *are, respectively, unit vectors along the x, y, z axes.* It is a very convenient symbol because of its purely formal versatility. It has no meaning by itself, but when treated like a vector quantity and multiplied by a scalar quantity in the way that is usual with a real vector, then upon performing the differentiation which the formal multiplication indicates, the gradient of the scalar results. $\nabla s =$ grad S. Likewise, if the steps of taking the scalar or dot product of del with a vector are carried through, the divergence of the vector results. If the vector or cross product is made, the curl is obtained.

The operator ∇^2, which indicates that the symbol following it should be formally multiplied by ∇ twice, is of particular interest. It is called the Laplacian operator and $\nabla^2 S = 0$ is called Laplace's equation. In words $\nabla^2 S$ means the divergence of the gradient of S. Laplace's equation, $\nabla^2 V = 0$ shows the potential at any point in free space arising from a stationary charge. The location of the charge determines the boundary conditions under which a solution of the equation is written.

A particular advantage of employing the Laplacian ∇^2 is that the meaning is clear, quite independent of the coordinate system. In Cartesian coordinates

$$\nabla^2 \mathbf{A} \; is \left(\frac{\delta^2}{\delta x^2} + \frac{\delta^2}{\delta y^2} + \frac{\delta^2}{\delta z^2} \right) \mathbf{A}$$

although in other coordinate systems it is a rather more complicated expression. The system that is chosen for a given problem is a matter of convenience. In a general derivation, however, we need not commit ourselves, and relations such as Laplace's equation, can later be written in terms of whatever coordinates we desire.

In some texts the operator del is called *nabla*, as it is considered that the word del might be confused with delta.

Delta—Δ

The Greek letter delta, like any other letter in the Greek or English alphabet, may be assigned any meaning that is desired. It is common practice in algebraic operations to replace numerical values with letters, and then to perform the mathematical calculations with those letters just as if they were numbers. Only when the calculations are completed, are the letters replaced with the appropriate numbers or, alternatively, the calculation is used to find a numerical value of some letter the exact value of which was unknown up to that point. Several advantages accrue from such a procedure. For one, the calculations are made more general and the result can be applied to more than one problem by simply replacing the letters in the final result by various appropriate numerical values. For another, the letters are often more brief than the numerical expression for the corresponding quantity and the calculation is therefore less laborious. Still another advantage is that a given calculation may be performed without even knowing some of the numerical values. In order to assign a letter to stand for a certain quantity, it is actually only necessary to know that the quantity exists. Of course, in order to make use of the final result, all the quantities of that result except one must be known (that one is obtained from the calculation), but it often happens that in the course of the calculations certain letters symbolizing certain quantities may cancel out so as not to appear in the final result. No numerical value of these need be found at all.

In assigning letters to represent unknown quantities, it is convenient to follow certain conventions which are well established. Resistance is almost always represented by R; inductance by L; capacitance by

C; ohms by Ω; etc. In the same way it is customary to use Δ to represent any very small quantity. *The Greek letter delta is conventionally used to represent any quantity which is much smaller than any other quantity of the same dimensions which appears in the same problem.* Delta is often prefixed to another letter and the pair treated as a single symbol meaning a *change in the quantity of the same sort* but much smaller than the quantity to which Δ is added. For example Δ*s* may represent a very small change in length much shorter than a length represented by *s*. Similarly Δ**E** may represent a small change in a vector of much smaller magnitude than **E**.

Dielectric Constant

If the electric field **E** is defined as the field arising from all charge and the electric displacement **D** is defined as the field due only to free charge, we may make the definition that **K** *is equal to* **D/E**. If only free charge is injected into empty space, then both **D** and **E** measure the same field and **K** becomes a number depending only on the units assigned to **D** and **E**. In a dielectric, **K** will take on a somewhat smaller value.

A qualitative explanation is best given in terms of the polarization of a bound charge. Dielectrics are made up of paired positive and negative charges, which, however, are in general oriented at random so as to give rise to no net field. When the dielectric is under stress by the presence of a charge, the polarization charges are somewhat aligned, and the effect of a charge distribution, on the faces of the

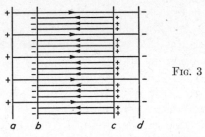

Fig. 3

dielectric is obtained. If surfaces *a* and *d* of Fig. 3 carry free charge as indicated and the volume between planes *b* and *c* is filled with dielectric, the bound charges in the dielectric tend to align themselves so as to give the effect of a charge distribution on surfaces *b* and *c*. If the field is measured in the medium without creating new interfaces on which the lines from the polarization charges may end, the field

E in the medium is measured. If a measurement is made between planes a and b, a value of the field is obtained that is equal to D in the medium.

Quantitatively we write $D = E + 4\pi P$, where P is the sum of the dipole moments per unit volume or, more simply, a measure of the amount of polarization arising from a given field D. It is clearly desirable that P be proportional to E so that $P = KE$ and $D = E$ $(1 + 4\pi K) = KE$. This is approximately true for most media.

Dielectric Constant in Free Space—K_o

In the Giorgi or MKS system of units, K_o and the permeability of free space are two numerical quantities which must be remembered in order to employ the units correctly. In that system E is measured in terms of volts per meter and D in coulombs per square meter. Since, in a vacuum, E and D measure the same field and since by definition $K = D/E$, it follows that K_o is just the ratio of the unit sizes. In other words, K_o represents the number of coulombs per square meter which corresponds to one volt per meter. To evaluate K_o we thus need to ask what positive charge density on an infinite plane will make it necessary to use a potential of one volt to hold a positive charge of one coulomb in front of that plane.

This is a simple problem although one which needs some care in transforming the electrostatic units, in which Coulomb's law is normally stated, to units of the MKS system. Its solution indicates that *in the MKS system $K_o = 8.85 \times 10^{-12}$ farad per meter.*

In the so-called Gaussian units, K_o has a value of unity. This is because E and D have units which cause them to give the same numerical value of a field in a vacuum. This unity value of K_o is very convenient in some calculations and Gaussian units are occasionally employed, but they are rather cumbersome when the many other conveniences of the Giorgi system are considered.

Diffraction, Fraunhofer

This type of diffraction is characterized by the focusing of energy after it passes through, or bends around, the edges of one or more apertures. As with the optical case illustrated by the telescope, the resolving power of a high-gain antenna may be limited by Fraunhofer diffraction.

Suppose two neighboring but very distant microwave sources are allowed to radiate at the same frequency. If the aperture of a receiving antenna is made large enough to give a sufficiently high gain it may be possible to distinguish between the two. If, however, an antenna of adjustable gain is used and that gain is gradually reduced, Fraunhofer diffraction will so spread the apparent direction of energy reception from each source as to preclude their resolution. This will occur before consideration of the antenna pattern alone would indicate loss of resolution.

Diffraction, Fresnel

Following the terminology used in the study of optics, *the ability of radio waves to travel in other than straight lines and to appear behind an obstacle, is called diffraction. When no focusing occurs after the obstacles are passed, the diffraction is specifically referred to as Fresnel diffraction.*

This phenomenon has nothing to do with reflection from a layer of ionized air in the stratosphere, nor with the ability of long electromagnetic waves to penetrate optically opaque materials. Likewise, it is not directly connected with the refractive bending of a beam of electromagnetic waves as they pass from one medium into another. Rather it is a fundamental property of wave motion which allows some energy to bend from a straight-line path.

The amount of energy which is diffracted depends upon the dimensions of the objects in relation to the wavelength of the radiation and upon the geometry of the space being investigated. If an opaque obstacle is placed in the path of a beam emerging from a small source, the width of the shadow is not only greater than is to be expected by straight-line geometric construction but may have boundaries which are bordered with further shadow bands.

If a slit of proper width is installed in a large opaque plane and one side of that plane radiated with energy from a small source, it will be found that energy is radiated through the slit over a much wider angle than would be expected. The more the slit is narrowed, the greater is the angle of divergence. If a small circular object of correct dimensions is placed in a conical beam, energy will be found at a distance behind the object exactly at the center of the shadow which the object is expected to cast.

These and other similar phenomena are examples of Fresnel diffraction. In optics, as with radio waves, the effects are closely connected in magnitude with the wavelength of the radiation. Thus the optical patterns are usually of small extent in space. With radio waves, all dimensions are much larger and, at least in some cases, the phenomenon is more important.

Divergence—div

Divergence, like the curl, is an operator and has no physical meaning associated with it except as it operates on a vector. If, however, **A** is a vector which is a function of the coordinates of a given space, so that it takes on a particular value at every point of the space, then div **A** has a definite physical meaning. *The divergence of a vector is a scalar quantity which gives the net amount of flow out of or into a unit volume.*

In the Maxwellian equation, div $\mathbf{D} = 4\pi\rho$, the generation of an electric displacement field by free charge, is described. At those points in space where there are no charges or where there is only bound charge, any small volume will contain a zero value of the charge density, ρ. This means that div $\mathbf{D} = 0$, and necessarily the same number of lines of **D** enter the volume as leave it. Since the volume may be made as small as we wish down to microscopic dimensions, it also means that the lines of **D** are continuous in such regions. On the other hand, at a point in space where charge does exist, the number of lines of **D** leaving a small volume in which the charge is located, will exceed the number entering by an amount equal to the number of lines originated by the charge. At such a point, ρ has a finite value and dictates that div **D** shall represent a number showing this increase in flux.

The divergence of a vector is useful in describing almost any vector field. It is commonly illustrated by a reference to hydrodynamics where the field represents the velocity of flow of an incompressible liquid. In that case the divergence is zero everywhere except at sources or sinks. In Cartesian coordinates

$$\text{div } \mathbf{A} = \nabla \cdot \mathbf{A} = \frac{\delta}{\delta x} A_x + \frac{\delta}{\delta y} A_y + \frac{\delta}{\delta z} A_z$$

Dyne

The metric unit of force is the dyne. In the English system of units the pound is the corresponding unit, although a very much larger one. In the English system pounds are used to measure both mass and force. We say that we buy 10 pounds of potatoes and mean that we are getting that quantity (mass) of potatoes, and we also say that we must exert an upward force of 10 lbs. to lift the potatoes. In the metric system this is not usually done. The *dyne* is almost wholly used as a measure of force and another unit, the *gram*, is used to measure mass.

The fundamental definition of the dyne is usually based upon the fact that force is needed to cause acceleration. If a body is at rest or moving with a constant velocity, then a force acting on the body will cause an acceleration or change of the velocity. *A dyne of force is defined as the force which will change the velocity of one gram of mass at the rate of one centimeter per second per second.* For instance, as a numerical example, one dyne of force acting on a stationary body which moves without friction is just enough so that after one second the mass will be moving with a velocity of one centimeter per second.

Electric Dipole

If equal amounts of positive and negative charges are distributed at random in a given volume, that volume as a whole may be said to be uncharged. It may also be that in the neighborhood of such a volume there is no electric field, or at least none the source of which can be traced to the mixture of positive and negative charges.

As a matter of fact, this is the situation with all uncharged physical bodies. The individual atoms of the body contain both positive and negative charges, but in such small units and so well mixed that they are not detectable by ordinary methods of measuring electrostatic fields.

When only a single positive and a single negative charge are involved, however, the situation is somewhat different. Except when they are actually coincident with each other, such a pair of charges does give rise to a field. Because charges (electrons, etc.) do occupy finite volumes, it is of course impossible that they really be coincident; but, since an element of charge may be very small, we can conceive of the charges being so close together that ordinary small volumes will be uncharged even though they contain an electric dipole.

An electric dipole is made up of a positive and a negative charge which are of equal strength and are placed at a small distance apart so that no macroscopic net charge is present and yet an electric field is generated. At distances large compared to their separation, s, the field arising from a dipole, is

$$\mathbf{E} = r_1 \frac{2p \cos \theta}{r^3} + \theta_1 \frac{p \sin \theta}{r^3}$$

where as shown in Fig. 4, θ is the angle between a line connecting the charges and a line drawn from the charges to the point of observation, p is the dipole moment, r is the distance from the dipole to the point

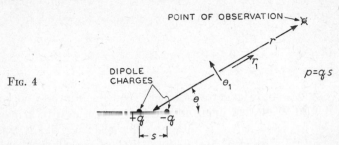

Fig. 4

of observation, and r_1 and θ_1 are unit vectors pointing respectively along r toward the point of observation and one constructed perpendicular to the line r in a plane determined by the position of the two charges and the point where the observation is made.

The *dipole moment* is a quantity which is often mentioned in talking about dipoles. It is the product of the charge (either the positive or the negative one) and the distance s. As can be seen in the expression just given, it is the dipole moment which determines the strength of the dipole as measured in terms of field strength.

Electric Displacement—D

In any medium, two sorts of positive and negative charges may be distinguished. One is called free charge and the other dipole charge. Free charge has a given sign and is separated from other charges; dipole charge is a combination of closely paired positive and negative charges. Dipole charges, when oriented at random in a medium, are without effect on any measuring instrument. When free charge is present in the same neighborhood, however, these paired charges are aligned, or polarized, and a test charge introduced into the neighborhood feels forces that are dependent on the location of both the free and bound charges.

As described under the heading *Electric Field—*E, all charges contribute to the value of E. *The electric displacement is the field resulting from free charge alone.* It may be computed at any point by summing vectors which are directed toward negative charge or away from positive charge, each with a magnitude given by Q/r^2, where Q is the charge in question and r is the separation.

D is somewhat analogous to *Magnetic Field-*H in that it, too, is a field quantity dependent on the cause of an electromagnetic state.

In the MKS system D is expressed in terms of coulombs per square meter. In the electrostatic system of units it would be the esu of charge per square cm.

Electric Field—E

A complete knowledge of any field requires information concerning both the direction and magnitude of a vector quantity at every point of space in which there is interest. The electric field is this sort of quantity. Like other fields, such as that of gravitation, or a vector field describing the flow of a liquid, it may be analytically expressible as a relation which specifies a vector for each point of space, or it may be represented graphically by a family of directed curves, which are often called electric lines of force.

These curves, or interpolated curves drawn between the given curves, pass through every point of space and by their direction at any point in question show the direction of the electric field at that point. The magnitude of the field is often indicated by the density with which the lines are drawn in the region of the point in question.

The electric field at any point in space may be found by (1) introducing a small positive charge, Q, at that point; (2) observing the electrical force, F, *exerted on it; and (3) performing a calculation according to* E = F/Q. It is assumed in such a measurement that Q is small enough to affect only negligibly other charge in the neighborhood by its presence.

E is somewhat analogous to *Magnetic Induction—*B. It is a measure of electric field in terms of its ability to influence a test instrument. In the electrostatic system of units E is expressed in terms of dynes per esu of charge, which is equivalent to esu volts per cm. In the MKS system the units are volts per meter.

Electrically-Long Lines

The treatment and action of long electrical lines is very different from that of short or constant-voltage lines. In the first place, if only a pair of ordinary conductors is considered and no reference is made to any circuit parameter except resistance, the resistance alone may nevertheless be so great that a very high voltage is required at the sending end in order to obtain a readable signal at the receiving end. The power which flows from the source is mostly dissipated in the line and, as far as the drain on the source is concerned, the nature of the load may sometimes be quite immaterial.

The problem of design is then no longer one of directly arranging for the maximum power transmission from source to load, but instead it is the twofold problem of first matching the source to the line and, second the matching of the line to the load. In such a case, to increase the response of the load to the source we may separately consider methods of increasing energy flow into the line and ways of extracting it at the far end.

With microwave transmission in waveguides, the problem of electrically-long lines is not usually concerned with resistance. The dissipative losses are generally quite negligible even with moderately long waveguides. The reactance components, however, have much the same sort of problems connected with them as do long lines at low frequency, such as are encountered in telephone transmission.

If an electrically-long line is defined as one in which the physical length is large compared to a wavelength, then all microwave transmission is concerned with long lines. The merit of such a line is usually best measured in terms of standing-wave ratio. It is important to know that such a measurement is valid only for the portion of the line farther away from the source than the point where the measurement is made. With electrically-long lines, changes in the source may of course affect the amplitude of the signal at the far end, but cannot make any change in the impedance-matching situation, as it exists at points farther along the line than at the point where the change is made. Energy reflected back from a point near the source does not reach more remote points at all.

Electromagnetic Units—emu

The electromagnetic system of units is based upon the study of magnetism quite apart from electric charge, except as electric currents give rise to magnetic fields.

The unit magnetic pole, which is an imaginary entity useful in setting up the system, is defined in analogy to a statcoulomb as a magnetic pole of sufficient strength to exert a force of one dyne on a similar pole one cm away. Since permeability, μ_o, is defined as unity in a vacuum, either **B** or **H** can be measured in terms of the force in dynes exerted on such a pole. Furthermore, an emu ampere is defined as the current in a circular loop of wire of one cm radius which will cause a force of 2π dynes to act on a unit pole placed at the center of the loop.

Electromotive force—emf

Whenever a source of electrical energy causes a charge to move around an electrical circuit, *the charge does work* in passing through the elements of the circuit. In a resistor, this work makes itself known in terms of the heat which is generated. In a condenser, the energy appears in the form of a potential energy due to the charging of the condenser. In an inductance, the energy is also stored up as potential energy but this time it appears in the magnetic field. The voltage which consequently appears across these elements is known as a *potential drop*. As distinguished from these, the voltage across a *source* of electrical energy is known as an electromotive force. As a charge passes through such a source, *work is done on the charge.*

The emf of a battery is the voltage across the terminals of the battery which is present because of the change of chemical energy into electrical energy. When a charged condenser is inserted into a circuit and used to supply power temporarily to the circuit, the voltage across its terminals is properly called an emf. It is then a voltage which is generated by the reduction of electric field between the condenser plates. Similarly, a generator may be considered as a source of emf. When two dissimilar metals are joined, a thermal emf may be encountered because of a temperature difference between the two junctions of the circuit. In brief, *emf is the work done on a unit charge as it passes through a source of electrical energy.*

Electron Trajectory

Particularly in vacuum tubes it is often convenient to trace the path of a single electron or, at least, the path of some average electron which is taken to be typical. *The path which an electron follows in going through the space between electrodes is called the electron trajectory.* Such a path is dependent upon the electric field components which arise due to (1) voltages on the various electrodes, (2) space charge, and (3) the rate of change of the electric or magnetic field. As a function of the electron velocity, the trajectory is also dependent upon the magnetic field arising (1) from currents and permanent magnets in the neighborhood of the tube, and (2) from the rate of change of electric field.

Electrostatic Units—esu

For calculations which involve only stationary charge and therefore do not deal at all with magnetism, the electrostatic system of units is the simplest choice of notation.

The esu coulomb is defined as the amount of charge which will exert a force of one dyne on an equal charge one cm. distant. The electric field E then becomes dynes per coulomb, potential becomes ergs per coulomb, and the electric displacement D is defined to be equal to E in a vacuum by virtue of defining k_o equal to unity.

If an attempt is made to carry this system of units over into the study of magnetic phenomena, a rather awkward set of numerical factors is obtained and no logical justification for doing so can be found. For example, an esu ampere is an esu coulomb per second and expressions such as $F = BIL$ for the force on a wire carrying current through a magnetic field would call for the use of electrostatic units of B which are inconveniently large, being 3×10^{10} times as large as a gauss. In such a system, we would find ourselves ordinarily dealing with small fractions of a unit of B which could easily lead to errors of statement.

Electrostatic units are often referred to as statcoulombs, statvolts, statfarads, etc.

Energy

Many textbooks define energy as an ability to do work. This is satisfactory from most standpoints and it covers most of the situations in which the term is used, although it does call for an exact idea of what is meant by work. It also means that the units of energy and of work are the same. The distinction is that energy is in the future tense and work is in the past tense. When it is said that energy travels through space from a transmitting antenna to a receiving antenna reference is made to something which will later be able to cause a motion in a pair of earphones or some other audio device. That motion is said to be work.

More basically, *work is force times distance measured along the direction of the force.* Alternately, and what means the same thing, *work is the component of a force which lies along the direction of a displacement multiplied by that displacement.* Strangely enough, a man standing quite still while holding a heavy load is considered to be doing no work at all in the engineering sense. If the load is on a cart and the cart is pushed, work is done because a force overcoming friction in the wheels is directed along the path of motion. A load lifted in an elevator, or an electric charge carried against an electric field also involve work, because a force is manifest in the direction of motion. When the charge moves with the field, it is capable of doing work on an external load. When it moves against the field, it must have work done on it in order to execute that motion.

Equation of Continuity

The equation of continuity is a mathematical statement that a quantity such as a charge can not, without cause, appear or disappear anywhere in space. In its most general form it may be stated as

$$\iiint \frac{\delta \rho}{\delta t}\, dv = -\iint f_n ds + \iiint P dv$$

This equation considers a small volume of space dv. The left member expresses the total rate of change of material in that volume, since $\delta \rho / \delta t$ is the rate of change of density and the integral signs indicate summation over the volume. The first term of the right-hand member represents the flow of material into the volume. The symbol f_n represents the component of the flow normal to the surface, the minus sign indicates the inward direction of the flow, and the double integral with ds shows that the flow is to be added up over the surface of dv. P is the rate of production within the volume. Thus, in words, the equation of continuity may be stated as: *The rate of increase of material in a given volume is equal to the amount flowing in plus the amount produced in the volume.*

In a steady state where density is independent of time, we may simply write div $f = P$, which shows that the rate of efflux is equal to the rate of production. The equation of continuity is a useful relation in many problems involving vector and scalar fields. For example, the basic contribution of Maxwell to electromagnetic theory may be shown to hinge on this relation. Ampere's circuital law, which may be written as curl $\mathbf{H} = 4\pi u/c$ in Gaussian units, does not obey the equation of continuity. This may be seen by taking the divergence of each side of the equation and recognizing that the divergence of any curl is always zero, in contradiction to the divergence of the current, which is certainly not always zero; for example, a charge may be allowed to accumulate on the plates of a condenser. Maxwell therefore added the term $\dfrac{1}{c}\dfrac{\delta \mathbf{E}}{\delta t}$, which caused the equation to become completely rigorous.

Equivalence Theorem

To obtain a given electric and magnetic field in an electrically empty section of space, it is not necessary to maintain a unique array of currents and charges in the neighborhood of that space. For example, the magnetic field in a region at the center of a long solenoid is given in oersteds by $\mathbf{H} = 4\pi nI/10$, where n is the number of turns per cm in the solenoid and I is the current in amperes.

The same field is obtained in the region under observation even if the position of the currents in space is changed by increasing the radius of the long solenoid. Likewise, if a region between two large charged plates is examined, an electric displacement field of V/d is found in which V is the potential between the plates and d the distance between them. The same field is maintained in the region under consideration by charges on plates separated by a different distance if the voltage is changed a compensating amount. Specifically, the plates may be placed so as to form part of the boundary of the observed volume.

Stated more generally in a form which is sometimes referred to as an equivalence theorem, we may say that *any field in a source-free region bounded by a real or imaginary surface, can be produced by some distribution of electric and magnetic currents on that surface.* Thus, any actual currents and charges anywhere in space which generate a certain field in a limited region, may be replaced as far as that region is concerned by other electric and magnetic currents on the surface of the limited region.

At least one application of this theorem is possible in the study of microwaves. It has to do with the calculation of the radiation fields coming from an opening in a waveguide or resonant cavity. The actual currents from which these radiation fields arise are very difficult to know with precision. Instead of trying to calculate them and then use the Biot-Savart Law or some more complicated method of field calculation, it is sometimes simpler to consider all space outside the waveguide or cavity as the limited source-free region and replace the opening and waveguide surface by equivalent currents. These equivalent currents may be calculated from actual field measurements at the opening and once they are obtained, the radiation field is computed as if arising from the equivalent currents.

Erg

The unit of work or energy in the cgs system of units is the erg. *It is defined as the work done when one dyne of force causes a displacement of one centimeter along the direction of the force.* The erg is of particular interest in the study of electricity because its definition forms the basis for the mechanical definition of the watt. Ten million ergs are equal to one joule, and a watt is equal to one joule per second. Thus, a power of one watt means an energy flow (or a rate of doing work) equivalent to 10 million ergs per second.

Faraday Induction Law

The discovery that changing magnetic field gives rise to an electric potential is generally attributed to Faraday. The statement that *an electromotive force is generated around any closed path by a changing magnetic flux through the circuit formed by that path* is generally called the *Faraday Induction Law.*

Quantitatively, the law may be stated as

$$E = -\frac{\delta N}{\delta t}$$

where E is the voltage generated in emu volts, and N is the total flux of B through the loop in gauss cm². A partial derivative is written, because N in general may be a function of coordinates as well as time.

The minus sign is a matter of convention and indicates that the field must be decreasing to generate a voltage around the circuit in the direction that a right-hand screw would turn to move forward in the direction of the magnetic field.

It should be emphasized that the Faraday Induction Law applies to any closed path whether there is a conductor present along that path or not, although only if a conductor is present can a current be made to flow. Thus, in a waveguide or resonant cavity which is fed magnetically by circulating a varying current through a loop inside the device, the changing magnetic field can cause a voltage or electric field to appear at appropriate places and create an internal energy flow in accordance with Poynting's vector.

Fermat's Principle

In the study of geometrical optics, Fermat's principle allows a very general statement to be made of the path that a ray of electromagnetic radiation will follow, even though it passes through various media and is subject to refraction. Similarly, the principle may be applied to rays of microwave radio beams and, although, as in the optical case, its value is of a theoretical nature, it still does possess interest because of its generality.

The principle states that *the path of a ray between two points will be such that the time required to traverse the path is a minimum (or in some very rare cases a maximum).*

In a homogeneous medium where the velocity of propagation is everywhere the same, it is at once apparent that Fermat's principle is obeyed by the passage of radiation along a straight line connecting the source and the receiver. The proposition of geometry that a straight line is the shortest distance between two points is proof of the statement.

If, however, the source is located in one medium which supports a high velocity of propagation, and the receiver is in another medium in which the propagation is slower, it is not so easy to understand that Fermat's principle can predict the actual path. A straight line between source and receiver is still the shortest distance, but less time may be consumed by following a somewhat longer path. The extra distance may be more than made up by allowing more of the travel to occur in the medium where a high velocity is possible.

For the case in which there are only two media, in each of which definite velocities of propagation can occur, it can be shown that Snell's law of refraction may be derived from Fermat's principle. When one medium shades into another or the velocity of propagation varies throughout a volume in an irregular way and Snell's law cannot be applied, Fermat's principle is still valid as a description of the path that any given ray will follow.

Foster's Reactance Theorem

If a four-terminal network is imagined to serve as a transmission line by virtue of a source connected at two of the terminals and a load connected at the other two, the network may take on any one of an infinite number of forms even if its elements are all pure reactances. For example, it may be made up of like or unlike sections containing combinations of inductance and capacitance in series and in parallel, see Fig. 5, or it may even be a waveguide assembly equipped with input and output coupling loops or probes. Together with the load,

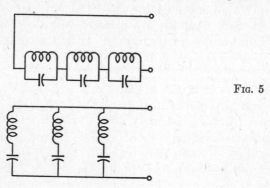

Fig. 5

such a system will have a certain source impedance, which is a function of frequency.

Foster's reactance theorem indicates that there are limitations on the sort of source impedance characteristics which are physically realizable. It does so by showing that complicated networks may always be replaced by others relatively simple, which have the same impedance characteristics. Specifically the theorem states, *if two reactance networks have the same resonant and anti-resonant frequencies, they can be made to have identical reactances at all frequencies by a proper choice of a multiplication factor.*

A resonant frequency is one at which the input impedance to the network is zero; an anti-resonant frequency is one at which the network has infinite impedance.

Fresnel's Equations

When a beam of microwave radiation passes through a plane interface between two media, it is in general both reflected and refracted. If the incident beam approaches the interface at an angle θ to the normal, the reflected beam also travels back at an equal angle to the normal in the same way that light is specularly reflected from a mirror. The transmitted beam is bent and proceeds into the second medium at a new angle θ'.

The relation between these angles θ and θ' which show the respective direction of the beams with respect to a line perpendicular to the interface at the point where the beam passes through, is given by Snell's law. *The ratio of the amplitude of the reflected beam to that of the incident beam is given by Fresnel's equations.*

For the most part in the form in which the equations are stated, it is necessary that the permeability of the two media be the same. In other instances, it is quite feasible to write the equations in a different form to take account of the variation.

At oblique angles of incidence two cases must be considered: one when the electric vector of the wave is tangent to the surface of the interface, and the other when the magnetic vector is tangent to that surface. Since in isotropic mediums, the electric and magnetic vectors are always perpendicular to each other, no generality is lost in writing relations for these two cases alone. If an intermediate degree of polarization is present in an actual beam, that beam may always be resolved into two beams which fit into these specifications.

Fresnel's equations for tangent **E** and tangent **H** beams are respectively $B/A = \sin (\theta - \theta')/\sin (\theta + \theta')$, and $B/A = \tan (\theta - \theta')/\tan (\theta + \theta')$. B is the amplitude of the reflected beam and A is the amplitude of the incident beam. Thus B/A gives the fraction of the beam reflected. The fraction of the beam transmitted is $1 - \dfrac{B}{A}$.

It is interesting to notice that in the case of a tangent magnetic field, the reflection may be zero. Specifically, if $\theta + \theta' = 90°$, $\tan (\theta + \theta')$ will be infinite and no reflection will take place.

Fresnel Zones

In analogy to the optical case, we may under certain conditions use Huygen's principle to find the radiation intensity at some point in an unknown radiation pattern. The general method is to choose an aperture nearer the antenna where the beam intensity is known and then find, by the use of Huygen's principle, the contribution of each point in that aperture to the radiation intensity at the point under discussion. A vector sum of these components then yields the desired intensity.

This was the method first used to find the free-space pattern of radiation out of the open end of an unterminated waveguide. It is in error there, as it may be in some other cases, because it does not include the portion of the pattern arising from currents induced into the outside surfaces of the waveguide. It gives a good approximation of the pattern in the forward direction, however, and is often useful. The aperture chosen may be, for example, the focal plane of a parabolic antenna or, in certain cases, it may be the region surrounding an obstruction to the beam. In the latter case, the calculations may well be aimed toward an examination of the shadow cast by the obstruction.

The main difficulty in such calculations lies in performing the integration necessary to sum up the components arising from the various points in the aperture. The use of Fresnel zones allows a rather simple approximation of this integration to be made in many cases. The aperature space is imagined to be divided up into zones in such a way that the optical distance from the center of one zone to the point where a field value is desired, is just one-half wavelength different than the distance from an adjoining zone. In other words, *a Fresnel Zone is an area in the aperture of a radiating system which is so chosen that radiation from all parts of it reach some point at which the radiation is desired at a common phase within 180°.*

When such zones are set up, it is often feasible to assume an average value of the phase and intensity of radiation from each whole or fractional zone and to replace the integration mentioned above by a simple sum. Moreover, because of the obliquity factor of Huygen's principle, it often happens that the average intensity of successive zones decreases slowly. Often each zone, except the first, may be considered as canceled by half of the preceding plus half of the following zone. In that case, the radiation from the whole aperture may be calculated in terms of only half of the first zone.

Gauss

The gauss is a common unit for the measurement of magnetic fields. In the gaussian system of units it is now well accepted as the name of the unit for **B**. The unit of **H** is the oersted. In the older literature this distinction is not always made. Especially among physicists, the gauss was once used indiscriminately for both **B** and **H**. This led to some confusion.

In the most recent books published in the field, most authors have adopted the MKS system of units which does not make use of the gauss at all. Because so much experimental data are available in terms of gauss, it is frequently desirable to reduce results to that unit even when the MKS system is used throughout the calculations. Since the numerical factor between webers per square meter as used in the MKS system is equal to 10^4 gauss this reduction is not difficult.

A definition of a gauss may be satisfactorily made in several ways. It may be defined as that amount of flux of **B** which will appear at the center of an evacuated long solenoid, which is wound with n turns per cm and which is carrying a current of $\frac{4\pi n}{10}$ amperes. It may be defined equally well in terms of the force on a wire carrying current through a magnetic field, or it may be defined by the potential generated in a loop which is rotated in the field. Since actual measurements of magnetic fields are ordinarily made with search coils or, in the case of steady fields, with flip coils, a definition based on induction is the most fruitful.

The magnetic induction at a point is one gauss when the maximum voltage that can be induced in a conductor moving through the point with a velocity of one cm per second is one emu volt. The maximum voltage will be obtained when the magnetic flux is perpendicular to the plane in which the wire moves.

Gaussian Units

Except for the Giorgi, or MKS, system of units which has only recently become very popular, the so-called Gaussian system of units is most used in calculations related to Maxwell's equations. If the centimeter, gram, and second are taken as basic quantities on which to build a unit system, the Gaussian units are logical to use. If electric and magnetic phenomena were entirely dissociated from each other, two systems of units might suffice and would logically be needed. The emu (*electromagnetic unit*) system would be used for magnetic measurements and the esu (*electrostatic unit*) system would serve for electrostatic work.

Actually, there is a need to define emu currents as well as esu currents and we know by actual measurement that the ratio of these unit sizes is c, where c is a number equal to the velocity of light in free space. It turns out that a factor of c or c^2 is invariably the ratio of the unit sizes in the two systems.

The Gaussian system of units is a combination of emu and esu which uses each in places where they are most logical and overcomes the discrepancy of unit size between the two systems by inserting some factor of c or c² into the equations in a proper manner.

An example of the way emu and esu are mixed in writing equations in Gaussian units is afforded by the expression for the force on a charge. If the equation is naïvely written, we would have $F = qE + q (v \times B)$ where the first term which represents an electrostatic force is written in terms of the esu system and the latter term for the magnetic force is in emu. It is obviously bad to have charge written in two sets of units in the same equation. The Gaussian system gets around this by writing the equation as $F = qE + (q/c) (v \times B)$, whereupon q is in esu throughout the equation, even though B remains in emu.

Gauss' Theorem

In dealing with vector fields such as those of E and H, there are several simple relations that are often helpful in making calculations. Gauss' theorem is one of them. It deals with the so-called vector flow out of a volume and shows an equivalence between the net flow outward through the surface and the integrated effect of the divergence of the vector field throughout the volume.

For example, a vector field may be expressed by equations into which the coordinates of any point in space can be substituted and the magnitude and direction of a vector associated with that point in space found as a result of the substitution. In this way a vector may be associated with every point in the space and the resulting array called a vector field.

If enough such vectors are plotted in a given space and especially if their magnitude is shown by the density of the plot, electric or magnetic fields may be portrayed as lines of force. Since these lines of force have a direction, they appear to be like lines of flow, as indeed they actually would be in the hydrodynamic case in which the vector field is one specifying the velocity of motion of various small measures in a liquid. Whether or not the problem is one of actual flow, however, the concept is useful.

For example, in the electrical case, if the number of lines of E which pass through a surface of area A are known, it is only necessary to divide the number by A to get the average value of E. *Gauss' theorem states that*

$$\int \nabla \cdot E dv = \int E \cdot da$$

or in words, that the volume integral of the divergence of a vector is equal to the surface integral of the normal component of the vector. E is considered positive when it points outward from the volume. If the meaning of div E is understood (i.e., that it gives the excess of the efflux over the influx for any very small volume, dv), it is easy to see that the left member of the equation gives the total flux generated in the large volume.

Gauss' formula simply says that the net amount of this generated flux added up over the whole volume, must leave the volume and show up as an outwardly directed flux through the surface. If a certain volume contains a charge density ρ, the integral over the divergence will be $4\pi\rho v$, since 4π lines of force arise from each charge.

Gauss' theorem states that the total efflux of the force lines out of the volume will also be $4\pi\rho v$.

Giorgi Units—MKS

In the last few years the Giorgi, or rationalized meter-kilogram-second, system of units has made great gains in popularity. In general, there are four reasons for preferring one set of units over another: (1) convenient magnitudes, which make the use of very small or very large numbers unnecessary in most calculations; (2) familiarity, that makes it unnecessary to refer constantly to tables and which makes magnitudes easy to visualize; (3) logical definitions, which make it possible in practice to define the units in a logical manner, and (4) avoidance of the use of factors such as π in most equations written in the units.

The Giorgi system of units meets these requirements as well or better than any other system. Electric field intensity, E, is measured in volts per meter. The volts are the same as those used in conventional circuits. Magnetic induction B, is in webers per square meter, where one weber per square meter equals 10^4 gauss. Charge density, ρ, is in coulombs per square meter. Current density, J, is in amperes per square meter. Both the coulombs and amperes of the Giorgi system are the same as those ordinarily used in conventional circuit theory.

The use of all these and other units, so that they fit in with the scheme used in practical circuits and so that they are of useful magnitude, is made possible in the theory of electromagnetism by assigning numerical values to K_o and μ_o, the dielectric constant and the permeability of free space.

These numerical values, $\mu_o = 4\pi 10^{-7}$ henry per meter and $K_o = 8.85 \times 10^{-12}$ farad per meter, are basic constants of this system of units and must be remembered. In this respect, the Gaussian system of units is preferable, since both these constants are unity.

It is now agreed by many workers in the field, however, that for most calculations it is better to have numerical values of K_o and μ_o than to keep straight all the powers of 10 and c that must be remembered in changing from the Gaussian system to practical units in order to interpret results in terms of practical volts and amperes.

Gradient—Grad

The gradient is an operator which has no physical meaning by itself, but takes on such meaning when it operates on a scalar quantity. For example, if each point in a certain space is labeled with Cartesian coordinates x, y, z, then V (x, y, z) may be a scalar function giving the voltage, with respect to some reference level of each point in that space. $V = V$ (x, y, z) is a symbol indicating an equation containing x, y, z, and V.

For a given point x, y, and z are certain numbers; substituting these numbers into the equation causes it to specify a value for V at that point. Now if the gradient operator works on V, a new equation is obtained which specifies a vector at each point in space. This vector becomes one which points in the direction in which the voltage is most rapidly changing, and one the magnitude of which gives the rate of change of voltage per unit length along that direction.

In other words, the gradient of the voltage is the electric field. Grad $V = -\mathbf{E}$.

More generally, *the gradient of a scalar is a vector which shows the direction and rate of change of that scalar in space*. It is an operator that is useful in working with scalar fields. It is encountered in the study of hydrodynamics, aerodynamics, acoustics, etc., as well as in electrodynamics.

In the case of Cartesian coordinates the gradient is

$$\text{gradient of } \mathbf{A} = \nabla \mathbf{A} = \mathbf{i}\frac{\delta A}{\delta x} + \mathbf{j}\frac{\delta A}{\delta y} + \mathbf{k}\frac{\delta A}{\delta z}$$

In other coordinate systems the form is somewhat more complicated.

Group Velocity—U

Two velocity quantities are associated with wave motion; these are group velocity and phase velocity. Very often group velocity is represented by U and phase velocity by V. If only a steady signal having a single frequency is employed, we are never concerned with group velocity. The concept of group velocity needs to be used only when we deal with transients or have a modulation present on the carrier. *Group velocity is the velocity with which a signal is transmitted along a wave and is numerically different from phase velocity only if the medium is such that the phase velocity varies with frequency.*

Suppose, for example, we have two waves of slightly different wavelength, both traveling in the same direction through a medium. Assume, further, that these two waves are continuous so that by measuring over a long portion of the wave train, we can accurately specify the wavelengths. Now, since the wavelengths are different, it must be true that if a snapshot of these waves could be taken, the picture would show cancellation in some regions and reinforcement in others. If, at one point along the path, the two waves are cooperating so as to disturb violently the medium, then, at other points which are an even number of half wavelengths distant for one wave and an odd number for the other, there will be complete cancellation. Thus, the medium will appear to be excited by groups of waves which appear at points of reinforcement and to be separated by null points where the interference is complete.

The velocity of these bundles of waves is called *group velocity*. The velocity of the individual constant-frequency waves is called *phase velocity*. If the phase velocities of the two constant-frequency waves are the same, it is clear that the group velocity will also have that value. On the other hand, if the phase velocities of the two continuous waves are different, then the group velocity will be different from both the phase velocities. This is true because the velocity of the group depends not only on the velocity of the continuous waves, but also upon the way in which one wave catches up with the other and thus influences the position of the reinforcement regions.

Velocity measurements of electromagnetic waves in actual apparatus usually yield group velocities. In general, it is only possible to make the measurement by marking a point on the wave by the use of modulation. Energy in a wave travels with the group velocity. The relation between the two velocities is

$$U = V - \lambda \, \frac{dV}{d\lambda}$$

In this expression λ is wavelength and $\dfrac{dV}{d\lambda}$ is the rate at which phase velocity changes with λ.

Hertz Vector—II

Generally, an electromagnetic field is given by specifying both **E** and **H** throughout the space in which we are interested. **E** and **H**, however, are interdependent in a way which is determined by the physical arrangement. Sometimes it is convenient to establish this interdependency by expressing **E** in terms of a scalar potential and **H** in terms of a vector potential and then writing down a relation between these potentials. Also, *it is possible to write the interdependency of* **E** *and* **H** *by expressing both of them in terms of a single vector. That vector is called the Hertz vector and is often symbolized by* **II**.

By the use of the Hertzian vector it is possible to describe the whole electromagnetic field with a single vector. For example, the Hertzian vector representing radiation into free space from an electric dipole has a magnitude given by

$$\mathbf{II} = \frac{p \, (t - r/c)}{r}$$

and always points along a direction that is the same as the direction of motion of the oscillating charge. The dipole moment which is represented by p is here a function of time; t is the time of flight from the source to the point of observation, r is the distance, and c is the velocity of light.

A charge for example, may be imagined to be oscillating along the z-axis and about the origin of a Cartesian coordinate system. An equal stationary charge of opposite sign is at the origin. The dipole moment by definition is the product of the value of one of the charges and the separation between the two. The value of p is thus itself an oscillating function of time. The distance away from the dipole (always large compared to the dipole) at which a value of II is desired is r; t represents time; c is the velocity of light. The electric field is given by

$$\mathbf{E} = grad\ div\ \mathbf{II} - \left(\frac{1}{c^2}\right)\frac{\delta^2\mathbf{II}}{\delta t^2}$$

and the magnetic field by

$$\mathbf{H} = \frac{1}{c}\ curl\ \frac{\delta\mathbf{II}}{\delta t}$$

where these equations are all written in Gaussian units. When we substitute for II its value for a dipole in free space and perform the indicated operations, we get expressions for $\mathbf{E}$ and $\mathbf{H}$ which show the usual directional radiation pattern that is well known for a dipole.

Huygen's Principle

If the position of an electromagnetic wavefront is known at some given time and if the transmission and reflection properties of the surrounding media and media-interfaces are known, Huygen's principle furnishes a simple method of locating the position which the wavefront will occupy at a later time.

The method consists of assuming that points on the known wavefront are sources of spherical waves, which emit new wavefronts at the instant at which the real wave's position is known. By measuring distances radially outward from each of the imaginary sources and by using the velocity of travel and the time elapsed to establish the proper distance, we can locate the wavefronts of these spherical waves at a later time. Huygen's principle then states that an envelope of these waves will give the anticipated position of the actual wave.

Several difficulties enter into the simple statement of Huygen's principle as just given. For one thing, it is clear that our statement would predict the formation of a backward wave as well as one in the forward direction. This may be overcome by introducing an obliquity factor into the intensity of the spherical waves. The spherical waves are then said to be imagined to have an intensity given by some constant multiplied by $\cos^2(\theta/2)$ where θ is the angle away from the direction of propagation of the original wave. This means that the intensity of each spherical wave is of cardioid form and no energy proceeds backward from the secondary sources.

The use of Huygen's principle in calculating microwave radiation patterns is also of somewhat limited value, because it does not easily adapt itself to superposition with field components arising from currents in the neighborhood.

As an example of the use of Huygen's principle, the derivation of the rule for specular reflection from a plane mirror may be described. If the position of a plane wavefront obliquely approaching a mirror is known, it is easy first to extrapolate the positions of various points on that wave and to find the time at which each will reach the mirror. At those times, in accord with Huygen's principle, we may construct spherical waves at the mirror surface and if we draw them with systematically varying radii so as to give a common time position, the envelope will give the position of the reflected wave. Only simple trigonometry is then required to establish the familiar rule that the angle of incidence is equal to the angle of reflection.

Interference

In much the same way that two batteries of equal voltage connected in series opposition can cancel each other so that no current flows, so two electromagnetic waves of precisely the same frequency may be so phased at certain points in space that no effect will be felt by a test charge or magnet that is imagined to exist at that point. *Interference between two waves is an effect due to phase differences between two waves which cause the resulting wave, existing as the sum, to be other than that which would be obtained by adding the energy present in the individual waves.*

In the study of optics, it is frequently said that two light waves will only interfere if they come from coherent sources. A pair of sources is said to be coherent when their phases stay exactly in step. In the optical case, this means in practice that the two interfering waves must arise from the same primary source, since the phase varies at random. This is because light is generated by the excitation of individual atoms.

With radio waves this is not true and interference between two transmitters is possible if they are very accurately held to the same frequency and phase. Directional antenna patterns formed by the use of dipole arrays depend upon this fact for their operation.

Isotropic Antenna

An isotropic antenna is one which can radiate energy equally in all directions or which when used with a receiver is equally sensitive to signals received from any direction. By any and all directions is not only meant any or all points of the compass, but also any or all angles of elevation. In other words, the radiation pattern of an isotropic antenna is a perfect sphere with the antenna located at the center. It is very seldom that an isotropic antenna as such is desired for actual use. Some directionality, at least in the vertical direction, is invariably desired. The isotropic case, however, is a convenient one to use as a basis of comparison. *Antenna gain,* for example, is defined as the ratio of the maximum signal strength in a given direction to that of an equivalent isotropic radiator. Also, isotropic antenna elements, or at least elements closely approaching isotropic, are often made and then combined to produce a desired radiation-pattern arrangement.

Joule

The unit of work which is known as the erg and which is defined as the work or energy involved in the action of a force of one dyne through a distance of one centimeter, is too small a unit for most practical calculations. Instead a larger unit known as the joule is generally used. *A joule is equal to ten million (10^7) ergs.* A joule of work is the amount accomplished by one watt of power acting for one second.

Klystron-Bunching Parameter—x

With simple bunching theory in which the velocity change in the beam is small compared to the average velocity of the electrons, the bunching parameter is a convenient quantity in terms of which the power available from a klystron catcher can be discussed. The bunching parameter depends upon the beam voltage, the r-f voltage applied to the buncher, and upon the drift distance of the tube as well as upon the frequency for which the tube is designed.

A plot of power available from the catcher resonator versus the bunching parameter is a Bessel function of the first order and degree. Such a curve somewhat resembles a damped sine wave and thus indicates that there is more than one value of the bunching parameter which may give satisfactory output, although only one that gives maximum power.

This corresponds physically to the fact that those electrons which are speeded up by the buncher, will catch up with the slower ones ahead of them in a more or less satisfactory manner, depending upon the time allowed for them to do so, the excess of their velocity over that of the slower electrons, and the average speed of all the electrons.

Specifically, moreover, the bunching parameter versus power plot takes account of so-called overbunching, in which the faster electrons overtake and pass the slower ones before reaching the catcher. *The bunching parameter x is defined as*

$$x = \pi N \left(\frac{V_1}{V_0} \right)$$

where N is the number of cycles of the output frequency which occurs while an electron is traversing the drift space, V_1 is the r-f voltage applied to the buncher, and V_0 is the beam voltage.

For a given tube, N is ordinarily fixed, since it depends only on the length of the drift space and the frequency of the tube. To keep a given value of x and thus maintain a given output, it is therefore desirable to vary V_1 and V_0 together.

Laplace's Equation

Probably the most used of all differential equations is that of Laplace. *In Cartesian coordinates it has the form*

$$\frac{\delta^2 A}{\delta x^2} + \frac{\delta^2 A}{\delta y^2} + \frac{\delta^2 A}{\delta z^2} = 0$$

In other coordinate systems it has a somewhat different form but, of course, indicates the same physical situation. In terms of vector operators it may be written independent of the coordinate system as

$$\nabla^2 \mathbf{A} = 0.$$

In the study of electromagnetic theory, Laplace's equation is used in at least three distinct ways. First, the **A** in the equation above may represent vector magnetic potential; in that case Laplace's equation describes magnetic potential throughout free space. Second, **A** may represent and describe the electrostatic potential in a uniform dielectric. Third, **A** may show how the electric potential varies in the study of the steady flow of electric currents in solid conductors.

In all these cases, the equation must be solved subject to the **boundary** conditions imposed by the particular physical arrangement, but the mathematics may be the same in any event. It is this similarity of the mathematics involved in physically dissimilar problems that makes it possible for people skilled in such manipulations often to solve new problems quickly and from memory of other cases which employ the same mathematical equations.

Laplace Transformation

An important method of solving linear differential equations is that of the Laplace transformation. *An equation of the form*

$$\frac{d^2w}{dx^2} + p\frac{dw}{dx} + qw = O$$

is transformed by the relation

$$w = \int u e^{xt}\, dt$$

and the resulting differential equation in terms of the variable u is often simpler than the original equation expressed in terms of the variable w. The symbols p and q represent functions of x, while u is a function of the variable t.

Suppose, for example, that at some time $t = O$, a transmitter is turned on at the origin of a three-dimensional Cartesian coordinate system and allowed to generate a plane wave which travels out into free space along the positive z-axis. If the wave is polarized so that the **E**-field is parallel to the x-axis and the **H**-field is parallel to the y-axis, then by Maxwell's equations, the field is determined by the following differential equations:

$$\frac{\delta \mathbf{H}}{\delta z} + K_o\, \frac{\delta \mathbf{E}}{\delta t} = O$$

$$\frac{\delta \mathbf{E}}{\delta z} + \mu_o\, \frac{\delta \mathbf{H}}{\delta t} = O$$

The fields **E** and **H** may be transformed by

$$\mathbf{E} = \int \mathbf{E}'\, \epsilon^{t\alpha}\, d\alpha$$
$$\mathbf{H} = \int \mathbf{H}'\, \epsilon^{t\alpha}\, d\alpha$$

In these equations **E**' and **H**' are functions of t. The transformation is made with z considered as a parameter. That is, z is imagined to be a constant independent of t, which we can vary at will. Since we can choose any value of z that we wish and make the transformation, it does not restrict the generality of the argument to hold z constant.

The transformed equations are obtained by performing the indicated differentiations, which give as the transformed equations

$$\frac{\delta H'}{\delta z} + K_o \alpha E' - K_o E_o = 0$$

$$\frac{\delta E'}{\delta z} + \mu_o \alpha H' - \mu_o H_o = 0$$

where the terms involving E_o and H_o are of the nature of integration constants and represent the values of E and H at zero time. These equations involve the variable α only as a multiplier and not as a variable in a differentiation. Thus, the transformed equations can be solved simultaneously by separating E' and H'.

Lecher Wires

Two parallel wires which are long compared to a wavelength and spaced from each other by a distance equivalent to a small fraction of a wavelength, are called Lecher wires.

Such a pair of wires may be used to demonstrate standing electrical waves as well as other types of phenomena encountered in hollow rectangular waveguides and other types of microwave transmission lines.

Lecher wires like those shown in Fig. 6 are satisfactory for work with wavelengths about one meter long. An oscillator producing the

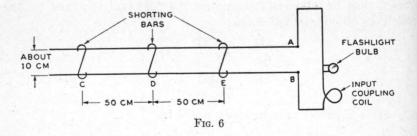

Fig. 6

proper frequency feeds energy to the system by means of the input coupling loop. If a flashlight bulb is adjusted in position in the input circuit so as to be midway between the input terminals A and B (taking account of the length of wire in the coupling loop), then such a bulb will be at a current maximum and will most sensitively indicate the positions of the shorting bars that cause resonance of the whole system.

If no shorting bars are used and if the wires are of arbitrary length, the indicating bulb will generally light only to partial brilliance. Waves are being reflected from the open ends of the wires but, except in special cases, they do not return to the indicating bulb in such phase as to completely cancel or reinforce the outgoing wave.

If, however, a shorting bar is moved along the wire, some position such as C will be found where the lamp glows most brightly. The position, which is also at a current maximum, is one where the waves reflected from the short circuit reinforce the outgoing wave a maximum amount at the indicating bulb. Other short-circuiting positions, such as D and E, can be found which have the same result. The distance between these points is just ½ wavelength and, because wave velocity over parallel lines is the same as that in free space, this is also just the wavelength of the generator's radiation. Such a scheme can be used to calibrate a wavemeter.

If only shorting bar C is in place and a suitable thermal galvanometer is moved along the wires, its deflection will be observed to vary sinusoidally, indicating that standing waves are indeed present on the wires.

Lenz's Law

When it is desired to associate the proper direction of a changing

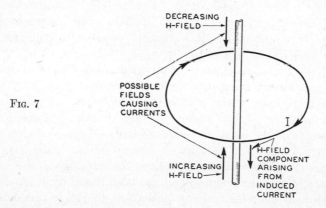

FIG. 7

magnetic field with the direction of an induced current, Lenz's law is a convenient rule to follow.

The direction of the magnetic field generated by an induced current is such as to oppose the change of the field causing the induction.

Thus, if a horizontal loop is observed to have a current induced in it which is flowing in a clockwise direction as viewed from above and shown in Fig. 7, the change of the field causing the induction must be opposed or compensated by an induced field directed downward. The right-hand rule in which the right hand is imagined to grasp the wire so that the thumb shows the direction of the current and the fingers show that the magnetic field passes downward through the loop, is proof of this.

Since the current generates a downward magnetic field through the loop, it follows from Lenz's law that the field causing the induction is decreasing in a downward direction. This may be either an increasing upward field or a decreasing downward field.

Line-of-Sight Range

Microwaves, unlike longer radio waves, are limited to transmission over distances that are short enough so that the curvature of the earth does not obstruct their passage. In other words, microwave transmission is all accomplished by means of a ground wave.

No microwave skywave is ordinarily detected, because the ionized layers of the stratosphere are not able to afford much reflection; instead, the microwave energy continues out into interstellar space. For this reason it is frequently said that microwave communication is limited to line-of-sight range. This implies that a microwave beam can travel from transmitter to receiver only if, except for fog and intensity requirements, it is equally possible to transmit a beam of light over the same distance.

All this is approximately equivalent to saying that the maximum range of microwave signals is limited to something like 200 miles and, even then, only if the receiver or transmitter can be well elevated.

Actually, it is not enough merely to take an average radius of curvature of the earth and proceed with simple geometry to find line-of-sight ranges for various elevations of the antennas, because of refraction effects. In an actual case, the intensity simply falls off with range in a regular manner, and has been found by K. A. Norton,[2] who made measurements and calculations at 46 mc, to become nearly zero at 200 miles for well-elevated antennas. Only when power measurements as a function of altitude are made at several ranges and the maxima of each altitude set are plotted, do we obtain a curve which we may interpret as the line-of-sight path.

It has been found that, for true microwave frequencies, this path allows ranges which are roughly equivalent to those which would be calculated geometrically if the average curvature of the earth were assumed to be 1.4 times larger than it actually is.

Line-of-sight range for microwave transmission is the maximum distance over which microwaves can be transmitted. Refraction makes the distance somewhat greater than simple calculations of the earth's curvature would suggest but does not prevent that curvature from being the limiting factor.

Loop or Anti-node

In a standing wave, the variation of the measured quantity varies sinusoidally at each and every point. *The points at which the variation is a maximum are called loops, or anti-nodes.*

Magnetic Dipole

Antennas that are used to insert energy into or extract it from wave-guides or resonant cavities may generally be divided into two classes. One is of the sort which, to a first approximation behaves like an electric dipole and the other is more like a magnetic dipole.

A small probe, inserted in a waveguide so as to lie along the direction of the electric field, is something like an electric dipole, because charge oscillates back and forth along its length. A small loop inserted so that the magnetic lines of force pass through it, may approximate a magnetic dipole, since the current in the loop and the field passing through it act like variable magnetic poles of opposite sign on each side of the loop.

In terms of permanent magnets, the concept of a fixed magnetic dipole is easy to understand, because it is well known that no matter how many times a bar magnet is cut in two, both a south and a north pole continue to exist on each piece. A very small piece of magnetized material is itself a fixed magnetic dipole. *A magnetic dipole is a pair of equal north and south magnetic poles spaced closely together.*

In the same way that an electric field may be observed to surround an electric dipole with a peculiar directional pattern, so also may a magnetic field be observed in the neighborhood of a magnetic dipole, even though the dipole contains both magnetic north and south poles of the same strength.

The equivalence of a current loop to a permanent magnet is well known because of the common use of electromagnets in relays, etc. The statement that a current flowing in a one-inch loop is equivalent to a whole array of magnetic dipoles arranged in the plane of the loop, is due to Ampere and is explained in terms of the so-called Amperian currents. The idea is that if a current flows clockwise in a horizontal loop, that current may be replaced by a large number of equal currents flowing clockwise about each elemental area of the plane enclosed by the loop. Except for the area elements adjacent to the wire, the current around each element will just be canceled by that going around a neighboring element and only the current along element edges which are coincident with the wire, will have a net value.

This consideration demonstrates that a current circulating in a wire loop will give rise to an array of magnetic dipoles or, as it is often called, a *magnetic shell* in the plane of the loop. Now if the current in the loop varies, the magnetic field of the dipole will also vary. By Maxwell's equations we know that a changing magnetic field must be accompanied by a changing electric field and radiation from the loop will occur. Similarly, if the electric field changes, current of varying strength may appear in the loop.

Expressions for the distribution of the field from a sinusoidally varying dipole moment are readily found although they are of rather complicated form. In a spherical coordinate system, $r \theta \psi$, if the magnetic poles are arranged along the axis from which ψ is measured $\mathbf{H}$ is found to have a component along r and another around the dipole with ψ. The electric field goes around the dipole with θ, as that symbol measures angles from some reference plane containing the dipole. Maximum radiation from an oscillating magnetic dipole occurs in a plane perpendicular to a line connecting the equal but opposite poles which form that dipole.

Magnetic Field—H

If it is desired to measure the magnetic field at a given point in a certain material, there are two general approaches. The measurement called $\mathbf{H}$ is one obtained by considering the *cause* of the magnetism. For example, if we wish to know the magnetic field at some point,

A, in a certain medium which may be in the neighborhood of certain other magnetic and nonmagnetic materials, we can do so in five steps. First, a very tiny but pivoted permanent magnet is installed at A and allowed to point as it wishes; second, the torque necessary to deflect this magnet through some convenient angle is measured; third, the cause of the field at point A is removed by shutting off all currents in the neighborhood, by removing permanent magnetism from all nearby bodies except the tiny test magnet, and by bucking out the earth's field; fourth, the neighborhood is surrounded by a properly oriented and very long solenoid so that point A is at the center of the solenoid; and fifth, a current is passed through the solenoid so as to produce the same torque as before and so as to turn the tiny magnet at A by the same amount. The magnetic field—H will then be given by $\mathbf{H} = (4\pi ni)/10$ oersteds, where n is the number of turns per cm on the solenoid and i is the current in amperes which passes through them.

Briefly then, $\mathbf{H}$ *is a measure of the magnetic field in terms of a current which can duplicate that field.* Its measurement is independent of the medium and neighborhood in which point A is located, since any such effect is canceled out by leaving the physical arrangement undisturbed between the two torque measurements.

Magnetic Induction—B

A magnetic field can be measured in terms of an *effect* it has on a certain test instrument as well as in terms of its cause as was discussed under the heading of *Magnetic Field*—H.

A field measurement in terms of effect is usually called magnetic induction and represented by $\mathbf{B}$. Thus, if it is desired to measure the magnetic induction present at some point P, which may be in any medium and may have any sort of magnetic or nonmagnetic materials in its neighborhood, we may do so by placing a small loop in such a position at point P so that none of the magnetic flux passes through it.

Now, if we turn this loop through 90° in a time Δt so that in its final position a maximum of flux is surrounded, we can compute the strength of the magnetic induction at P in terms of the average voltage that is induced into the loop. The computation can be made from $\mathbf{B} = (V \, 10^8)/(A\Delta t)$, where V is the observed voltage and A is the area of the loop.

Magnetic induction, $\mathbf{B}$, *is a measure of magnetic field made by observing a voltage generated when a conductor cuts through the field.*

In the method of measurement just described, the loop is ideally so small and turned so rapidly that the field strength is constant and unchanged during the time Δt. How rapidly the loop must actually be turned depends upon the extent of the accuracy to which the measurement is desired.

B can also be measured in terms of the force on a charge, Q, moving through point P with a velocity v in a direction perpendicular to the magnetic field. In that case, $B = \dfrac{c \cdot F}{Qv}$ where F is the force on the charge and c is the velocity of light.

Method of Images

A great simplification in the plotting or calculation of electric and magnetic fields can sometimes be obtained by use of the method of images.

The method consists of replacing surfaces which may exist in the neighborhood of known charge and current by other charge and current which are so located and of such strength that we can show the field to be unaffected by the substitution.

When this can be done, it is relatively easy to proceed by calculating the fields arising wholly from free charge even when it would be very

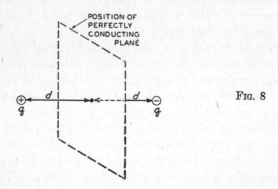

Fig. 8

difficult to make the calculation if we needed to take account of currents induced in conducting surfaces.

For example, as is shown in Fig. 8 consider a charge q, placed a distance, d, in front of a very large and perfectly conducting plane. No electric field can exist at the conducting plane since if it did, currents would flow to equalize it. Now if the plane is removed and a second charge, q, of opposite sign is placed a distance, d, behind the position that was occupied by the conductor, the same situation as was had before is duplicated. There is no tangential field along the surface where the plane was situated. The field of charge $+ q$ and its image $- q$ just cancel each other along that surface. This is sufficient to indicate that the electric field at every point in front of the conducting surface is unchanged by the substitution of an image charge for that conducting surface.

It may be even easier to see that the image case is an equivalent situation by thinking in terms of potential. Along the surface occupied by the plane, the potential must be zero with an image charge present because every point on that surface is equidistant from $+ q$ and from $- q$. It is likewise clear that the potential of a conductor must be zero or at least constant.

Nabla ▽

The symbol ▽, which some writers call *nabla* and which is called del in this book, has exactly the same meaning as has been ascribed to del. It is a vector operator having a purely formal meaning and a value lying entirely in its ability to allow these operations to be written in a brief form. See Del.

Nepers—N

The neper, like the decibel, is a ratio which measures the gain or loss of a signal in terms of a logarithmic scale. Also like the decibel, it is primarily useful because physical apparatus in general responds logarithmically; for example, the losses in a transmission line. The loss in each unit length of the line, is not a fixed amount as it would have to be if linear variables were to be an adequate measure of its operation, but instead the loss is a certain percentage of the amount entering that unit length. Strictly this is exactly the type of phenomenon that gives rise to Naperian logarithms to the natural base ϵ. While decibels are based on logarithms to the base 10, the neper uses logarithms to the base ϵ. This would seem to make the neper the more logical unit for many calculations, but since the difference between the neper and the decibel is only a numerical constant, its advantage is really trivial, for 1 neper = 8.69 decibels. *If two quantities W_1 and W_2 are said to differ by N nepers then*

$$N = \tfrac{1}{2} \log_\epsilon (W_1/W_2).$$

Newton

Just as the dyne is the unit of force in the centimeter-gram-second system of units, so the newton is the unit of force in the Giorgi or meter-kilogram-second system. *A newton is that force which can accelerate one kilogram of mass at the rate of one meter per second per second.* In either of these metric systems the distinction between force and mass is much clearer than it is in the English units of mechanical engineering where we use the pound to measure both the quantity of a commodity that can be purchased for a given price (i.e. mass) and the tension or compression that a mechanical member must withstand (i.e. force). Fortunately the electrical engineer and the physicist have almost universally avoided using English units. In expressions such as $F = BIL$, which gives the force on a conductor of length L carrying a current I through a field B, units are arranged so that F comes out either in dynes or newtons. In the MKS or Giorgi system of units, F is in newtons if B is in webers per square meter, I in amperes, and L in meters. A watt of power is equivalent to one newton of force acting through a distance of one meter each second. One newton is equivalent to 10^5 dynes and is of a convenient size for practical measurements. Roughly a newton is about equal to 0.22 lb of force while a dyne is the equivalent of only about 35 millionths of an ounce.

Node

In a pure standing wave, only the amplitude of the wave changes as a function of time. That is, if a particular point is chosen on a transmission line which contains a pure standing wave, and voltage or current is instantaneously measured there, a sinusoidal variation with time will be observed and, depending upon the point chosen, the variation will occur with some particular amplitude. Points at which maximum amplitude are encountered will at all times show measurements of greater strength than any other points on the line. *Points of zero amplitude will always remain of zero strength, and are called nodes.*

It should be recognized that true nodes of zero amplitude are very rare. In general, a transmission line of any sort has at least some small dissipation so that some net energy flow along the line is necessary. No energy at all can flow past an exact node. Consequently, most physical nodes fail to have a zero value. They fail by virtue of a small traveling wave component.

Oersted—H

Oersteds are used in the gaussian system of units as a measure of the magnetic field, **H**. *One oersted of magnetic induction exists at the center of a long solenoid of any radius when $H = 4\pi NI/10$ is equal to unity. I is measured in amperes and N is the number of turns per cm wound on the solenoid.* In the MKS or Giorgi system of units the quantity corresponding to the oersted has no special name and **H** is measured in terms of amperes per meter. The reasoning is that if a current flows in a device such as a coaxial line, the **H**-field is entirely restricted to the space between the conductors and depends only upon the current densities in the inner and outer conductors. These current densities may be measured in terms of amperes per meter of conducting surface width. Thus, if the outer conductor has an inside diameter of 3 cm and carries a current of 10 amperes, it has a current density of $10/(.03\pi)$ amperes per meter because the 10-ampere current is effectively spread over a conducting surface the width of which is equal to the inner circumference of the outer conductor.

The unit of **H** in the Giorgi system is best defined in terms of the field between two infinite but parallel plane current sheets carrying charge in opposite directions. The field there in Giorgi units is then equal to the current density and is expressed in the same units. It is reasonable to use these units because the induction field for such a pair of infinite plane conductors is completely independent of everything else, such as the spacing between the plates and the nature of the medium. The oersted is a much smaller unit than the ampere per meter.

Parasitic Oscillations

In an amplifier or an oscillator, wanted or unwanted feedback coupling between stages is often encountered. These may often introduce a strengthening of a certain frequency in the input circuit and even cause the device to oscillate at that frequency. *An unwanted oscillation of a circuit is known as a parasitic oscillation.*

Permeability—μ

If currents flow in conductors located in a certain region, the magnetic field at a point in that neighborhood can be measured in terms of the magnetic field **H** or in terms of the magnetic induction **B**. *The ratio,* **B/H**, *may be defined as permeability and is usually represented by* μ. Since **H** depends only upon the currents and not at all upon the medium, while **B** is in general larger than **H** by an amount dependent on the permeability of the medium, it follows that μ is a quantity which describes the medium. Iron materials may have very large permeabilities; some other materials such as pure nickel and certain alloys also cause **B** to be much larger than **H**; most other materials have a permeability approximately equal to that of free space.

It is very important to understand that permeability is not a constant of a material. With a certain iron, for example, it is not safe to say that the permeability is 2500 gauss per oersted. If a **B-H** curve is drawn for such a piece of iron, the familiar hysteresis curve showing saturation of **B** for large values of **H** is obtained. Thus, although for small values of **H**, μ may be 2500 showing that **B** is 2500 times larger than **H**, for larger **H** values the permeability drops off and eventually may become very small. The permeability of a given material may also be affected by grain orientation or by cold working of the iron.

Permeability in Free Space—μ_o

Two numerical constants in the rationalized Giorgi system of units must be remembered. One is the dielectric constant in free space and the other the permeability. The permeability is especially important because it is approximately the same in free space and in all media except magnetic materials. In Giorgi units, $\mu_o = 4\pi \times 10^{-7}$ henry per meter; in the gaussian system $\mu_o = 1$. The simpler value obtained in gaussian units is a great advantage of that system, but is not always one that outweighs the use of powers of 10 and c, which must be used in changing to practical units. *By definition* $\mu_o = $ **B**$_o$/**H**$_o$ *where* **H**$_o$ *and* **B**$_o$ *are the values of the magnetic induction* **B** *and the magnetic field* **H** *respectively at a point in free space.* With rationalized Giorgi units, it is interesting to notice that expressions for wave velocity and impedance in free space are expressed very simply in terms of μ_o and K_o. Starting with Maxwell's equations, we may derive wave equations for E and H as

$$\nabla^2 \mathbf{E} - K\mu \frac{\delta^2 \mathbf{E}}{\delta t^2} = 0$$

$$\nabla^2 \mathbf{H} - K\mu \frac{\delta^2 \mathbf{H}}{\delta t^2} = 0$$

For a plane wave traveling along the z-axis of a cartesian coordinate system, the x-axis may be arranged so as to have the E vector point along it and the H vector will then lie along the y-axis; in that case we have only $\mathbf{E}_x$ and $\mathbf{H}_y$ for which to solve these differential equations. Furthermore, we may anticipate that our solutions for $\mathbf{E}_x$ and $\mathbf{H}_y$ will be of the form of a sinusoidal traveling wave. If we assume such a form and use an arbitrary constant for the velocity, we may substitute the tentative solutions back in the differential equations and not only show that they are indeed solutions, but also that the wave velocity is given by $1/\sqrt{K_o\mu_o}$. In free space, therefore, $1/\sqrt{K_o\mu_o} = c = 3 \times 10^8$ meters per second. Also having found E and H for a plane wave, we can form the quotient as the impedance and show that the impedance of free space is given by $\mathbf{E}_o/\mathbf{H}_o = \sqrt{\mu_o/K_o} = 377$ ohms.

Phase Velocity—V

The wave or phase velocity of a traveling wave is just what the name implies: the velocity with which a point of given phase moves in a traveling wave. The most important consideration in understanding the distinction between phase and group velocity has to do with the flow of energy. Energy always moves in accord with the group velocity of the wave, and not at a speed dictated by the phase velocity. The phase velocity is essentially a phenomenon of a steady state in which the wave has neither beginning nor end other than in the source or load. When the source is first energized and the beginning of the wave train travels to the load, the situation is such that we must consider that beginning as traveling with the group velocity, because its frequency is not single-valued even though the source oscillates at only one frequency. Only if the wave extends indefinitely in both directions, can it be exactly measured even in principle and thus be said to have only a single frequency component. In other words, the beginning of the wave is the equivalent of a 100% modulation and modulation by definition travels with group velocity.

When a wave motion is traveling in a steady state, however, phase velocity is a very real concept and subject to measurement and calculation. If, for example, a length of waveguide is imagined to be perfectly matched to a source and load and to have a unity standing-wave ratio, we can at least imagine measuring the phase velocity by using a very agile probe which moves along the guide in coincidence with a point of maximum electric field. Since such a probe would be moving with a velocity equal to that of a phase point (the point of maximum **E**), it must be moving with a speed equal to the phase velocity. Phase velocity is numerically different from group velocity only when the phase velocity changes with frequency. Under certain conditions the phase velocity of a wave may be greater than the velocity of light. This does not contradict the principles of special relativity, because energy is not transported at that velocity.

Plane Polarization

It is customary to speak of the plane polarization of a wave which is traveling more or less parallel to the surface of the earth as being vertically polarized, horizontally polarized, or sometimes as being polarized in a plane inclined at some angle between vertical and horizontal. Since any vector inclined at any angle between the vertical and the horizontal, may be thought of as being made up of a vertical and a horizontal component, polarization in a plane at an intermediate angle may also be thought of as a mixture of vertical and horizontal polarization. *A plane-polarized wave is one in which the electric field is restricted to a single plane (or a group of parallel planes).* The magnetic field is in consequence restricted to another plane (or set of planes) which is perpendicular to the first plane, and the energy is propagated in a direction determined by the plane intersections.

Vertical polarization refers to the case in which the **E** *vector lies entirely in vertical planes* (and **H** is restricted to horizontal planes). *Horizontal polarization, on the other hand, calls for horizontal* **E** *vectors and vertical* **H** *vectors.*

Point Impedance

The concept of impedance like that of many other physically

measurable quantities is one which has more or less grown with time. The term was first used to allow writing an alternating-current analogy of Ohm's law as applied to an alternating current through an impedance. Gradually the term impedance has been applied to more complex situations, until now its meaning is not always clear except in the context in which it is used, especially since it has proven convenient to define certain impedances in terms of the electric and magnetic fields in a waveguide as well as in terms of the voltages and currents that are involved. It is usual to refer to several sorts of impedance, which although closely related in meaning, still indicate somewhat different measuring techniques. There is not complete agreement on the exact terminology used, but at least characteristic impedance, input impedance, intrinsic impedance, surface impedance, equivalent impedance, and point impedance may be found in various books on the subject and serve a useful purpose at least as far as their names are self-explanatory.

Point impedance is defined as *the ratio of the maximum* **E**-*field to the maximum* **H**-*field that is observed at a given point in a waveguide or transmission line due to the energy flow under consideration.* The point impedance of a given point in a waveguide system in general will depend upon the geometry of the whole system, but its measurement may be made by considering the situation of the single point alone. When the impedance of free space is said to be 377 ohms, there can be no question of the measurement of current or voltage. What is meant is that the point impedance of any point in free space is 377 ohms. The **E** vector at any such point is in proper units 377 times larger than the **H** vector. On the other hand, when the task is one of matching two waveguides of different size by the use of some type of coupling section, it is certainly not enough merely to arrange to match point impedances. It is more a matter of smoothly transferring the electric field from one waveguide to the other over the whole area of cross-section. This is accomplished when the voltages and currents generated in the walls of the guide are matched. Such an impedance based on voltage and current is frequently referred to as an *equivalent impedance.* For reasons of practical measurement it is normally estimated or calculated from measured values of the point impedance.

Poisson's Equation

The differential equation which may be conveniently written in the form

$$\nabla^2 V = 4\pi\rho$$

is one of especially wide application and hence well known in the fields of hydrodynamics, astronomy, and aerodynamics, as well as in the study of electromagnetic theory. Its most important use in the electrical case is occasioned by its ability to describe the electric potential arising from electric charge no matter how that charge is distributed throughout the neighborhood of the space in which we are interested. It is only necessary that the position of all the charge be known and specified by an equation involving ρ (the charge density) and the coordinates of some coordinate system. When such an expression is available it is only necessary to solve it for ρ, substitute for ρ in Poisson's equation, and solve the differential equation for V, subject to whatever boundary conditions are in force. The resulting expression for V will give the potential as a function of the coordinates, and upon substituting numbers corresponding to the coordinates of any point, a numerical value of V is obtained, which is the potential of that point. When the space contains no charge, so that the equation reduces to zero, it is known as Laplace's equation.

Polarization

In order for radiant energy to travel in a given direction in free space or in any medium of uniform properties, the electric and magnetic vectors must always remain perpendicular to that direction of propagation and at the same time be perpendicular to each other. These conditions do not completely specify the directions of the electric and magnetic vectors. For example, if energy is being propagated to the north, the **E** vector may be vertical and the **H** vector may be horizontal, or equally well, the **E** vector may be horizontal while the **H** vector is vertical. In fact, there are an infinite number of directions ranging between vertical and horizontal which either vector may take up at a particular instant provided the other takes a complimentary position at the same time. If the radiation is not polarized, the directions are completely random. An observer at a given point in such a radio beam who is measuring the direction of one of the vectors at various times, will find no correlation between the successive measurements. *A polarized beam of radiation is one in which the* **E** *and* **H** *vectors are oriented in some systematic way. Plane polarization* requires that the vectors always point in the same direction. *Circular polarization* means that the vectors rotate like the radius of a circle.

The term polarization as applied to radio waves and to light means the same thing.

Polarization, Dielectric—P

A conductor differs from a dielectric inasmuch as it contains free electrons. These free charges are able to move about through the conductor and when they do under the influence of a voltage, they constitute the flow of an electric current. A dielectric, on the other hand, contains only bound charges which are not free to move away from each other, although their binding is somewhat elastic thereby allowing their relative positions to be somewhat distorted under the influence of an electric field. *The distortion in the positional relations of groups of bound charges in a dielectric is referred to as polarization.*

If equal quantities of positive and negative charge are oriented at random in every small volume of a dielectric, then because the atomic charge unit is so very small, the net charge density of the dielectric is zero and no external field or potential is occasioned by the presence of the bound charge. If an external field is applied to the dielectric, polarization takes place and the bound charges are no longer oriented at random; instead the pairs or groups of bound charges, tend to line up in accordance with the direction of the field. If, in such a situation, a small flat cavity is cut into the dielectric and the field measured in that cavity, it will be found to be greater than the applied field, because positive bound charges in trying to move with the field will distort their bounds so as to accumulate on the side of the cavity from which the field is coming, and negative charge will do the same on the other side. Charge appearing on the walls of the cavity in this manner is called polarization charge and is the reason why the dielectric field **D** is larger than the electric field **E**. The relation between the two in gaussian units, is

$$\mathbf{D} = \mathbf{E} + 4\pi P$$

where P is the polarization of the dielectric.

Polarization, Wave

The polarization of electromagnetic waves is a phenomenon which is well known in the study of optics as well as radio waves. The direction of propagation of electromagnetic energy, the electric field vector, and the magnetic field vector are generally all perpendicular to each other. As may be seen in Fig. 9, however, this still makes it quite possible for the **E** and **H** vectors together to be rotated to either of the positions shown or to any position in between. *When the mutually perpendicular* **E** *and* **H** *vectors are governed in this rotation by some simple law, the electromagnetic beam is polarized.* When the rotational

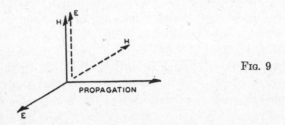

FIG. 9

orientation is random or when the **E** and **H**-fields exist simultaneously with various angular orientations, the beam is said to be *unpolarized.*

The simplest type of polarization is called *plane* polarization. In this case the rule is that the **E** vector shall always point in a certain direction and the **H** vector shall indicate a direction 90 degrees away. For example, if we are considering a radio wave and the **E** vector points only upward or downward the plane wave is said to be vertically polarized. Similarly, a horizontally plane-polarized beam is one in which the **E** vector is always horizontal.

Circularly polarized beams are those in which the **E** and **H** vectors at a given point in space rotate together but with a constant amplitude. *Elliptically polarized beams* are those in which the **E** and **H** vectors rotate and change their magnitude so as to trace out an ellipse.

Ground-wave signals received from a vertical transmitting antenna are generally plane polarized and are usually best detected by a vertical receiving antenna. Frequently under such conditions the signal strength may even be zero for a horizontal antenna. The sky wave, which is reflected from the ionosphere, on the other hand, generally will be elliptically or circularly polarized. In certain cases the sky wave may even be nearly plane polarized in the horizontal direction. With microwaves, where no sky wave is ever encountered, the polarization is more completely under the control of the designer. The merits of vertical versus horizontal polarization for all applications have not been entirely settled as yet.

Power

The term power is used to mean either the time rate of utilizing or creating energy or, alternatively, it may mean the time rate at which energy is transmitted from one point to another. Thus, when a watt-meter is connected into a transmission line it reads the number of watts passing through the line. When an electric heater is rated at 100 watts, it is meant that 100 joules of electrical energy is used up each second. Various units for measuring power include the watt (joule per second), the horsepower (ft-lbs per second divided by 550), and certain other less commonly used units such as the erg per second.

Poynting's Theorem

In gaussian units Poynting's theorem may be written mathematically as

$$ div\left[\frac{c}{4\pi}\ (\mathbf{E} \times \mathbf{H}) \right] + \frac{\delta}{\delta t}\left[\frac{1}{8\pi}\ (K\mathbf{E}^2 + \mu\mathbf{H}^2) \right] = -\ \mathbf{E} \cdot \mathbf{J} $$

Its meaning in general is the same as the principle of the conservation of energy. Electrical energy, like energy in any other form, is in-destructable. The theorem says specifically that in any small space during any very short length of time, the net energy removed from that space per unit time plus the amount of energy stored in the space per unit of time, must be equal to the net rate of production of electro-magnetic energy within the space. In the first term of the equation which states the theorem, $(c/4\pi)$ $(\mathbf{E} \times \mathbf{H})$ is the familiar expression for Poynting's vector which describes the flow of energy in the small space in which we are interested as well as in the neighborhood of that space. Wherever $\mathbf{E}$ and $\mathbf{H}$ have components perpendicular to each other, Poynting's vector is perpendicular to both and indicates by its magnitude the amount of energy flowing in the direction in which it points. Taking the divergence of Poynting's vector makes the first term of Poynting's theorem tell the excess of the outward flow of energy over that which enters the volume. If more energy is enter-ing the space than is leaving, the term becomes negative.

It is well known that it takes energy to build up electric or magnetic fields. To charge a condenser, voltage must be applied to the con-denser. Likewise an electromagnet obtains its magnetic properties only after a current has flown long enough to overcome the inductive effect which at first causes a voltage drop to be present also. The amount of energy necessary to build up these fields is respectively given by $(1/8\pi)$ (KE^2) and $(1/8\pi)$ (μH^2). The partial time deriv-ative of the sum of these tells the rate at which energy is being stored in the space. The right member of the equation gives the energy pro-duced in the volume. Here μ is the current density (statamperes per cm²) flowing in the space under consideration.

If, for example, the space contains no batteries but only resistance material of resistivity σ (statohms per unit cube), then by Ohm's law, $\mu = \sigma E$ and the right member of the equation becomes $-\sigma E^2$, rep-resenting a negative amount of power generated or a positive dissipa-tion into heat. On the other hand, if a battery is present, the electric field there is opposite in direction to that appearing across a resistance, since it is the cause rather than the result of the motion of the charge. Thus, the force on a charge in a battery is $-E$ and the rate of work-ing of the force on unit charge is $-E$ times the velocity of the charge. To change this rate of doing work on a single charge to the rate at which work is done by the battery per unit volume of space, we multiply by the charge per unit volume. Since the charge per unit volume times the charge velocity is just μ, this again gives $-E \cdot J$, with the minus sign combining with the inherent negative value of the field of the battery to cause the whole expression to result invariably as a positive quantity when electrical energy is being manufactured by a source.

Poynting's Vector—P

As radio waves travel through space they carry energy with them. Poynting's vector is a quantity which may be calculated for every point in the wave at every instant of time. Its value at a certain point and time gives the direction of the energy flow and the rate of that flow. *It is a vector the magnitude of which is the product of E and H and the direction of which is that of a right-hand screw placed and rotated as if to turn E into H.* If H is in oersteds and E in electro-

static volts per cm, Poynting's vector is $\dfrac{c}{4\pi}$ (E $\times$ H) ergs per square

cm per sec; if H is in amperes per meter, and E in volts per meter, Poynting's vector is E $\times$ H watts per square meter. A certain amount of arbitrariness is inherent in the interpretation of Poynting's vector as a flow vector. For example, if an electric charge is isolated and placed at the center of a small permanent bar magnet, the radial electric field is at right angles to the well-known magnetic field distribution and Poynting's vector calls for a continual circulation of energy around the magnet. This situation, although possible, does not yield a valid flow of energy. On the other hand, the energy flow interpretation of **P** is very helpful in many places and is not known ever to lead to contradictions; it is therefore worthy of use when the electric and magnetic fields are changing.

Propagation Constant—γ

The wavelength of a traveling wave is a simple concept and as long as the attenuation is negligible in the wave, it is easy to measure. When the wave is damped rapidly, however, it becomes more difficult to consider wavelength and frequency. Indeed if by a wave of a certain length we mean one which is like a sine curve that makes a complete oscillation in that distance, we will find that sine waves of many wavelengths must be added up to get a sum equal to the damped wave we have in mind. This is the same as saying that a damped wave contains many wavelengths. For this reason and because the form in which the propagation constant is written allows a very simple expression to portray a wave with or without damping, it is common to omit direct reference to wavelength in symbolizing traveling waves.

In writing a mathematical expression to represent a traveling wave we must in general consider three factors: we wish to indicate that (1) the wave position will progress along its line of action with time; (2) at any given value of time the wave disturbance will extend with oscillating values along its line of travel; and (3) we want to show the effect of damping by indicating a lessening of strength with greater distance along the path of travel. These three properties are shown by three factors of the expression. The variation-with-time factor is taken care of by $\sin \omega t$ or $e^{-i\omega t}$. If the propagation direction is chosen as the x-axis of a coordinate system, the oscillation with x and the damping may be respectively expressed by $\sin (2\pi x/\lambda)$ or e^{-ibx} and e^{-ax}. Choosing the exponential form of writing the sinusoidal variation with x, these last two factors may be combined and written as $e^{-(a+ib)x}$. If it is chosen to replace the complex number $a + ib$ with a single symbol γ, then that symbol is the propagation constant. *The propagation constant is in general a complex number whose real part measures the damping of a wave and whose imaginary part describes the wavelength that wave would have without damping.*

Q of a Resonant Cavity

A convenient definition for the Q of a resonant cavity is

$$Q = 2\pi \frac{Energy\ stored}{Energy\ loss\ per\ cycle}.$$

This definition indicates that Q is an inverse loss factor just as when it is applied to wired resonant circuits. The usual definition which is given as $Q = (\omega L)/R$, is not used with cavities because the meaning of the inductance L for a cavity is rather indeterminate and at best only a derived property of no direct interest. For either the cavity or the wired tank circuit, Q is a factor of merit which is large in proportion to how small the losses of energy from the cavity can be made.

Shape and size determine the frequency of a resonant cavity. The resistance of the walls with due reference to the skin effect, influences the Q. For a given shape, the cavity of the greatest volume is the one of highest Q. This is because the greater surface area will in general allow the current flowing on any one part of the wall to be smaller and yet cause the same total energy storage in the cavity. Since the power consumed by the need of overcoming resistance is given by i^2r, this can be quite important. By the same token, reëntrant cavities, which by their nature call for high current densities at corners or bends, are to be avoided if a high Q is desired.

Silver and copper are the best materials for the construction of cavities since they keep the losses to a minimum. Since the skin depth for microwave frequencies is very small indeed, silver plating of any material makes it satisfactory for the construction of high Q cavities. Joints must be soldered with great care and should preferably be plated after assembly. In certain cases it is possible to make designs so that the soldered joints will be at points where no current flows.

In actual practice there is very little choice in the Q's which are possible in cylindrical, spherical, and rectangular cavities although the first type is most used for practical reasons. In general, the higher modes of the cavity give the best Q because they permit larger dimensions. The extent to which one can go in this direction, however, is usually limited by the practical necessity of limiting operation to a single mode.

Quarter-Wave Attenuator

Microwave wattmeters are usually built in accord with thermodynamic principles. Either a medium such as water is circulated through the instrument so as to absorb the energy directly, or a device, such as a thermocouple, is heated by a portion of the energy flowing into the meter. In any event, the amount of radio-frequency power present is usually measured in terms of temperatures or temperature differences. Because of this it is not convenient to have extended ranges of measurement and it is usually considered better to use calibrated attenuators.

When very high powers are to be measured, the energy is first run through an attenuator, which is known to remove a certain percentage of the power, and then a measurement on the remainder makes it possible to calculate the actual total power. Likewise, when a very weak signal of known strength is desired in order to calibrate a receiver, it is usually convenient to measure a power of medium magnitude and then use an attenuator to reduce that power by a known fraction.

For these applications it is therefore clear that an ideal attenuator is a device which, when inserted in a transmission line, absorbs power without introducing reflections. The simplest, although somewhat idealized, form of such a device is one which is known as a quarter-wave attenuator. *It consists of two energy absorbing grids or other structures placed in the transmission line. These are separated by an odd number of quarter wavelengths and are not only designed so as to absorb energy, but also fixed so that reflected energy from the second grid just cancels that which is reflected from the first.* Fig. 10 shows such a device in schematic form.

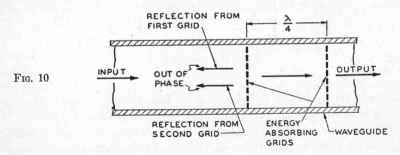

Fig. 10

To accomplish this it is only necessary that a certain numerical relation exist between the impedance of the two grids and the imped-

ance of the waveguide transmission line. This causes the two reflections to be equal in magnitude and since one has twice traveled the
quarter-wave section, they are out of phase and completely cancel
each other. In this form, the attenuator functions only for waves
traveling along the guide in one direction. By the addition of a third
grid, it is possible to remove this restriction.

Quarter-Wave Termination

It is frequently desirable to terminate a waveguide transmission
line so as to absorb all the energy traveling through it without reflection. To do so is to accomplish the same thing that is done in circuit
theory when a line is terminated with its characteristic impedance;
the waveguide or transmission line then acts as if it were infinite in
length. One way of accomplishing this is by the use of the so-called
quarter-wave termination. When it is used *an energy absorbing grid
or film is stretched across the waveguide at a distance ¼ wavelength
from the shorted end and arranged so that reflection from it is just
canceled by the multiple reflections from the shorted end.* The film
may consist of a piece of semi-conducting material, or, if a grid is
used, wires may be stretched across the guide so as to parallel the
electric field. When such an arrangement is properly made, it is said
that the impedance of the grid is matched so as to give a perfectly

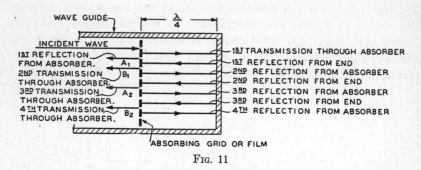

FIG. 11

absorbing termination. By referring to Fig. 11 a qualitative description of how the scheme functions may be understood.

Suppose a wave of unit strength is incident upon the film. A certain
fraction of it will be absorbed, another part reflected, and a third part
transmitted. The transmitted portion proceeds to the shorted end
of the waveguide and after reflection there it again becomes incident

upon the film although this time from the opposite side. As is indicated in the diagram, this energy reflected from the closed end of the waveguide is again in part absorbed, in part transmitted, and in part reflected. Moreover the reflected portion of the wave which arises from the second encounter with the absorbing film is again returned to the closed end of the waveguide where after reflection it returns to the absorbing film for the third time. This process repeats not just three times as shown but an indefinitely large number of times. After each encounter with the absorbing film the wave involved becomes weaker because of the absorption. If the impedance of the film is properly arranged, the waves marked A and B will completely cancel each other so as to give the desired perfect termination. This is possible because the quarter-wave section causes those marked A to be out of phase with those marked B. Waves indicated as B_1, B_2 have respectively traveled one-half wavelength further than the corresponding waves marked A_1, A_2. Because the film can be adjusted to transmit a prearranged amount more than it reflects, the magnitude of all the energy transmissions like those marked A can be made to be very nearly equal to those marked with B.

Quarter-Wave Transformer

In much the same way that an output matching transformer may be used as coupling between the plate of a vacuum tube and the voice coil of a loud speaker, so may devices be used at microwave frequencies to couple between a high-impedance source and a low-impedance load. By analogy, such devices are called transformers even though they bear no physical resemblance whatever to the sort of transformer which has a primary and secondary windings of wire. Nevertheless the fundamental functions of these transmission-line devices is the same as that of the more familiar sort of transformer. In either case, a large current at a small voltage is made into a smaller current at a larger voltage, or vice versa.

An important case of a transmission-line transformer is the quarter-wave transformer, which, however, is limited to use in matching two dissimilar impedances that have no imaginary components. In other words, a quarter-wave transformer is useful for matching a source to a load of different impedance, provided the load is capable of presenting a unity standing-wave ratio and the source is capable of delivering maximum power into a matched load which does present a unity standing-wave ratio. *A quarter-wave transformer is a length of lossless transmission line which is an odd number of quarter wavelengths long and which has a characteristic impedance that is a geometrical mean between the real impedance of the source and the real impedance of the load.*

The simplest method of giving a qualitative explanation of such a transformer is the one involving traveling waves. A traveling wave from the source is normally transmitted in part and reflected in part as it encounters the different impedance of the transformer. As the portion which is transmitted reaches the still different impedance of the load, it is again reflected in part. The wave from the second reflection, however, travels the length of the quarter-wave transformer twice and hence is just a half-wave behind the wave from the first reflection. If the impedances are correctly arranged, these two reflections are equal and, because they are out of phase, they entirely cancel each other, only a continuous flow of energy from the source to the load remaining.

Quasi-Stationary Processes

Maxwell's equations in gaussian units are

$$Curl \ \mathbf{H} = \frac{1}{C}\frac{\delta \mathbf{D}}{\delta t} + \frac{4\pi \mathbf{J}}{C} \qquad Curl \ \mathbf{E} = -\frac{1}{C}\frac{\delta \mathbf{B}}{\delta t}$$

$$Div \ \mathbf{B} = 0 \qquad\qquad Div \ \mathbf{D} = 4\pi\rho$$

$$\mathbf{B} = \mu\mathbf{H} \qquad\qquad \mathbf{D} = k\mathbf{E}$$

These may be given not only in this final form, which is rigorous for all macroscopic phenomena, but also in at least three specialized forms. In their order of increasing generality, these are the static case, the stationary case, and the quasi-stationary case. The static case does not allow moving charge nor any change of the fields with time; thus all the terms containing time derivatives and the one which contains the current density $\mathbf{J}$, then become zero because other than zero values of these quantities indicate change with time. For static phenomena the magnetic and electric equations are completely independent of each other. The stationary case refers to a situation in which currents are allowed but the fields are kept constant with time; this means that the current density term is present but the time derivatives are still zero. *For quasi-stationary processes* $(\delta \mathbf{D}/\delta t) << 4\pi\mathbf{J}$ *and the time derivative of* $\mathbf{D}$ *is omitted although the time derivative of* $\mathbf{B}$ *is retained.*

This arrangement of Maxwell's equations is by its very nature always an approximation since it is an incorrect application of Maxwell's equations to the general case, but in a very wide field of application it is an approximation that may be successfully used. It is valid wherever the magnetic field is dependent in the main on circulation currents and hardly at all on dielectric currents. This is the case for practically all of the classical field of electrical engineering. Since the term involving $(\delta \mathbf{D}/\delta t)$ represents the main contribution of Maxwell to the theory, however, it is obvious that no completely rigorous tests of the equations can be made without the inclusion of that term.

Radiation Resistance

The input impedance of an antenna has the same meaning as does the input impedance for any non-radiating load. If, for example, a non-radiating coaxial line runs from a transmitter to an antenna, then at the point where that line connects to the radiating conductors, the voltage across the line and the current through it may be measured. The ratio of these two values gives the magnitude of the impedance; and the phase angle between the current and the voltage shows if the load is capacitative, inductive, or a pure resistance. If the transmission line to the antenna is a hollow pipe waveguide, the measurements will probably deal with values of electromagnetic fields, but again a perfectly definite impedance value will be obtained and it will contain a resistive component and probably at least a small reactive term as well. The resistive component in the main is not due to ohmic resistance in the antenna, but rather it is caused by the radiation of energy. If one can see only the inside terminals of two wires which run out through the wall of a building and see with the aid of meters that a net amount of power is being sent out through the wires, one cannot tell without further test whether that energy is being radiated or only dissipated in a resistor mounted on the outside of the building. It is because of the similarity of the two effects that *the portion of the resistive component of the input impedance to an antenna which is caused by radiation is called the radiation resistance of that antenna.*

The radiation resistance of a dipole antenna may be calculated by integrating Poynting's vector over a spherical surface which is imagined to surround the dipole. From the known antenna pattern of a dipole the integrated value of Poynting's vector will come out in terms of i^2, where i is the current fed to the antenna. Setting the calculated value of the radiated power from the dipole equal to i^2r which measures the power put into the antenna, a value for r is found. The result of 80 ohms is in agreement with measured values.

Rationalized Units

With any set of electromagnetic units such as the electromagnetic system, the electrostatic system, the gaussian system, or the Giorgi system, the constant 4π enters into many of the equations which are used. *The so-called rationalized units, of which the Heaviside-Lorentz units are an example, attempt to suppress these 4π factors by adjusting the unit size so that the 4π is absorbed into the new unit.* Two advantages are sometimes claimed for rationalized systems. They are: (1) calculations which involve 4π are encountered only in relations which are used infrequently; and (2) the removal of the 4π factor leads to greater symmetry in the way in which electrostatic and electromagnetic quantities enter into the equations.

In the Heaviside-Lorentz rationalization of gaussian units, Gauss' law takes the form Div $\mathbf{D} = \rho$ instead of $4\pi\rho$ as it does in the unrationalized system. This is possible because the rationalized units of $\mathbf{D}$ and ρ are respectively $(1/\sqrt{4\pi})$ and $\sqrt{4\pi}$ times the size of the unrationalized units. This sort of thing extends fairly well throughout the theory with one exception. Rationalized units require Coulomb's law to be written $\mathbf{E} = Q/(4\pi Kr^2)$ or $\mathbf{H} = m/(4\pi\mu r^2)$ instead of the simpler form without the 4π. These 4π quantities may also be eliminated by changing the units of K and μ and when this is done, the system is said to be subrationalized. At least in the case of the gaussian units, subrationalization is frequently objected to on the basis that it spoils the convenience of having μ and K equal to unity in free space.

Refraction

An electromagnetic wave which obliquely approaches a boundary surface between two media will in general change its direction of motion upon traversing the boundary. This change in the direction of propagation is called refraction. It is caused by the fact that the velocity of propagation is different in the two media. If, for example, a plane wave approaches an interface as is shown in Fig. 12, it is clear that the A ends of the wavefronts will reach medium 2 ahead of the

B ends. In the case shown this means that the *A* ends will spend more time traveling in the slower medium 2 and thus get behind and cause a wheeling motion just as the inner men of a column of soldiers do when in drill they execute a turn while marching four abreast.

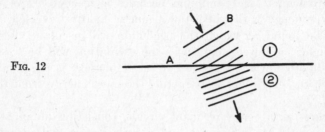

FIG. 12

A quantity called the *index of refraction* is defined as the ratio of the velocity of propagation of a wave in a medium to that in free space. If the indices of refraction are known, Snell's law is sufficient to predict the bending which will take place at any interface. We may show from Maxwell's equations that the index of refraction is equal to $\sqrt{K\mu}$, where K and μ are given in gaussian units.

If instead of encountering a definite interface, an electromagnetic wave finds a gradual change in the medium, refraction will cause the direction of propagation to change slowly and the wave will travel in a curved path. This happens with microwave radio because the lessening density of air with increased altitude bends the beams toward the earth. This bending is obviously not able to return the beams to the earth but only makes the earth's radius of curvature seem to be greater than it is. In computing line-of-sight paths, it is convenient to approximate the situation by neglecting refraction and making up for the neglect by assuming that the earth's radius is one third larger than it is.

Resonance

One of the simplest criteria for distinguishing a resonant frequency in any electrical or mechanical device has to do with the energy involved in the oscillation. *When a resonator of any kind is excited rhythmically by a drive of constant voltage or mechanical amplitude, resonance is encountered whenever the flow of power into the resonator passes through either a maximum or a minimum.* At resonance, changes also occur in the phase and in the amplitude of the oscillation in the resonator. These or other properties of a resonator may equally well be used as a definition of resonance if it is so desired. If a simple pendulum with soft-iron bob is caused to swing back and forth by regularly reversing a magnetic field which is supplied by a near by electromagnet, the pendulum becomes a resonator. As we increase the frequency with which the magnetic field is reversed, a frequency will be found at which the pendulum will oscillate violently, while at higher or lower frequencies the oscillation will be less. The most violent oscillation, which occurs at resonance, is the condition under which the pendulum is extracting the most energy from the magnetic field.

Likewise, a series resonant circuit, consisting of an a-c source in series with an inductance and a capacitance, will draw its largest current when resonance is obtained. This largest current means the dissipation of the largest amount of energy in whatever resistance is present in the circuit. On the other hand, for a parallel resonant circuit consisting of a power supply connected in parallel with an inductance and capacitance, the current out of the generator is a minimum when the frequency is adjusted to resonance. Such a condition of minimum current response is sometimes referred to as an *anti-resonance*.

Retarded Potential

If a charge of strength q is isolated in free space and it is desired to bring a test charge of unit strength and of the same sign up to within a distance r of the original charge, the amount of work which must be done to accomplish the task is given in gaussian units as q/r ergs. Because of this, we say that the potential of a point r cm away from charge q is q/r. If, instead of having only a single charge in space, we have several or a great many, the potential of any point in the neighborhood (i.e. the work necessary to bring a distant unit charge to that point) is influenced by each charge, and we must calculate q/r for each of the charges and then as scalars add all the results together to get the actual potential of the point in question.

Now if the charges are themselves moving, it is clear that there may be some question as to what distance should be used for various r's. The answer is that if the potential of a point is wanted at a certain time $t = A$, then the contribution to that potential of each charge in the neighborhood should be calculated not in terms of the position of that charge at time $t = A$, but at some previous time which is earlier by an amount given by r/c, where c is the velocity of light. The reason for this procedure is easily seen: the amount of time which elapses between the time when a charge is at a given point and the time when the potential at another point is affected by the presence of that charge is r/c, because the effect must travel across the intervening space r with a velocity c. *The retarded potential of a point in space is the potential of that point at a given time with due allowance made for the fact that the charges which gave rise to that potential may have moved to new positions while their influence was en route to the point in question.*

Sheet Grids

A three-dimensional grid may be placed in a hollow waveguide so as to remove effectively all modes of propagation except the one desired. In Fig. 13 an example of such an arrangement is shown.

FIG. 13

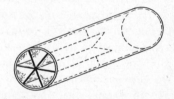

Such a grid or grating when viewed from the end is like any other grid structure but instead of being made of wires, the end view shows only the edges of metal sheets which extend along the guide for approximately a wavelength.

The effectiveness of sheet grids depends upon the fact that thin conductors may be placed along an equal-potential surface (i.e. perpendicular to the electric field) without disturbing the field in any way. The reason is that a metal sheet so placed finds every free charge that it contains to be at the same potential and hence the charge is under no compulsion to move. Since the charge of the metal sheet does not move, it cannot affect the field. On the other hand, if a metallic conductor is placed in a waveguide so that a component of the electric field is tangent to the sheet, the free charges in the metal move in such a way as to cancel out the tangential field component.

Thus, if a circular waveguide is transmitting in both the TE and TM modes and it desired to remove the TM energy, a radial sheet grid structure like the one shown would be used. The *TE* electric field would be perpendicular to the sheets and hence be unaffected, but the longitudinal component of the electric field in the *TM* mode would be forced to lie tangent to the grid sheets; hence it would be damped out. In practice, although sheet grids may easily be constructed to remove the unwanted component, it is much harder to arrange them so as to have a minimum effect on the desired mode.

Shunt Admittance

Four terms must be distinguished and understood to discuss the meaning of shunt admittance successfully. These are shunt impedance, series impedance, shunt admittance, and series admittance. Either series impedance or shunt admittance is usually chosen to describe a given situation because either of these add directly, while the others must be converted into reciprocals before an addition is made. *The shunt admittance of an element which is to be added to a transmission line, is a quantity which may be properly added to the known admittance of that line so as to give the new admittance, which will be found after the element has been installed.*

To clarify this, it is helpful to consider an ordinary two-wire line. If a circuit is connected between the two wires somewhere along such a line, we conventionally refer to the addition as an impedance or admittance in shunt with the remainder of the line. We find this convenient particularly if we consider admittance, because with good judgment as to details, the new admittance of the whole line may be found by adding the admittance of the shunt to the original admittance of the line. Similarly, it is clear that if one conductor of a two-wire line is broken and some element connected between the broken ends, we normally refer to the addition as a series impedance. In that case, the new impedance is the old impedance plus that which is added. The word *shunt* is therefore an indication to add *admittances*, while the word *series* indicates that it is *impedances* which are to be added.

In certain waveguide cases, there is less immediate basis for deciding whether the properties of an additive element shall be described as a series or shunt arrangement. The decision as to which to compute is then based on convenience, along with some guidance which is available from the continuity of the electromagnetic fields. For example, a diaphragm may be installed in a rectangular waveguide and used as a matching impedance. An expression may be calculated for the

approximate shunt impedance of such a diaphram. It is not immediately clear that the diaphram is in shunt rather than in series with
the load and since we have departed from wired circuits, the question
has no definite physical reality. The name shunt admittance, as
applied to the diaphram, nevertheless has a very definite meaning
inasmuch as it indicates how the expression is to be used.

Shunt Resistance

If a pure inductance and a pure capacitance having no resistance
at all could be connected in parallel, a resonant circuit with no dissipative loss would be obtained. If, with such an arrangement, a resistor
were also connected in parallel with the condenser and inductance, a
power loss into the resistance would be found and by adjusting the
resistor to a proper value, that loss could be made to simulate the loss
in an actual circuit containing imperfect condensers and coils. *The
shunt resistance of any resonator is the resistance which would have
to be connected across the terminals of a hypothetical equivalent circuit, which is made up of pure inductance and capacitance so that the
dissipation losses of the two devices would be equal.*

Skin Depth—δ

When an electromagnetic wave strikes the surface of a conductor
or a semi-conductor, in general it is subject to damping and its intensity falls off exponentially with penetration. For microwave frequencies the penetration is rather small and only the surface of the
conductor has any effect on the microwave properties of the assembly.
This is important in the construction of hollow waveguides, since it
means that almost any material may be used as long as it is plated
with a good conductor, silver and copper being the most satisfactory.
*The skin depth is the distance into the material in centimeters or
meters, depending upon the units employed, at which an incident
electromagnetic wave is attenuated to the 1/ε of its original strength.*

If waveguides were made of a material having a true infinite conductivity, the skin depth would be zero. The free charge of the conductor with its perfect mobility would shift at the surface to cancel
the incoming electric field completely. This shift of charge at the
surface would constitute a current, however, which would be entirely
lossless because of the absence of resistance. Thus, the criteria for

excellence in a material for microwave conductors is that of the thinness of the skin depth. In practical cases the skin depth of materials is greater than the minimum amount obtained for pure copper for several reasons. In the first place, if the conductivity is low, penetration into the conductor occurs because the fields are not neutralized at the surface by the moving charge. Secondly, if an imperfectly conducting material is magnetic, the penetration is increased by internal magnetic coupling to the surface currents. In Giorgi units, the skin depth in meters is given approximately by

$$\delta = \sqrt{\frac{\lambda_o}{\pi \sigma \mu c}}$$

where λ_o is the free space wavelength, σ is the conductivity, μ is the permeability, and c is the velocity of light. Even at frequencies corresponding to a one-meter wavelength, δ is only 3.8×10^{-4} cm for copper, while at true microwave frequencies it is much smaller. For a poorly conducting medium such as sea water, the skin depth for one-meter radiation is of the order of one centimeter.

Snell's Law

When a wave passes from one medium into another, its direction of propagation is usually changed as it goes through the interface. Snell's law tells us about this change in direction. *If a wave approaches the interface at an incident angle i degrees to the normal and leaves at an angle r degrees from the normal, Snell's law is stated by sin i/sin r = V₁/V₂, where V₁ and V₂ are respectively the velocities of propagation in the first and second media.*

It can be seen that when the radiation moves from a fast to a slow medium so that the ratio of the V's is greater than unity, any value of i may be chosen and r works out to be a smaller angle, which may always be found. On the other hand, when motion from a slow to a fast medium is involved, the situation is quite different. V_1/V_2 is then a number less than one and if i is chosen nearly equal to 90 degrees, Snell's law is found to require *sin r* to be more than one, which is of course impossible. Physically, this sort of a situation corresponds to the phenomena of total reflection. At angles where Snell's law would require impossible values of *sin r*, there is no transmission through the interface at all. Total reflection occurs for incident angles greater than the critical angle which is specified by *sin i = V₁/V₂*.

It is not to be inferred from a discussion of the critical angle that an abrupt change to total reflection occurs when that angle is reached; rather the ratio of the energy transmitted to the energy reflected decreases in an orderly manner throughout the whole range of increasing r and only becomes zero in actuality at the critical angle. At slightly smaller angles, transmission is possible but is very weak.

Standing Wave

When two sinusoidal traveling waves of equal amplitude and frequency move through a medium in opposite directions the medium is said to be supporting a standing wave. As the waves move past each other, the disturbance felt at each point in the medium is the algebraic sum of the disturbances that would be felt because of the presence of each wave alone. This sum may be anything from zero to twice the amplitude of one of the waves. It develops, however, that certain points spaced a half wavelength apart along the propagation direction, are always disturbed by a zero amount. Excitation of those points by one wave is always just canceled by that of the other. Such points are called *nodes*. Midway between these nodal points are other positions which are subject to very violent oscillations, because there the two waves continually cooperate in disturbing the medium. These points of maximum activity are called *antinodes* or *loops*.

Standing waves are usually obtained by reflecting a wave back on itself. Under such conditions, at least, a perfect standing wave is a practical impossibility. In a really pure standing wave, the nodes would be absolutely stationary and no energy could flow past them along the wave. In practice, some flow is always necessary to overcome friction and other types of dissipative loss. Standing waves therefore are usually accompanied by at least a very small traveling wave which moves away from the source.

Standing-Wave Ratio—SWR

To understand SWR measurements it is necessary to know the cause of standing waves and the way in which traveling sinusoidal waves, which are moving in the same direction with the same velocity, may be added. Briefly, a standing wave is obtained when a medium supports two waves which are equal but traveling in opposite directions. If the waves are not equal, the larger of the two may be considered as being composed of two waves, one equal in magnitude to the opposing wave and the other of such a size as to take up the remainder of the amplitude. A medium supporting two opposing traveling waves may generally be equally well said to be supporting a standing wave plus a traveling wave. With only a traveling wave present, a time average of the magnitude will be the same everywhere in the medium, since all parts of the wave travel by every point. With a pure standing wave, nodal points in the medium can be found at which no amplitude ever exists, and loop points can be found where the oscillation is a maximum. Since *SWR may be defined as the ratio of the maximum to the minimum wave amplitudes that can be observed at various points along the propagation path of a wave,* it follows that a pure standing wave corresponds to infinite SWR, while a single traveling wave indicates unity SWR.

SWR measurements are particularly useful in waveguides, where dissipative losses of energy may well be less important than reactive losses. Reactive losses are a reflection of energy back along the guide toward the source; hence, a large SWR marks the presence of a standing wave and reflection due to reactive mismatching in the waveguide. An SWR measurement, if made near the source, will show the net reflections from the overall system. It will not show losses due to radiation or dissipation.

Stoke's Theorem

If any closed curve is constructed and the tangential component of a vector around it is integrated, the result is equal to the surface integral of the normal component of the curl of that vector over an arbitrary surface bounded by the curve. Mathematically this may be stated

$$\int F_s ds = \int\int curl_n \, F dS.$$

The proof of the theorem is simple enough although strictly mathematical in character and may be found in any book treating of vectors. To understand the physical uses of the relation, special cases must be considered.

If a vector specifies a field in which the curl is everywhere equal to zero, it is clear that the integral of the curl will be zero no matter what closed curve or what surface is chosen. This in turn means, according to Stoke's theorem, that in such a curl-free field the tangent integral taken about any closed curve will be zero. If the field is a gravitational one, for example, and **F** represents the force on a certain mass, that mass may be carried over any route and returned to its original position without a net loss of energy. Similarly, a charge may be carried around a closed path in a stationary electric field without a net loss or gain of energy. Such fields are called *conservative fields* and Stoke's law shows that the curl being identically equal to zero, is a necessary and sufficient condition to insure that a given field is conservative.

If a magnetic pole is moved around a wire carrying current, a net amount of energy is involved even though the pole does return to its starting point. Magnetic fields are not conservative even in the stationary state case; in fact, Maxwell's equations show that curl **H** = $4\pi J/c$ even when the electric field is constant with time.

Stationary Fields

Stationary electromagnetic fields are those which are independent of time. They may be regarded as a special case of the general situation which is covered by Maxwell's equations. Specifically in the stationary case, we may write Maxwell's equations without the partial time derivatives since they are identically equal to zero. Thus we have in gaussian units

$$\text{curl } \mathbf{H} = 4\pi J/c \qquad \text{curl } \mathbf{E} = 0$$
$$\text{div } \mathbf{B} = 0 \qquad \text{div } \mathbf{D} = 4\pi\rho$$
$$\mathbf{B} = \mu\mathbf{H} \qquad \mathbf{D} = k\mathbf{E}.$$

In this case the electric field arises entirely from a charge density and may either be found by a vector integration over the charge or through the use of a scalar potential. The vector integration of Coulomb's law,

$$\mathbf{E} = \int \frac{d\rho}{k\mathbf{r}^2} \, \mathbf{r}_1$$

is clumsy at best and calculations are more frequently made by first setting up a potential. The curl **E** equation shows that a scalar potential may be used and it is defined as $\mathbf{E} = -\,grad\ V$. Let us assume in general that we know how the charge density is distributed throughout the space in which we are interested. Furthermore let us present these data in terms of a function of ρ, which has a particular value at each coordinate corresponding to the charge density at that point. The potential V is obtainable from Poisson's equation

$$\nabla^2 V = -4\pi\rho$$

and a solution of that equation yields an expression giving values of V at each point in space. For the H-field we cannot set up a scalar potential even for the stationary case, because the curl of H is not zero. Therefore it is found convenient to set up a vector potential defined by curl $\mathbf{A} = \mathbf{H}$ and div $\mathbf{A} = O$. Here, too, $\mathbf{A}$ can be determined by Poisson's equation,

$$\nabla^2 \mathbf{A} = -4\pi \mathbf{J}/c,$$

involving the current density $\mathbf{J}$ which is presumed to be known in the space in which there is interest.

Target Cross-Section

In specifying the reflection ability of an object which is observed by a radar beam, it is customary to use a quantity called *target cross-section. The target cross-section of a radar target is defined as an area near the target which, when placed perpendicular to the direction of the incident radar energy, is just able to intercept enough energy so that if that energy could be fed into a perfectly matched isotropic antenna, the radiation back toward the radar set would duplicate that actually obtained from the target.* It is seldom possible to calculate target cross-section from known dimensions of the target, because a dependence upon the exact shape is very strong. Experimental values for various types of aircraft are well known, however, and this quantity is useful in comparing the vulnerability to radar detection which these various types possess.

Thermal Noise

In an electrical circuit, noise is characterized by spurious voltages of a random character and may arise from any one of several causes including many that can be minimized or circumvented by good design. Thermal noise, however, is intimately connected with natural causes and establishes the upper limit to the sensitivity that can be built into a radio receiver. *Because the free charge in conductors and semiconductors is subject to thermal agitation, random voltages are generated in strength given by*

$$\begin{matrix} \textit{square of effective value} \\ \textit{of voltage components lying} \\ \textit{between frequencies } \mathrm{f}_1 \textit{ and } \mathrm{f}_2 \end{matrix} = 4kT \int_{f_1}^{f_2} R df$$

where

$k = Boltzmann's\ constant = 1.374 \times 10^{-23}\ joules\ per\ degree\ Kelvin$

$T = absolute\ temperature\ in\ degrees\ Kelvin$

$R = resistance\ component\ of\ impedance\ across\ which\ the\ noise\ voltage\ is\ developed$

$f = frequency.$

When the element in which the noise originates is a pure resistance so that R is independent of frequency, the integration may be performed at once. The expression then becomes simply

$$E^2 = 4kTR(f_2 - f_1).$$

The free electrons in the conductor are in constant motion, moving at random and constantly colliding with each other just like the molecules of a gas. This motion is in fact heat. When a body of any sort is warmed, the motion of its atomic particles is increased and we say the body is warm or hot. Likewise if any body is cooled, the motion of its free electrons and molecules is reduced and, if we could cool the body to absolute zero, they would be stopped entirely. In a conductor these randomly moving electrons constitute an erratic current and generate the emf which is called noise. It is particularly noteworthy that the energy of each electron is well known on the average. It is given by $(3/2)kT$, in which k is Boltzmann's constant and T is in degrees Kelvin. A statistical analysis of the effect of many electrons having this average energy can give rise to the formula quoted above.

It will be noticed in the expression for the square of the effective noise voltage that the noise is independent of the frequency being amplified but it does depend upon the bandwidth of the amplifier. Thus, if a 1-megohm resistor is operated at room temperature (about 300 degrees K) in an amplifier which passes all frequencies between f_1 and f_2, which are 5000 cycles apart, that resistor must be considered, as far as the rest of the circuit is concerned, to be a source of noise voltage of $(4 \times 1.37 \times 10^{-23} \times 300 \times 10^6 \times 5000)^{1/2} = 9.1 \times 10^{-6}$ volts. This is true whether f_1 and f_2 are of the order of a few kilocycles or have values equal to many megacycles. The peak value of the noise will be 3 to 4 times greater than this rms value.

Torque

The rotation of a wheel or the opening of a door may be described as clockwise or counterclockwise. Evidently such a motion is a vector quantity which has direction as well as magnitude. Similarly, a force causing a rotation is certainly a directed quantity but one which may constantly change direction. Furthermore, it is apparent that force alone is not the only factor to be considered in describing the cause of a rotation. A bolt and nut which cannot be loosened with the fingers alone can be turned with the same force when a wrench is used. The quantity which does describe the effectiveness of an effort to ?ause rotation is called torque. *Torque is the product of a force and the perpendicular distance from the axis of the rotation to the line of action of the force. It is often represented as a vector drawn along the axis of rotation with a length equal to the magnitude just described, and a direction that is the same as that in which a right-hand screw would advance if the torque caused the rotation of such a screw.* Its magnitude is expressed in terms of a unit such as the centimeter-dyne.

Traveling Wave

A sine wave is one in which some quantity such as current, voltage, **E**, or **H** has a value which varies sinusoidally along a given path. This is instantaneously true of either a standing wave or a traveling wave. The distinction between the two must be made in terms of the way in which sine-wave distribution changes with time. *A traveling wave is one in which the sinusoidal properties of some quantity successively change their space coordinates at successive instants of time so that the wave appears to move smoothly along through space with no other change.* Any measurement made at any point which, for example, might be labeled as being at a distance s from some reference mark, will presently be true of a point at $s + \Delta s$, and successively at later times it will be true at points $s + 2\Delta s$, $s + 3\Delta s$, etc.

It should be emphasized that it is not necessary to have any flow of physical material in the direction of propagation of a traveling wave. Even in an entirely mechanical case such as is encountered with waves produced in a rope by shaking one end, it will be recognized that energy can be transferred to the far end even though the rope remains connected to the mechanical source causing the excitation. Such a wave is called a *transverse* wave, since all motion is restricted to a plane perpendicular to the line along which the traveling wave moves. Similarly, all electromagnetic waves are said to be of the transverse kind, because the electric and magnetic fields are always perpendicular to the direction of motion of the traveling wave.

Sometimes the term *attenuated traveling wave* is used. Such a wave is not a pure traveling wave because in addition to the progressive phase shift which is encountered as the space coordinates are increased, the amplitude gradually decreases.

Tubes of Force

A vector field is a space which has a vector of a given direction and magnitude defined at each and every point. Such a field may be described by an equation or a pair of equations which give vector magnitude and direction as a function of some coordinate system, or it may be represented graphically by the use of lines of force. Even when the mathematical method of specification is used, it is often desirable to supplement that description by graphical methods so as to allow a more ready physical conception of the situation.

To represent a vector field with lines of force, imaginary lines are drawn throughout the space so that the vector for any point has a direction tangent to the lines of force in that neighborhood and a magnitude equal to the density with which the lines have been drawn. *If a bundle of lines of force, which pass through a certain neighborhood, are considered together and if the outer lines of that bundle are spanned by a tubular surface, that surface is called a tube of force.*

Tubes of force are particularly useful in some calculations because they have certain properties. For instance, no two lines of force can ever cross since such a crossing would make the specification of the vector at the crossing point ambiguous. This means that a tube of force contains the same flux (same number of lines of force) throughout its length and any change in its cross-sectional area indicates a strengthening or weakening of the field. Tubes of force may be considered as carrying lines of force much as pipes carry a liquid. Indeed, if the vector field is one giving the flow velocities in a liquid system, the tubes of force may actually correspond to physical pipes carrying the fluid.

Vector Potential—A

In the steady state, the electric potential of a point in space is the energy necessary to bring a unit charge to that point from some place which we call zero potential. This method of describing the electrical properties of a space has several advantages. It is intrinsically simpler than the statement of the three field components; it allows certain mathematical calculations to be carried out simply; and it makes use of the volt, which has considerable physical significance.

In the magnetic case, however, it is not generally possible to consider such a scalar potential. The energy involved with a unit magnetic pole is not uniquely determined by the position of that pole in space and, since that is what is meant by scalar potential, we can not assign unique potential values to such points. An example of this is apparent in the case of a magnetic pole located in the neighborhood of a wire carrying a current. The work involved in moving the pole to such a position may be anything, depending upon the number of trips around the wire that were made en route.

The magnetic vector potential is a means of overcoming this difficulty and allowing a potential function to be set up that will salvage at least some of the advantages of scalar potential theory. For example, in the case of a wire carrying a steady current, the magnetic vector potential is a vector pointing along the wire in a direction opposite to the current flow. In gaussian units, the magnitude of the vector potential falls off with distance from the wire in accordance with

$$A = -(2i/c)\log_\epsilon r$$

This is in contrast to the way the scalar potential falls off from a charge with distance, which is given by

$$\phi = \rho/r.$$

To find H from A it is necessary to take the curl of A, while in the scalar potential case the negative gradient of ϕ will give E. *The vector potential of a vector H is given by curl $A = H$ together with some specification on div A which in the steady state case is taken as div $A = O$.* In the general case where the electromagnetic fields may change with time, neither E nor H have zero curl, which is the criteria for setting up scalar potentials. We may nevertheless use ϕ and A by setting $E = -grad\ \phi - (1/c)\ (\delta A/\delta t)$ instead of simply $-grad\ \phi$ and by defining A *with div* $A = -(1/c)\ (\delta\phi/\delta t).$

Velocity of Light—c

The velocity of light in free space is usually taken as 3×10^{10} cm per sec. This is equivalent to 3×10^8 meters per second or 186,000 miles per second. Although c is usually referred to as the velocity of light, it is actually the velocity with which all electromagnetic radiation travels in free space quite independent of frequency. Echo sounding devices using electromagnetic waves, can, for example, determine range by multiplying one half the transmission time by c. In accordance with the theory of special relativity (not to be confused with general relativity which is a rather complicated subject), neither matter nor energy can travel faster than this. Special relativity has had ample experimental verification by many people.

Phase velocities in waveguides may seem to be an exception. They very often involve velocities greater than c. Close examination, however, shows that no energy moves with the phase velocity. Group velocity is the velocity of the energy motion and that is always equal to or less than c. In fact, in any medium or under the restraint of any boundary condition, electromagnetic energy always travels slower than in free space.

Volt

The volt is the potential difference between two points when one joule of work is involved in transferring one coulomb of charge from one point to the other. Since energy is an ability to do work, voltage may also be said to be the energy per unit charge that is associated with a given motion. It is important to realize that two points must always be specified in order to give a voltage measurement. In the rare case in which it is good practice to talk of the voltage of a single point, it is implied that the voltage with respect to some ground reference is really meant.

Watt

In electrical measurements the watt is universally used to measure power. It is also used for mechanical power measurement in those countries where the metric system of units is prevalent. *In terms of volts and amperes the watt is the energy released by a current of one ampere flowing through a voltage drop of one volt. Mechanically, it is the rate at which work is done when one joule of energy is used each second.* Confusion sometimes arises when it is not clearly understood that the watt measures the *rate* at which work is done. The kilowatt-hour (thousands of watts multiplied by the number of hours during which the power flows) is the unit in which electricity is usually

purchased. Notice that the unit is not just the kilowatt which measures how fast the electricity is used, but rather the kilowatt-hour
which brings in the time over which the use was made of the energy,
and hence causes the consumer to pay for the total electrical energy
used.

Waveguide Cutoff Wavelength—λ_c

Hollow-pipe waveguides have characteristics that are in many ways
similar to those of high-pass filter networks. If a wave of a given
frequency and strength enters the input end of a waveguide, equal or
smaller amounts of power will emerge from the far end. The decrease
in energy during transmission is called attenuation and may be due
not only to actual losses into heat, but also to the reflection of energy
back along the path from which it came. Even if it is assumed that
the guide is made of a perfectly conducting material, attenuation,
which is usually measured in db per foot, is possible because of reflection and in general it is found to depend upon frequency in such a
way that at some frequency it increases very rapidly with a further
decrease in frequency. *The wavelength λ_c corresponding to the cutoff
frequency f_c beyond which the attenuation of a waveguide rises very
rapidly is called the cutoff wavelength.*

In an actual waveguide, where dissipative attenuation is also taken
into account, a plot of attenuation versus frequency usually shows a
minimum at a point just above the cutoff and gradually increases
again at higher frequencies. This high-frequency attenuation is due to
the finite conductivity of the material and it is so much smaller that
it is not easily confused with the large attenuation experienced with
wavelengths that are longer than the cutoff wavelength.

A slightly more mathematical but also more accurate way to
describe cutoff in a waveguide, concerns the propagation constant
and the characteristic impedance. When the wavelength is small, the
propagation constant is a pure imaginary quantity, indicating a
traveling sinusoidal wave, and the impedance is real, showing that no
energy is reflected from points along the interior of the guide. On the
other hand, for long wavelengths, the propagation constant becomes
real and thus designates an exponential diminution of the energy
transmitted, while the impedance becomes imaginary to show the
presence of a reflected component. The frequency or wavelength at
which these quantities change from real to imaginary, is called the
cutoff frequency or wavelength.

Waveguide Modes

A given piece of hollow-pipe waveguide is capable of transmitting electrical energy in one or more of an infinite number of ways or modes, which are distinguishable from each other because of characteristic patterns of the electromagnetic field which are formed within the guide. In a particular case only one or a limited number of modes may be excited, depending upon the frequency that is employed and how the energy is introduced into the waveguide. For example, with a rectangular waveguide all the possible modes may be included under two main groups which are commonly called transverse electric and transverse magnetic modes. These names are usually abbreviated as TE and TM. They indicate in the TE case that the electric field is only directed crosswise of the waveguide and not at all along its length, while in the TM case the magnetic field is transverse only. The various modes existing in each class are given by subscripts as TE_{mn} or TM_{mn}. In the case of a rectangular waveguide, the subscript m tells the number of half-wave variations in field intensity that are to be found in traveling one way across the rectangle, while n gives the same information for the other transverse dimension.

That mode of a waveguide, which can be utilized with the lowest possible frequency for a given set of dimensions, is called the *dominant mode.* It is generally the most useful, because it can be used under conditions that prevent the transmission of any higher modes which are then well beyond cutoff. In the case of rectangular waveguide, the $TE_{1,0}$ mode is dominant, and is the only mode that will propagate if the narrow dimension of the guide is sensibly less than a wavelength. With a circular waveguide, only the dominant mode is transmitted without severe attenuation if the radius of the pipe is appreciably less than 0.38 times as great as the wavelength λ but greater than 0.29λ.

Wavelength in Waveguide—λ_g

In coaxial lines using an air dielectric, the wavelength is always the same as in free space, and is given by $\lambda f = c$, where c is the velocity of light. In all types of hollow-pipe waveguides, the wavelength is longer than it is in free space so the phase velocity given by $V = \lambda_g f$ is greater than the velocity of light, and the group velocity, which is the speed with which energy is carried along the waveguide, is less than the velocity of light. *The wavelength λ_g is related to the cutoff wavelength λ_c and the free-space wavelength λ by the relation*

$$\lambda_g = \frac{\lambda}{\sqrt{1 - \left(\dfrac{\lambda}{\lambda_c}\right)^2}} \, .$$

From this expression it is clear that if a waveguide is operated very near its cutoff frequency, λ_g becomes very large. In a practical waveguide, however, the attenuation due to current losses in the walls of the guide also becomes large as cutoff is approached, so that a practical upper limit to the magnitude of λ_g is encountered rather soon.

Weber

The unit of magnetic flux in the Giorgi or mks system of units is the Weber. *If an open-circuited loop of wire is initially in a field-free space and if a magnetic field is allowed to build up through the loop at a rate such that one volt appears across the terminals of the loop, then at the end of one second the magnetic flux through the loop is one weber.* Thus the weber is not a unit of B directly as is the gauss in the gaussian system of units, but rather it is analogous to the more infrequently used flux unit called the maxwell. Magnetic field strength, B, is measured in terms of webers per square meter. This is in accord with the usual graphical device in which lines of flux are defined as a family of imaginary curves drawn in a space in such a way that at any point a tangent shows the direction of the field and the density of the lines gives its strength. A weber is, in this picture, the name of one of these imaginary curves and by the convention, the number of webers per unit of area is the strength of the field.

Work

Work is defined as the product of the magnitude of a force and the distance through which that force is applied. If a man raises a 10 lb weight to a height of 3 ft, he is doing 30 foot-pounds of work. If a tractor pulls forward on a wagon with a force of 200 lbs and moves the wagon 500 feet while continually exerting that force, the tractor has done 100,000 ft-lbs of work on the wagon. If a fixed electrical charge attracts a distant unit charge with an average force of 3 dynes while causing the unit charge to move 3 cm, 9 dyne-cm or, in other words, 9 ergs of work will have been done. Since the moving charge had unit strength, this means that the motion took place through a potential drop of 9 esu volts.

FOOTNOTES
1. For example, $h = 0.5gt^2$ is used to calculate the time of fall of a body. If the body falls 64 feet with $g = 32$ ft. per sec.² then the solution of $t = -2$ sec. is disregarded and $t = +2$ sec. accepted as the proper answer.
2. K. A. Norton, Proc. I.R.E. 29, 623, 1941.

INDEX

A

Admittance, 289
Airplanes as radar targets, 107
Alternating current, 43
  sine-wave representation, 45
  vector representation, 46
Ampere, 290
Ampere's circuital law, 289
Ampere's rule, 292
Amplitude modulation, 286
Amplitude modulation tubes, 224
Antenna, 199
  aircraft, 221
  array, 216
  beam width, 206
  biconical type, 220
  cosecant squared, 208
  cross section, 292
  dipole, 211
  gain, 215, 273, 293
  half-wave dipole, 89
  horn, 219
  isotropic, 215
  loading, 219
  microwave types, 199
  patterns, 204, 206
  pattern dependence on ground, 221
  radar, 221
  radiation from discontinuities, 90
  reciprocity theorem, 294
  slotted waveguide type, 219
Applegate diagram, 232, 294
Attenuation constant, 295
Azimuth angle, 296

B

Bandwidth, 286
  pulse and cw service, 261
Barkhausen-Kurz tubes, 248
Beam loading, 224, 296
Bessel functions, 297
Biconical horn antenna, 220
Biot-Savart law, 30, 298
Black-body radiation, 298
Bound charge, 11

Boundary conditions, 299
  at a perfect conductor, 120
  at an interface, 118
Bunches, 225
Buncher grids, 225
Bunching parameter, 235, 333

C

Cable loss, 273
Capacitance, 35, 40
  in transmission lines, 54, 135
Catcher grids, 227
Cavities, resonant, 170
  applications of, 194
  coaxial, 175
  cylindrical, 182
  development of, 173
  disk-seal tubes, 254
  frequency of, 185
  klystron, 228
  limitations of, 175
  magnetron, 252
  rectangular, 177
  Rhumbatron, 173
  tuning, 193
  types, 175
  waveguide, 177
Centimeter-dyne, 300
Characteristic impedance, 55
  coaxial line, 60, 76
Charge, 7
  bound, 102
  free, 102
  nature of, 71
  unit of, 16
  sign, 10
Charged bodies, 1
  forces between, 8
Charging bodies, 10
Coaxial line, 59, 127
  cavity, 175
  connection to waveguide, 166
  charge distribution in, 69
  current waves in, 60
  impedance, 133

381